UNFIT FOR
HUMAN CONSUMPTION

Ruth Mulvey Harmer
has also written
The High Cost of Dying

UNFIT FOR HUMAN CONSUMPTION

RUTH MULVEY HARMER

Prentice-Hall, Inc.
Englewood Cliffs, New Jersey

Thanks are due the editors of THE NATION for
permission to use material in Chapter 6,
which the author first published in that
magazine.

Unfit for Human Consumption
by Ruth Mulvey Harmer

ISBN 0-13-936906-6
Library of Congress Catalog Card Number: 76-143581

Printed in the United States of America T

Prentice-Hall International, Inc., London
Prentice-Hall of Australia, Pty. Ltd., Sydney
Prentice-Hall of Canada, Ltd., Toronto
Prentice-Hall of India Private Ltd., New Delhi
Prentice-Hall of Japan, Inc., Tokyo

For
Moth
who always cared

ACKNOWLEDGMENTS

That public policy is ultimately shaped by the citizen rather than an elite corps of technicians and scientists is the great strength of a democracy. Public policy is weakened and democracy subverted when citizens are misinformed or kept ignorant of the issues by those whom they trust to advise and protect them. That is why we are threatened even more today by the rising tide of economic poisons than we were in 1962, when Rachel Carson, that wise and good woman, issued the warning of the *Silent Spring.*

I am grateful to the public officials, scientists, lawyers, conservationists, and writers who have alerted me to the dangers which I have attempted to describe in this book and who have advanced alternate ways to solve pest control problems. I am entirely responsible for whatever errors the book may contain, but I think it seemly to thank those who furthered my education.

The text, the notes, and the bibliography are designed to make clear the extent to which I, as a citizen in a democracy, am indebted. Additionally, I owe particular thanks to many experts and friends who took the time to help me personally—directing me to proper sources, providing me with material, allowing me to interview them.

Among them are U.S. Senators Alan Cranston, Philip A. Hart, Walter A. Mondale, Gaylord Nelson; Congressmen George E. Brown, Jr., and Richard Ottinger; California's Chief Deputy Attorney General Charles O'Brien and his assistant, Paul Richmond; California State Senator John Nejedly, and Assemblymen George W. Milias and David

Roberti; Lu Haas, Senator Cranston's aide in California. Dr. Barry Commoner, Dr. Paul DeBach, Dr. Samuel S. Epstein, Kevin Shea, Dr. Charles Wurster, and Miss Mildred Greenberg provided me with a considerable amount of scientific material; Jerome Cohen and David Averbuck of the United Farm Workers Organizing Committee and Victor J. Yannacone, Jr., former counsel for the Environmental Defense Fund, gave me information about legal matters.

Special thanks are due many friends and acquaintances who made contributions: the staff of the Arroyo Seco Branch of the Los Angeles Public Library; Marti Lisowski and Mai Shields of the Cal Poly Library; Douglass Adair and David Fishlow of the staff of *El Malcriado;* Mildred Cowger, Howard Lorbeer, Grant Hegranes, Commander Edsel Fussell, Eleanor McBean, Friend Deahl, Jenifer Schroeder, Helen Perkins, Albert C. Oliver, Ted Weissbuch, and Anni Landauer.

Most of all, however, I am indebted to C. M. Vandeburg, my agent—an eco-activist since he discovered the first pesticide-poisoned robin on his lawn in Bronxville years ago—who insisted that I write this book; to Bram Cavin of Prentice-Hall, whose patience, kindness, and helpfulness make him the very model of the editor every writer hopes to work with; to Lee Howe, our good neighbor and friend, who shared with me the results of his research; and, of course, to my family, who helped me to endure.

CONTENTS

• FOREWORD

THIS BOOK HAD its beginning at a luncheon several years ago. All of us, in the way of people on such occasions, were doing more talking than listening until I found myself straining to hear the words of a middle-aged businessman sitting opposite. Others began to do that, too. And suddenly, except for his voice, there was silence.

"Imagine," he said, "walking through this series of security locks in a test laboratory in Savannah. It was only the Communicable Disease Center of the United States Public Health Service, but my credentials were checked as carefully as if I were being admitted to an ultimate defense installation. We walked down a corridor, past rows of bolted doors. Then my guide opened one of them, and we stepped inside. There, ranged against the wall, were racks of cages—seething with flies and mosquitoes that were totally immune to pesticides." He shook his head as if to rid himself of the memory.

"In one cage I saw descendants of a species that began to evolve nearly twenty years ago, when the first of their ancestors were given DDT. That treatment has been repeated every single day since that time. Imagine," he stressed slowly: "Every single day. The daily dose is a 'lethal' one. Yet they survive. And breed. I have heard the expression that fear makes the hackles rise. Well, this was the first time in my life—and I've been frightened many a time—that hackles on the back of my neck came right up. Those flies and mosquitoes were so fierce and so big and so healthy . . . so indestructible. . . .

"Then a man in a white smock—and everyone in the place wore white smocks—led me over to a cage of mosquitoes that had been treated daily for almost ten years on a type of organic phosphate pesticide so deadly that the smallest fraction of an ounce would kill you or me instantly. 'In a minute they'll form up,' the man told me calmly. Then, as I watched, these black mosquitoes swarmed up from the bottom of the cage, massing on its sides in perfect V-shaped echelons. Once they were all hooked to the side of the cage, they began to buzz, rhythmically and outlandishly. Then it became quiet again. Their strange ceremony over, the mosquitoes began to climb down the walls again. They didn't fly. They didn't run. They just walked, slowly and deliberately.

"I have never been so shaken in my life."

It was not hard to understand why, nor to appreciate why the creatures are guarded so carefully that no one may leave the bolted room until checks are made to insure that none of them has escaped. The reproductive capacity of ordinary mosquitoes and flies is staggering: if the descendants of a pair of average houseflies lived and mated fully, their family would number 190,000,000,000,000,000 by the end of four summer months.[1] What, then, the capacity of the superflies and the supermosquitoes? If they were infected with diseases and turned loose in the manner proposed by biological warfare advocates, might they not be able to bring pestilence and death to the population of an entire continent in a single season? Since they are immune to the most powerful weapons developed against their kind, who would be shielded? Which of us could escape?[2]

"But I thought," I protested, "that pesticides do protect

us against those disease carriers—that the risks are worth it since they are our *only* real protection."

"Yes," the man across the table smiled wryly, "that's what most people do think."

That is how this book began.

Since then, I have learned that the argument is false—as is the argument that without unrestricted use of pesticides we would soon starve. Yet pesticide makers have used those fallacies as bases for subjecting the planet and its every living thing to a tide of poisons unbelievable in magnitude and uncontrollable in consequence. Although a wide variety of safe, economic, and efficient measures exist to control pests that threaten our health and our food supply, pesticide makers have gained consent for the all-out chemical war from:

• Agribusinessmen seeking a bigger bang for a buck, who have transformed farming—that most civilized of activities—into the violent science;

• Scientists, including educators, who have bartered objectivity and expertise for the financial rewards of pushing pesticides;

• Regulatory officials who have set aside their responsibility to protect the public and who have allowed the poisoners, themselves, to act as regulators;

• Legislators who have permitted industry lobbyists to draft pesticide laws and to set penalties for their abuse.

As a consequence, it is easier to buy one of the deadly poisons than an even mildly potent medicine; it is cheaper to violate the laws than to obey them.

I have felt a need to share what I have learned because perhaps the most painful knowledge I gained is that the rest of us, the majority, have become unwitting allies. Deceived by propaganda, misled by many whom we trust, elated over short-term results whose consequences are unknown, we have encouraged, subsidized, and actively participated in the extermination campaign.

The cost of the damage done to our environment, to our health, and to the well-being of generations to come is beyond estimate. It is my hope that the tide can be reversed, that this book may make some contribution to the store of information that will lead to a lasting truce in the mad struggle against nature—a truce that will help to make the world once again safe for people and other living things.

PART ONE

1. AMONG THE SURVIVORS?

MITHRIDATES VI WAS an extraordinary person. The ancient king of Pontus held history at bay for a quarter of a century in a series of wars that almost prevented the eclipse of the "glory that was Greece" by Roman grandeur. At once a most barbarous and civilized man, Mithridates was an expert equestrian and warrior, able to out-eat, out-drink, out-womanize any of his retinue. An accomplished linguist, he had such command of 22 languages that interpreters were not needed at his court. He revered art and music and was a generous patron of Greek poets, scholars, and philosophers. He was also a ferocious adversary, ordering the massacre of 80,000 Italians in Asia Minor on a single day, crowning one victory by pouring molten gold down the throat of a captured foe. To protect his throne, he killed his mother, his brother, and six of his own children.[1]

But what made him legendary was simply that, as A. E. Housman noted in one of his bitterest poems: "Mithridates, he died old."

He knew how to cope with poisons. After inheriting the throne at the age of 11, he fled to the woods to escape his mother and guardians, who had conspired to kill him. There, he lived for seven years as a wild hunter. When he was restored to the throne, he determined to protect himself against further plots by drinking a little poison every day until he became immune to all the known toxins.

He succeeded so well that at the age of 69, defeated and deserted, he was unable to find refuge in suicide. His hands lacked the strength to drive home the sword: his system totally resisted the great draughts of poison he downed.

No one could possibly develop such tolerance to the poisonous hazards in our environment today, although there are persons who develop partial immunity. Swiss mountaineers still eat arsenic to increase their endurance and get a pleasurable "jolt"—stepping up the daily intake until they can consume quantities far greater than the fatal dose for an ordinary person.[2]

Generally, however, we lack all the advantages that enabled Mithridates to cope: the knowledge of kinds, effects, and sources of poisons. Instead of confronting only a few for which antidotes have been and can be developed, we are submerged by a tide of poisons so new and so numerous, so complex and so potent that not even scientists know what all their ultimate—or even immediate—biological consequences are. Increasingly, the more responsible among them are expressing gravest concern about what Dr. Barry Commoner in *Science and Survival* called "the huge experiment" we are conducting "*on ourselves.*"[3] Not long ago an even more explicit warning was issued by Dr. Richard Felger at a meeting of the Population Crisis Committee: "*Life will probably persist on earth for millions of years, but as things are now it is not likely that man will be among the surviving species. If he continues poisoning the environment at the present rate, he doesn't have more than half a century or a century to go.*"[4]

The bright promise of the Age of Chemistry that was ushered in shortly before World War II with cries of "miracles" and "wonders" has tarnished as each succeeding bill has been presented—as we learn the price to be paid for poisoning the air we breathe, the earth we walk on, the water we drink, the food we eat, the tobacco we smoke, the clothes we wear. "America the Beautiful" has become "America the Toxic," celebrated bleakly on campuses across the country with such anti-hymns as:

> *Oh cancerous for smoggy skies, for pesticided grain . . .*
> *Irradiated mountains rise above an asphalt plain.*
> *America, America, thy birds have fled from thee;*
> *Thy fish lie dead by poisoned streams from sea to fetid sea.*[5]

Chemical pollution of the atmosphere is perhaps most noticeable, since we take in about 6,000 gallons of air a day. Yet presently, as one black humorist has it, "All you have to do to feel rotten is to take a deep breath." Contamination of air by "the dirty animal" is old stuff, going all the way back through pre-history to the moment the first savage kindled a flame and allowed wastes of his Promethean gift to be wafted off. Highly toxic pollution, however, dates back only to about the nineteenth century, when industries began to generate chemical fumes and gases on a large scale and when industrialists appropriated the air—that most public property—for use as a sewer for their poisonous garbage: hydrofluoric acid; sodium and calcium fluorides; compounds of arsenic, sulfuric, and hydrochloric acids; compounds of zinc and lead. A major twentieth-century contribution was "smog"—the irritant gases produced by photochemical reactions of petroleum products obtained through the catalytic cracking process.[6]

Air pollution, old style and new, had reached such a point by the summer of 1969 that an official of the Department of Health, Education, and Welfare estimated that every year more than three-fourths of a ton of "toxic matter" was being released into the air over this country for each man, woman, and child in it.[7] Principal victims of atmospheric poisoning are those in urban centers, but even in less densely populated areas lethal effluents make life miserable.[8] Potent enough to destroy rubber, metal, glass, and stone, the airborne poisons cost Americans at least $13 billion a year.[9]

Their biological consequences are still not fully known. First warning of them occurred shortly after World War II, when a Los Angeles farm family became destitute in the single hour it took a smog attack to bleach several acres of spinach plants to an unsalable ivory color. By 1969, smog and other forms of air pollution were killing an estimated $500 million worth of agricultural products annually[10] and irreparably damaging parks and forests. Animals and men have also suffered assaults on hearts, bones, bone marrow, bladders, and respiratory organs. Many specialists believe poisons in the air to be a primary cause of lung cancer. In 1970, Dr. Joseph Boyle of the California State Air Resources Board reported to the American College of Chest Physicians that persons with early lung cancer can sometimes reverse progress of the disease by moving out of a smoggy city.[11]

Water is also a vehicle for conveying poisons to plants, animals, and persons. Just as with air, a hundred years ago it was possible to tell what was polluting water— unless one happened to be "above all that" as was Queen Victoria. According to one story, while standing on a bridge over the Cam River (then as now a sewer), she regally demanded an explanation of "all those pieces of paper in the water." The Master of Trinity College at Cambridge, with remarkable presence, replied, "Those, Your Majesty, are notices saying that bathing is forbidden."[12]

There is plenty of sewage in United States waters today. The Mississippi is referred to as the "colon of mid-America," a not inappropriate description if one knows that fish placed in a sample of its sewage-laden water recently died in less than a minute, even though the sample had been diluted ten times with pure water.[13] Other rivers are in scarcely better shape. The Potomac has been described during cherry blossom time as "the best-dressed cesspool in America," and several years ago a random sample of the Connecticut River disclosed the presence of such disease bacteria as typhoid, paratyphoid, cholera, salmonella, tuberculosis, polio, anthrax, tetanus, plus a large assortment of viruses.[14] Even more sinister than human wastes —more toxic and less apparent—are many of the effluents poured into rivers and lakes by agriculture and industry, "the most flagrant abuser of water quality."[15]

The earth, too, that thin skin of soil that sustains life, is also a dumping ground—for the five and more pounds of refuse each individual discards every day, and for the rain of chemical and radioactive wastes that fall to earth, are absorbed by plants, and presently make their way into the systems of men and animals. Many of those things, along with a host of other poisons, become integral parts of our daily bread and everything else that is served at the dinner table.

The precipitous ban on cyclamates in the winter of 1969 brought home to most Americans a new awareness of how unprotected they were from toxins in their foods. In the ensuing uproar, Senator George S. McGovern, chairman of the Senate Committee on Nutrition, urged a halt to government policies and practices which permitted the sale of more than 680 everyday food additives that had not been tested for safety. Among the substances was a "taste enhancer" in baby foods that had been demonstrated, at a level only three times higher than that customarily employed, to produce eye and brain damage in young monkeys and mice.[16]

The kinds of hazardous substances range from embalming fluid in hamburger, to give it a "fresh" taste; to coal tar dyes, to give foods a colorful appearance; to calcium peroxide and other chemicals, to keep bread soft. Antibiotics and hormones, substances so dangerous that they may not be obtained without prescriptions and should not be taken except under careful medical surveillance, are among other staples of American diets.[17]

But of all the pollutants invading our environment and contaminating our systems, none is more clearly and immediately hazardous than radioactive wastes and pesticides. Not even the astronauts, sealed in their capsule a quarter of a million miles into outer space, could escape them. So far as they are concerned, far more than has been the case with other man-made dangers, the wait-until-all-the-facts-are-in syndrome has proven murderous.

We have learned a lesson of a sort with fallout. For years we allowed strontium 90 and other substances to be released into the atmosphere by nuclear explosions or dumped into the oceans and rivers—eventually to be absorbed by people—on the grounds that no one *really* knew how harmful they might be. Thus, in 1956, misled by Atomic Energy Commission estimates about fallout levels and genetic damage risks, President Eisenhower was insisting that H-bomb testing "by the most sober and responsible scientific judgment . . . does not imperil the health of humanity." Yet only eight years later President Johnson was hailing the limited nuclear test-ban treaty for having halted "the steady, menacing increase . . . beginning to threaten the safety of the people throughout the world . . . the health of every unborn child."[18]

Pesticides, those other by-products of World War II, threaten much the same thing. Only more so. Acutely as well as chronically toxic, the vast arsenal of economic poisons has been wiping out whole species of animals in some places and threatening the existence of others, including man.

Because pesticides were designed to rid man of those creatures that menace health, comfort, and happiness, little concern arose among the general public for years about the possibility that these chemical weapons might boomerang. Conservationists have known, of course, and scientists too. But the warnings, first uttered in 1946 and most tellingly sounded by Rachel Carson in 1962, have become more difficult to ignore. In 1963 more than five million fish in the lower Mississippi were killed by minute amounts of endrin and dieldrin dumped into the water. More recently, world attention was called to the effects of pesticides on lower forms of life when in 1969 a "relatively small amount" of endosulfan, considered "relatively harmless" to animals and humans, fell from a barge into the Rhine River. The 185-mile stretch of water was transformed into a death trap, where 40 million fish were killed before the stuff washed into the sea.[19]

Pesticides, some of which are variants of nerve gases, are deadly for people, too. By 1951 they were being produced in this country in sufficient quantity to kill fifteen billion human beings—approximately six times the population of the world.[20] Kill has since been multiplied by "overkill," with more and more toxic products being turned out. They are being sprayed, dusted, fogged, and scattered over the surface of the earth at such a rate that there is not a person in the country—even an embryo— who is not carrying around cumulative deposits of the poisons. Scientists jest grimly that the milk of nursing mothers contains so much pesticides that in any other container it could not legally be carried across state lines. Western Europeans jibe that no self-respecting cannibal would eat an American. In many communities the fable of a "silent spring" has become a reality. Some scientists now fear that pesticides are disrupting the earth's most vital system—the oxygen-carbon dioxide cycle. That would spell the doom of all life.

Mithridates had other advantages over modern man. He could identify his assailants and act against them. We can't. The Borgias of the environment do not resemble ordinary poisoners—those criminals who wield the "coward's weapon." They are corporate "entities" and organization "un-persons," concerned only with profits and with means to get a job done quickly. Consequences? Ends? People? Posterity? All are irrelevant.

If an individual can be held culpable, action is swift and sudden, as it was in Florida several years ago when a sharecropper was sentenced to death for having fed his seven children parathion, a potent insect killer, to collect the $14,000 in life insurance policies he had taken out on them.[21] Yet less than a month later, when 67 persons in Colombia died in a single day from eating bread baked with parathion-contaminated flour and at least 130 persons were hospitalized, the casualties were simply written off as an "unavoidable" accident.[22] It is not hard to imagine the cries for punishment that would arise if students who are now being arrested for protesting the fouling of the environment were to deliberately spill poisons into the reservoir of a city—as is being done every day by agriculture and industry. Nor is it hard to imagine how swift action would be if a group of militants tossed into a public dump, as a California chemical company did, 55 barrels of a discarded poison—enough to paralyze most

of the people in Los Angeles County if it had become
exposed to air.[23]

Because people in executive suites are remote in time
and place from the effects of their decisions, they are
rarely called to account. Indeed, they are usually outraged
to be charged with responsibility for what happens. I saw
this for myself in the summer of 1968, in an improvised
courtroom in the mining town of Alsdorf, Germany. De-
fendants in the trial—occasioned by what European newspapers labeled "the crime of the century"—were directors
of the West German company that had developed and
marketed the tranquilizer known here as thalidomide. Government prosecutors charged them with having peddled
the drug *after* scientific investigation had revealed the
dangers—dangers made obvious by a long parade of witnesses: elderly persons trembling because of irreversible
motor damage; children who were armless, legless, hide-
ously deformed. I found one of the most striking aspects
of the affair to be the attitude of the company officials—
indignation and astonishment at being held accountable.

Although it is true that many of the polluters are not
aware of the effects of their actions, a good many are. A
prosperous Arizona rancher was expounding not long ago
to a friend of mine about his personal pesticide problems.
Lettuce is a delicate vegetable, and in order to insure
that it reaches the market unflawed, some farmers, illegally, have their workers pour little pools of poison on
the leaves when the plants are being headed. "Sure my
stuff is loaded," the rancher was frank. "But what the hell
can I do? I have $128,000 riding on that crop. There's
about one chance in a hundred—if that—that my shipments will be inspected. I'll take that chance."

Another rather grim instance was given to me by a
manufacturer of pesticide-free cigarettes. It is his theory,

supported by some solid scientific opinion, that the most
hazardous thing about smoking is the amount of pesticides
drawn into the system in 'mainstream' smoke. Tobacco,
long the only crop without federal regulations, is loaded
with pesticide residues of all kinds. Cigars have even
more than cigarettes since they must have "perfect"
leaves. The manufacturer told me that in one experiment
juices were extracted from a cigar bought at a retail outlet in North Carolina and mixed with food. The stuff
was lethal enough to kill twenty-two test rats within ten
hours. Yet his company found it all but impossible to
break into the cigarette market with their pesticide-free
products. The project was actively discouraged by state
agriculture extension workers. (In 1969, the USDA halted
the use of DDT against tobacco pests after West Germany
and other European countries threatened to halt all tobacco imports; yet the state agency recommended for
"preventive" treatment highly toxic disulfoton, applied at
the rate of forty pounds an acre.) Radio and television ads
were rejected by the National Association of Broadcasters
on the ground that the "code" prohibits *health claims*—
as offering the public a choice between pesticide-loaded
cigarettes and pesticide-free cigarettes was held to be.

Interestingly enough, one of the company's best individual customers was an heir to a great tobacco fortune—
an emphysema victim who sent his personal check every
two weeks for years to take care of his smoking needs.[24]

When the major polluters are called to account, they
either take evasive action or insist that they be allowed to
police themselves.[25] Reynard appointed to guard the
chickenyard!

Thanks to lobbying activities, penalties for large-scale
pollution are so preposterously low that most companies

find it more economical to pay them than to stop polluting. In Los Angeles, "litterbugs" can be fined up to $500 and jailed for up to six months for strewing paper or refuse. But a company there doing a $30,000,000 annual business in vegetable oils acknowledged not long ago that quite illegally—and without punishment—it had been dumping wastes into the harbor regularly for 36 years.[26]

Lobbyists have exercised heroic efforts, usually successful, to place corporate polluters beyond the reach of laws that apply to individuals. In February 1969, when world attention was focused on an off-shore oil drilling accident that turned 500 square miles of ocean off the California coast into what many observers dramatically labeled a "dead sea," oil industry lobbyists were busy at a legislative hearing on water pollution. Their argument was the standard: "We are the experts. We can police ourselves."

The public relations screen the polluters have erected to protect themselves has allowed them to go unmolested about the business of defacing the landscape, shattering the life chains, jeopardizing the health and lives of all earth's species—present and to come. Thus, smog makers in the oil and automotive industries, with the aid of government agents, have been able to persuade urban dwellers to reject the evidence of their own senses as well as documented scientific studies pointing out the danger in the air. Instead, smog has been likened to harmless smoke and fog. For two decades, official reports and news communications euphemistically called it an "eye irritant," while people, particularly children, were allowed to damage hearts and lungs as a "calculated risk."[27]

The public relations of the pesticide industry has been even more successful. Publicists have made articles of faith the notions that those direct poisons not only taste good, but are good for you, that any attempt to minimize their overuse would be against public interest. Their damaging effects—at least some of them—have been widely known since 1950, when Congressman James J. Delaney of New York organized an inquiry into the use of chemicals in foods. Yet for two decades anyone who has questioned them has been branded "unscientific" at best and "unpatriotic" at worst—derided as a "kook" or a "Commie."

That kind of abuse is popular not only among the paid publicists, but among academicians, government employees, and legislators sensitive to the pressures of the chemical and farm industries. The "education" of the public has been so thorough that millions of housewives regard pesticides as no more harmful than scouring powder. More than a few women have been so indoctrinated that they have developed "pest hallucinations," summoning exterminators to rid their houses of "invisible infestations" of unwanted creatures.[28]

Farmers, who use most of the more than a billion pounds of poisons produced here annually, are in little better shape, dousing fields and orchards with a chemical rain to exterminate imaginary as well as real pests. Although they are dealing with some of the deadliest substances ever devised by man, many of them are totally ignorant of what they are about. A study made recently in a midwestern state revealed that at least 50 percent of the farmers did not know what the word "toxic" meant. They thought simply that it meant dangerous to bugs and weeds.[29] That curious definition is by no means limited to the ignorant and illiterate. Quite the reverse; the more they read agricultural journals and listen to expert advice, the more inclined they are to believe in the safety of economic poisons. That point was made clear to me in the spring of 1970 by a friend, a widely read man who had set off on a trip around the country with his wife, a newly retired librarian. I had mentioned in a letter to them that I was doing some research on pesticides. A week later I had a reply. In it was a clipping from the Amarillo *Daily News:* "Dieldrin Cause of Robin Deaths."[30] In the accompanying note my friend wrote that he had spent $600 on dieldrin the year before; the man who was renting his place had spent a similar sum: a total of $1,200 on 160 acres planted in corn and soybeans. "When I get to Illinois," he sounded indignant about the death of the birds, "I will surely check up on this chemical."

It is not surprising that even sophisticated persons have been victimized by the advertising and propaganda barrage. The overkill program has been sanctioned and promoted by those persons and institutions in whom there is the greatest trust. Chief among them are the state agricultural colleges, which have worked closely with the chemical industry, and the federal and state regulatory agencies.

All have been what may only be considered casual about the public interest, as will be seen in detail in later chapters. The agricultural scientists have compromised themselves to such an extent that one manufacturer of a pest control device scoffed to me recently, "Grant is just another word for bribe." The record of state and local agencies is not glowing; that of federal agencies little better. A panel of the American Bar Association said recently of the Federal Trade Commission, which is supposed to protect consumers against false advertising and other deceptive and predatory practices, that "if change does not occur there will be no substantial purpose to be served by its continued existence."[31] The Food and Drug Administration? According to its own recent study, it has done little more than the FTC: "The consumer is

literally surrounded by an arsenal of products which can
kill or maim him."[32] As for the USDA . . . That has simply
allowed the food supply to be poisoned, while its officials
indulge in such effusions as:

> Making an honest dollar through honest effort has,
> historically in these United States, been considered
> as American as Mom's apple pie. That's what the food
> industry in this country does. It makes an honest
> dollar through an honest effort to protect your food
> and mine against all hazards.[33]

In all fairness, much of the responsibility for the low
level of performance by government agencies must be
assumed by legislators, who determine their course of
conduct. Characteristic of a particular type is Representative Jamie L. Whitten of Mississippi. As chairman of the
House Appropriations Subcommittee on Agriculture, he
is in an excellent position to shape USDA programs and
policies. His attitude about pesticides has been quite
clearly stated: "The worst residue problem we have to
face today is the residue of public opinion left by Rachel
Carson's book, *Silent Spring*."[34]

Equally statesmanlike concern for the public was ex-
hibited by Senator George Murphy of California in the
summer of 1969, when a select subcommittee was investigating farm labor problems. To underscore the argument
by the United Farm Workers Organizing Committee that
workers are being flagrantly exposed to poisons, Attorney
Jerome Cohen introduced a report showing that grapes
purchased in a Washington, D.C., supermarket, three
thousand miles away from the California vineyard where
they were harvested, contained 18 parts per million of
aldrin. Senator Murphy branded the report "a vicious
type of deceit." Only some papers that had headlined that

story carried his later apology and the news that the grapes did indeed contain aldrin—180 times the amount considered safe for human consumption.[35]

Although there are notable exceptions—for instance, Senator Philip A. Hart, Senator Mark Hatfield, Senator Walter F. Mondale, Senator Edmund Muskie, Senator Gaylord A. Nelson, Senator Alan Cranston; Congressmen like Richard Ottinger of New York, Paul N. McCloskey, Jr., and George E. Brown, Jr., of California, L. H. Fountain of North Carolina—the record of politicians, foreign and domestic, is not generally encouraging. In his successful appeal to the United Nations to call a conference on pollution not later than 1972, Swedish Ambassador Sverker Astrom warned against allowing them to do the planning rather than scientists, who are "well aware of the exact magnitude of this problem."[36]

In the case of pesticides, the planning has not even been done by politicians, but by the home officers and the traveling salesmen of the manufacturers, who are literally merchandising death.

Some progress has been made during recent years against DDT. Many countries have followed the lead taken by Sweden in banning it, including, in a limited way, our own. But that victory should not be allowed to obscure the larger issues. Very little attention is being given to biological and physical means of coping with pest problems; but a great deal to chemical replacements for DDT, many of which are far more poisonous. The attitude of many users was summed up succinctly by a California rancher. Told about a state-ordered ban on DDT on grapes, he snapped his fingers and said casually; "That's all right with me; I'll just use TEPP." That pesticide is so toxic that a single drop on the skin is more than enough to kill a man.

People don't know about these things, is his theory; and what they don't know won't. . . .

But pesticides can and do hurt. The hope is that people will recognize that and work to prevent further damage. How much can be done by "ordinary" citizens was made apparent during the battle against radiation. That we are now even partially shielded is due largely to groups like Consumers Union, which undertook the first large-scale investigation of the fallout hazard and led the campaign to halt further exposure to it.[37] The matter is urgent. As long ago as 1963 Dr. Jerome B. Wiesner of President Kennedy's Science Advisory Committee told Senate investigators that chemicals in the environment could be "potentially a much greater hazard than nuclear fallout."[38] The quantity has increased astronomically since then. It is no longer a question of merely reaching a point of no return. As one scientist noted gloomily a short time ago, "Already it may be too late."[39]

2. WITHOUT KNOWLEDGE, WHAT CONSENT?

ON A FALL afternoon in 1961, one of the most curious medical-detective stories of recent times began, when Dr. John F. Conrad, Jr., a staff member of a children's hospital in Fresno, California, received a call from a colleague asking him to admit a patient. When the 8-year-old boy arrived, it was obvious that he was in need of help; his face was pale, his eyes glassy, his heart beating rapidly, his breathing irregular. He was also suffering from muscle twitches, diarrhea, nausea, vomiting, and abdominal pain—"confused in mind and almost comatose."

Why? What? How?

In the manner of the Scottish physician who provided Sir Arthur Conan Doyle with the model for Sherlock Holmes, Dr. Conrad managed to avert the deaths of at least six youngsters and prevent the illness of a number of others.[1]

According to the story, first reported in the *Journal of the American Medical Association* in 1963 and brilliantly related not long ago by Berton Roueché in *The New Yorker*,[2] the beginning of the happy ending occurred when Dr. Conrad deduced correctly that the child had been poisoned by an organic phosphate insecticide. He revived him. But it became imperative to find the source after the lad, who had been released, had to be admitted to the hospital a second time in shock and after another

8-year-old boy was hospitalized with the same kind of acute poisoning.

Dr. Conrad, according to Mr. Roueché's account, suspected that the boy he was treating had been poisoned by either something in the family car or by something he was wearing, since the second episode began between the time he left the hospital cured and the time he reached home. He had the most likely item, the jeans the boy had worn on the two occasions, sent to the State Department of Public Health. There, they were tossed into a cage with a colony of mosquitoes bred for experimental purposes. An investigator described what happened next:

> I tell you, it was a sight to see. Those mosquitoes just curled up and died. It took only fifteen minutes. At the end of that time, every mosquito in the colony was dead. There was another breeding colony about twenty feet away, and in about five more minutes all *those* mosquitoes were dead, too. The poison was that volatile.[3]

How had the jeans acquired the lethal burden of pesticide? Investigation showed that they had been included in a shipment sent from a Fresno clothing factory to a Los Angeles retailer eight months earlier. The truck carrying them was also transporting machinery, farm equipment, and 120 gallons of an emulsified concentrate of Phosdrin, one of the organic phosphate poisons. One of the metal containers sprang a leak, spilling some of the stuff on a bundle of jeans. When they reached the warehouse in Los Angeles, a shipping clerk noticed the stain and rejected them. The jeans were hauled back to Fresno, stored, and finally put on sale at a salvage depot. The bargain had been an almost fatal one for the six who were stricken and for others who were warned in time.

The story of the "Clothing-Borne Epidemic" undoubtedly has entertainment value; it is also an instructive one since it indicates how deadly pesticides are, how ubiquitous, how ignorant we are of their presence, how casually they are handled by those who are supposed to know about their effects.

The notion is current that pesticides are hazardous only on the farm. That is why the U.S. Department of Agriculture has chief responsibility for their registration and use; that is why those laws we do have apply chiefly to farm work, why educational campaigns have been chiefly for farmers.

Farms continue to be dangerous places, largely because of pesticides—so dangerous that a California superior court judge ruled recently that farm work does not constitute "suitable employment" and that a man's unemployment compensation cannot be terminated for refusing to accept it.[4]

Farmers are careless about themselves and their families. According to *The Farm Quarterly*, pesticide poisonings are serious and frequent. Children have died from eating food dropped on sprayed floors, drinking out of pop bottles that had been used to store pesticides, inhaling the poisons from open containers. So have adults. Because older pesticides, chiefly arsenic-based ones, did not easily penetrate the skin—a route through which modern ones travel readily into the bloodstream—people feel secure as long as they are not eating them. But among deaths reported during recent years was that of a 28-year-old farmer, who was found sprawled face down in a field of lettuce he had started to spray the evening before with a mixture of Phosdrin, DDD, and parathion. He had shortly before completed a two-week chemical training program and had started work fully armored in protective clothing—rubber gloves, rubber suit, and respirator. But at one point he had apparently torn one of his rubber gloves and discarded it. The toxicity of the chemicals he was using was so great that only one-half a gram on the skin could cause death. He must have gotten at least that on his bare hand.[5]

Farmers are even more careless—sometimes homicidally negligent—with their workers. Consider the case of a 16-year-old laborer who was killed recently in California as the result of spraying a field of strawberries:

> The permit to purchase and apply the pesticide had expired, so that it was purchased and applied illegally. The highly toxic phosphate ester was applied by hand duster, a primitive and entirely unsafe method of application. The container label was not read by anyone until after the illness was discovered. No advance arrangements were made with a physician for prompt, adequate care for an emergency. The worker was not instructed about hazards and precautions for using the pesticide.

Moreover, as Dr. Irma West, former coordinator of the Injury Control Project with the California Department of Public Health, noted, when the boy was taken to a physician, no one could provide any information about the pesticide he had used. In any case, it would have been almost pointless since the product was found to have been misbranded.[6]

Although every single one of the series of errors was in violation of the laws and regulations, no one was held responsible for his death.

Other examples of negligence are common. In Texas, for example, which is also a highly regulated state, there has been a "significant increase" in pesticide poisonings

in the Rio Grande Valley since methyl and ethyl parathion were introduced to control bollworms. A report in
the *Farm Journal* noted that 23 hoe hands were stricken
"almost simultaneously" when they entered a cotton field
that had been treated twelve hours earlier.[7] To permit
workers to go into a field only twelve hours after being
sprayed with those organic phosphates is not merely
"hurried" and "careless," as was held to be the case; it
was downright murderous. Permissible time limit in California is from 14 to 28 *days*, depending on the concentration. Even that may be too short a time. A case has been
cited in which 16 of 24 workers were overcome when they
entered a vineyard 33 days after spraying; and Dr. John
E. Swift of the University of California at Berkeley told
me of an instance in which workers had been affected
when they entered an orchard *60* days after it had been
sprayed with parathion. Yet farmers have actually been
known to have fields sprayed by crop-dusting planes while
workers were in them.[8] It is no wonder that in the Southwest pesticides are now called *muerte andando*—walking
death.

Life off the farm has become just as hazardous—perhaps even more so since there are fewer regulations and
there has been relatively little effort to alert people to
dangers and to teach them how to protect themselves.
Pesticides are used with such abandon and handled so
indiscriminately that there is no hiding place.

A dramatic example of that was called to my attention
early in 1969 at a court hearing on the petition of the
United Farm Workers Organizing Committee to force
county agriculture officials to release spraying records.
Edward Lester, owner of medical laboratories in the
area, appeared in support of the petition, contrary to his
own financial interests. Lester provides testing services

for many of the large crop-dusting companies that were fighting the petition on the grounds that pesticide applications are "trade secrets." As evidence of the need for full disclosure of what poisons are being sprayed, where and when, Mr. Lester cited a case he had been called in on a few months earlier, when a truck driver had collapsed on the street in Fresno while changing a tire. Investigation revealed that some time earlier the man had driven through an area that had been sprayed with an organic phosphate pesticide. His truck tires had picked up and retained enough of the lethal stuff to fell him hours later while he was changing a flat.

That kind of thing is not unique, Mr. Lester told me, adding: "Obviously I feel quite strongly about the need to inform people. I see so many critically ill persons, including children and young people. If proper precautions were taken, people wouldn't die."

Proper precautions are not being taken, people are not being informed that they are exposed to pesticide poisoning dangers in the air, water, food, in the objects that surround them in their own homes. Of course, accidents do happen. But most of them occur because of the conspiracy of silence involving industry, science, and government agencies.

A report by the Human Relations Agency of the California Department of Public Health[9] recently called attention to a number of deficiencies in the law.

It noted that no regulation now forbids the storage or transport of highly toxic pesticides with food, clothing, or other commodities designed for close personal contact, despite the series of mass disasters that have been occurring since 1956. Among the most serious, in addition to the one in Colombia mentioned in Chapter 1, was an episode in Mexico in 1967 in which seventeen persons, mostly children, died after eating food made with sugar that was contaminated by parathion carried in the same truck. In that year, too, flour being carried by ship to Saudi Arabia and Qatar was contaminated by endrin; the toll, 26 dead, 874 ill. The largest single disaster occurred in 1958, when a cargo of flour being shipped to India was contaminated by parathion stored nearby; as a result, 106 persons died, 826 others became seriously ill.

Neither shippers nor stores provide adequate information or protective equipment for workers; as a consequence, those on hand during an accident cannot limit or control a spill except at personal jeopardy and have no way of protecting the general public.

Brushes with disaster are far more frequent than is generally realized, with over a billion pounds of synthetic organic pesticides being shipped around the country each year and stored in warehouses—sometimes several times before they are used. Accidents of all types occur to the stuff: ships collide, trains are derailed, planes crash, and trucks pile into other vehicles, roll over, or lose their loads.

Public tolerance for such activity is very high, but then public knowledge is very minimal. It was not until the summer of 1969 that protest was made about rail shipments of chemical warfare nerve gases, close relatives of organic phosphate pesticides. Efforts to halt that hazardous activity came after Congressman Richard D. McCarthy of New York announced and denounced the Army's decision to move by rail 27,000 tons of lethal nerve gas from Colorado, Alabama, and other parts of the country to New Jersey and ultimately into the Atlantic for a sea burial.[10]

No general concern has yet been expressed over pesticide shipments, despite the obvious hazards and despite past experiences. Since most pesticides are shipped at least once by truck, that means that at least a billion pounds a year are exposed to the vagaries of everyday traffic—and that everyone who drives a car is exposed to the possibilities of a pesticide disaster on the road. It seems to many observers a matter of sheerest luck that more fatalities have not occurred. Several years ago, only three persons were hospitalized when an American Potash Company truck carrying parathion from Los Angeles to Phoenix lost a ton of the pesticide. Low casualties were attributed not merely to luck, but to the prompt action of highway officials who sealed off a 50-mile stretch of road until crews could decontaminate it.[11] In 1968, three accidents involving parathion occurred on the San Francisco Bay Area freeways, which are some of the most heavily traveled in the world. Since many of the accidents involve leaks and spills rather than collisions and turn-overs, they pose hidden dangers. For example, the USDA reported 540 individual Class B poison container failures in transit during the first nine months of 1968.[12] There is no way of knowing how many persons were inadvertently exposed to poisons as a result of those, or the other failures which went unreported.

Storage poses less of a problem than shipment. However, contamination of food and other substances has resulted from careless practices and faulty containers. Additionally, fire danger is quite high since many pesticides are combustible and are often mixed with flammable solvents. Because the products of combustion of some pesticides are more toxic than the pesticides themselves, their dispersal in a fire could be "catastrophic in populated areas," the California report warned.[13]

Another problem is disposal of used pesticide containers, an increasing cause of people poisoning and environmental pollution. During the 1969 spraying season

about 20 million agricultural pesticide containers had to
be gotten rid of; the number of those used for household,
public health, and structural pest control operations might
well bring the total to 200 million and more. It defies
accurate estimate.

How to dispose of them is a major concern—at least to
public health officials and conservationists. A good many
of the producers as well as large-scale users seem singu-
larly unconcerned, however, disregarding what regulations do exist as if they were matters of no consequence.
For example, Velsicol Chemical Corporation's Memphis
plant was held a major source of the endrin pollution
that ruined the fishing industry along the Mississippi and
Atchafalaya rivers some years ago. Yet when an official
appearing before the Ribicoff Subcommittee some years
ago was questioned about the "dumping" practices, he
blandly set aside photographs showing drums heaped in
a nearby creek and scattered around the landscape as
entirely irrelevant.[14] That company is not alone: California health officials reported that at one site, "an un-
supervised open dump," there were on August 6, 1969,
approximately 100 Demeton, 10 Di-syston, and 40 parathion containers. "Many of these containers retained
significant quantities of their original contents of exceedingly toxic organophosphate pesticide."[15]

Children have been poisoned by picking up discarded
containers on farms and along airstrips used by commercial applicators. Some serious adult accidents have
occurred, involving workers for refuse departments and at
dump sites.

Because pesticides are so widely and readily available,
their safety is taken for granted by most persons. Mrs.
Terri Angell of a Denver suburb got a shock a couple
of years ago, when she decided to get rid of the stock she

had accumulated. It had suddenly occurred to her, she said, that the poison she was spraying on her roses had saturated the ground her children were playing on. "Frightened" by what she read on the label of one can (only a minority of the pesticide labels contain any directions for getting rid of the containers[16]), she called the Department of Agriculture to find out how to dispose of them safely. In a letter, she described her conversation with three different people there, two of whom had doctoral degrees:

> Shall I pour this down the sink?
>
> Good heavens, no! Don't ever put any of it in any form in or near the kitchen sink—or in any containers or vessels you'll want to use again.
>
> Well, shall I cap them all tightly and put them in the trash barrel?
>
> You can't do that. If the containers broke, the trashmen would be subject to injury, or the fumes and vapors would drift around the area, either in your neighborhood or in the dump. And at the dump they might mix with something else.
>
> How about burning?
>
> Never. Fumes would . . . We'll switch you to someone else. Hold the phone . . .

The third expert finally solved Mrs. Angell's problem. He urged that, wearing a mask and gloves, she very slowly saturate and dilute the poisons with water in a bucket in the basement, taking care to aerate the latter. She was told to do this one product at a time, since "no one had yet studied what compounds could be formed by the indiscriminate mixture of these various chemicals." The bucket could be emptied down the basement floor drain, it was reluctantly agreed, after she had added plenty of water so that the pesticide would be properly diluted and the pipes thoroughly rinsed.

Commenting on the episode, Mrs. Angell said: "Those people were genuinely horrified at the thought of dumping so much lethal material at one time, but they never questioned the fact that I could acquire it without limit. They were worried, and rightly so, about the fumes I might release into the air by breakage, but there would have been no question at all had I merely gone out and sprayed all the items at one time, creating a contaminated mist in my neighborhood."

The irony of making poisonous substances so readily available to persons who are not aware of their effects has troubled other persons, too. Among them is a young California State College student I know, 23-year-old Gilbert Voss. He returned from a summer study program in Antarctica in 1969 quite shaken. His particular concern was DDT, since at that area, remote from "civilization," he had seen its effects on penguins—the shells of their eggs becoming perilously thinner, the anatomy of the birds so modified that "the skeletons are all displaced." Young Mr. Voss is no anti-pesticide fanatic, although he and his family, who own a large begonia nursery, have always regarded them with what they consider healthy respect. "But," he fumes, "it really makes me mad that any little old lady can walk into a store and buy a can of that stuff. It should have been dumped off the shelves years ago." Any little old lady, any little old child, any little old deranged person, any little old anybody can buy a can of substances vastly more toxic from any little old grocery store—or hardware or department store.

Former Secretary of Agriculture Orville L. Freeman dismissed the idea of policing individual users, after conjuring up a picture of "Mother Brown" apprehended for spraying roses "illegally."[17] And it does seem an unfeasible notion. But all of the Brown family, as well as Mother and her fellow members of the Weeping Willow Garden Club, might develop a greater respect for pesticides if they were a little harder to buy and if greater emphasis were placed on their effects on humans and the environment.

Neither, out of deference for pesticide company profits, is now the case. The proximity of the poisons to food, cosmetics, garden tools, and other harmless items gives many persons the idea that reading the label on a bomb or bottle is about as necessary as reading the list of ingredients on a package of breakfast food or a bar of candy—although that might be a good idea, too. Moreover, the messages that appear in advertising and in the news and feature articles stress words like *safety, harmless to humans and pets, protection, clean*—in addition to such standard advertising diction as *amazing, remarkable, scientifically approved, perfect.* As a consequence, labels are ignored. A 1969 study of pesticide use in Charleston, South Carolina, showed that of the 83 percent white and 97 percent nonwhite families using pesticides:

> Both white and nonwhite families commonly ignored safety precautions in the use of household chemicals. Locked storage was not employed by 88 percent of all families; 66 percent stored the pesticide within easy reach of small children.[18]

It is possible, of course, that if pesticides were labeled informatively, and if they were read intelligently, the bottom would drop out of the house-and-garden market, on which consumers are now spending at least a quarter of a billion dollars a year.[19] Our family is reasonably

literate, and it is against the law in California to sell for
home use some of the most dangerous kinds of pesticides.
Nevertheless, when I checked the supply of moth-proofers,
ant-killers, weed-eradicators, bug-slayers, and similar
items that had accumulated over the years, I found all
categories—from highly toxic Class I through Class IV[20]
—in various cupboards and on various shelves. I asked
several friends to check; their findings were the same.

Even though we have no intention of using many of
them again, there is absolutely no guarantee that they,
and others even more deadly, will not become a part of
our world and ultimately of us. Like everyone else in the
country, we are absorbing them all day every day from a
thousand different sources without our knowledge and
against our will. We have no more to say about it than
the helpless people of Vietnam who have been subjected to
a rain of agricultural chemicals in the "defoliation" campaign that, scientists report, has left "miles of forest"
without a green leaf and has caused animal life to almost
totally disappear.[21]

Private "overkill" programs launched by farmers have
been supplemented by public ones, sponsored jointly by
the pesticide industry and government agencies. Both
have been characterized by what can only be termed
massive indifference for human beings and all else that
lives. Ordinary citizens, "enemies of progress," are kept
in the dark about the kinds and amounts of poisons. That
is true not only in California, where farmers and crop
dusters have persuaded the Department of Agriculture to
keep the spray records "confidential," but even in the
nation's capital, where a city official recently refused to
disclose how much pesticide was being sprayed on the
trees.[22]

Warnings are rarely posted. In some parts of the country the amount of poisons persons absorb from the atmosphere and water far exceeds the average daily dietary intake held permissible by the World Health Organization; that fact is kept secret. After all, there are no laws that say the pesticide content of anything but food has to be regulated. And even that regulating is uncertain. Government agencies authorized to keep the public informed seem more intent on keeping the chemical and agricultural industries happy. A few weeks before Thanksgiving in 1969, the USDA seized seven million pounds of turkeys and placed them "under retention"—the largest such action in the history of federal poultry inspection. The meat, all produced by Arkansas Valley Industries, Inc., was held for further testing after residues of heptachlor up to 2 parts per million (p.p.m.) had been detected by the Campbell Soup Company. Heptachlor is so toxic that the approved residue level is zero. As the editor of the *U.S. Consumer Newsletter* noted: "The whole affair does not evoke confidence in the Federal inspection program"—nor in its public information program. He pointed out that the original discovery by Campbell had occurred on October 9; yet it was not until November 7 that the USDA acknowledged any details, and then "only" after he insisted on an explanation for rumors that had reached him from outside sources. Moreover, the editor noted:

> USDA's eventual news release was deceptively worded to downplay the gravity of the situation . . . and no company names were given except for AVI. It makes one wonder how many other potential hazards have been filed away by USDA aides.[23]

The most hazardous ways of applying pesticides have been approved to keep the industries happy. Experiments conducted as early as 1960, long before commercial application became the big business it is today, indicated that crop dusting was dangerously wasteful. Only about 50 percent of the pesticides released in an aerial spray ever reaches the surface aimed at; only a small part of that—perhaps 10 percent—ever reaches the specific target. Yet communities as well as farm and woodland areas continue to be deluged all over the world, with most adverse results: monetary as well as health costs have been high, and pest problems have been created worse than the ones the public programs were designed to solve.

A classic example of how we have been forced, without knowledge or consent, to pay for the privilege of serving as guinea pigs was the fire ant program undertaken by the USDA in 1957. Dr. Paul Ehrlich of Stanford University, who originally protested the aerial spray campaign, described recently how his fears had materialized. The kill of wildlife in checked areas was high; more disconcerting, it was discovered during the course of the program that the heptachlor used had been transformed by weathering into a persistent and highly toxic derivative—heptachlor epoxide—that was turning up in meat and milk. Additionally, the $15 million program provoked new outbreaks of fire ants in many places held to have been freed of that pest.[24]

Dozens of similar stories have been reported since then. A malaria-control program in Bolivia aimed at killing off mosquitoes was apparently more successful in killing off cats. In their absence, the village thus "aided" was overrun by a mouselike mammal harboring black typhus virus. More than 300 villagers were killed in that health campaign.[25] Nor have many of the promised economic benefits been realized. Instead of an emphasis on rational agricultural and engineering practices in underdeveloped countries, sole emphasis has been placed on agricultural chemicals. Short-term benefits are offset by long-term losses, since some of the countries are poisoning their products out of the world market[26]—just as we have done in this country. Pesticide-laden U.S. foods and tobacco are no longer acceptable in many parts of the world, and farmers are being forced out of business by the high cost of "protecting" their crops from chemically induced pest explosions and from strains of pests so resistant that they can tolerate any amount of the toxins.

Whether or not living is better through chemistry is a moot point; the evidence now suggests that dying is faster and more expensive.

3. CHEMICAL WAR IS NOT HEALTHY FOR PEOPLE . . .

IN THE TRADE they are known as *economic poisons*—the more than 45,000 registered synthetic commercial killers of weeds, bugs, funguses, rats, and other organisms considered pests. Scientists are now calling them *biocides* because of their destructiveness to the web of life. A blunter, but perhaps more meaningful label for them, is *people poisons*.

That is what has been overlooked or minimized in the debate that rages over the uncontrolled use of pesticides. The lines of battle were clearly drawn two decades ago between those who advocated unlimited use until "facts" proved them harmful and those who would restrict them until "facts" proved them safe. During the Delaney Subcommittee hearings an exchange between chief counsel Vincent A. Kleinfeld and a professor of entomology revealed the opposing attitudes. Asked about the advisability of using pesticides without full knowledge of their effects on humans, Professor William M. Hoskins said he believed in animal studies, but considered them "only preliminary to use on human beings . . . there is no substitute for that." Then:

MR. KLEINFELD: I see. . . . Couldn't that be fairly called the human guinea pig approach?

DR. HOSKINS: I presume so.

MR. KLEINFELD: How do you think these human guinea
pigs feel about it?

DR. HOSKINS: Why, I believe they would object. . . .[1]

It is the human guinea pig approach that has prevailed
—with relatively few objections, since most of the experimental subjects have no notion of what is happening to
them. Neither do their doctors, if they have doctors. Experts say that only a small percentage of acute pesticide
poisonings are reported, or even identified. Chronic and
more subtle types of poisonings are frequently misdiag-
nosed or totally ignored: yet in some parts of the country
they have already reached near epidemic proportions.

The assault begins in the womb. Scientists have found
pesticide residues in the tissues of unborn babies as early
as the twenty-second week of development, residues of
the persistent pesticides like DDT, aldrin, and dieldrin
almost as high in embryos as in adults.[2] The under-5
population has even higher levels, particularly breast-fed
babies. A Swedish toxicologist testified recently that their
intake of DDT compounds, about twice the amount recommended by the World Health Organization, comes in
the range of exposure in which laboratory animals began
to show biochemical changes.[3]

The assault that begins in the womb continues for a
lifetime, with all of us absorbing appreciable quantities
from a thousand different sources—air, water, the surfaces
we touch, the garments we wear,[4] every bite we eat. It is
wishful thinking to imagine that laws and regulations pre-
clude our absorbing unsafe amounts. Even foods and
beverages, which are regulated, may contain dangerously
unsafe residues. "Tolerances" for residues considered
harmless are set by the Food and Drug Administration,

generally at 1/100th of the smallest amount known to cause effects in the most sensitive test animals. For any compound considered too toxic to be allowed in any amount, FDA sets a zero tolerance.

While that sounds reassuring enough, protection is actually very sketchy. Zero, it seems, is a stretchable term.[5] Further, no controls have been provided to insure that tolerances are not exceeded; the FDA's staff is so small that it checks only about one percent of the food shipments over which it has authority,[6] and many states are unconcerned about foods not under Federal jurisdiction. Moreover, United States tolerances have been set according to overly optimistic estimates of damage; and they have even been set for compounds like aldrin, dieldrin, heptachlor (epoxide), and chlordane, although a "no effect" level in animals has never been determined.[7]

Regulatory agencies in Western Europe have been far more wary in setting tolerances. Just consider a few of the differences in the amounts of residue of various pesticides allowed on United States citrus fruits in 1968 and those held permissible for them in Common Market nations:[8]

	Europe (p.p.m.)	U.S. (p.p.m.)
Captan	15.0	100.0
Lindane	2.0	10.0
Parathion	.5	1.0
Toxaphene	.4	7.0

The systematic poisoning of the country's food supply, along with the air, water, and other unregulated sources, has continued chiefly because people were not dropping dead after a pesticide-laden meal. Studies showing damage have been impressive; but they have been overshadowed, out-shouted, by industry-approved studies that bear out the claim of "harmless to humans."

One such study, of value to the industry, was conducted early in the 1950's by Dr. Wayland J. Hayes, Jr., on the effect of repeated oral doses of DDT in man. Former chief of toxicology of the U.S. Public Health Service, Dr. Hayes obtained permission from the Bureau of Prisons to study the dosage-storage rate of the pesticide on a group of 51 inmate volunteers. For periods ranging up to 18 months, he fed some of them up to 35 mg. of DDT a day—a quantity about 200 times greater than the average man was ingesting in his daily diet at that time. According to Dr. Hayes, after about a year the subjects ceased to store DDT. They began to eliminate it—a phenomenon, he concluded, that indicated "a large safety factor is associated with DDT as it now occurs in the general diet."[9]

The paper, first read before a panel of the American Association for the Advancement of Science (December 29, 1955) and later printed in the *Journal of the American Medical Association,* has been reprinted by the hundreds of thousands and cited in dozens of books and hundreds of articles. Never in the history of medicine have the urine samples and fatty tissues of a few men been so chronicled. And they were few. Only 5 completed 18 months of dosage and only 35 of the original 51 completed the final examination. Two of the men considered their health adversely affected. One of the dropouts complained after 155 days that he had bone pains, occasional headaches, and tearing of the right eye—complaints Dr. Hayes dismissed as "obviously . . . of psychoneurotic origin."[10]

Some of the findings were highly subjective. The sampling was small and the selection process was questionable: studies have indicated that convicts participating in experiments are so eager to be cooperative that they fail to report adverse effects.[11] Yet overnight, Dr. Hayes became one of the most famous medics in the country. And for more than fifteen years the National Agricultural Chemicals Association has had what it considers to be an ultimate weapon against spoilsports protesting the DDT deluge.

Dr. Hayes, who became a professor of biochemistry at Vanderbilt University after retiring from government service, continued to defend pesticides, particularly DDT, vigorously. At the 1969 Wisconsin hearing on a petition to eliminate that pesticide, he asserted: "You can eat Coho salmon containing 19 p.p.m. of DDT morning, noon, and night in your total diet for at least 19 years without any harmful effect." That statement was also widely publicized by the National Agricultural Chemicals Association, which had called him as witness.[12]

Not all scientists shared his profound faith. Nor did they shortly after DDT first made its appearance. In 1945 the *British Medical Journal* carried a number of reports of DDT poisoning. One researcher said his reactions included tiredness, heaviness, irritability, joint pains, and a "feeling of mental incompetence in tackling the simplest mental task."[13] Another, who applied a DDT solution to his skin, was bedded for three weeks and absent from work for ten.[14]

Dr. C. H. Curran, curator of the American Museum of Natural History, warned as early as 1951: "All of us who have experimented with DDT during the past years have recognized that we were dealing with a dangerous substance. From the very beginning most of us were afraid of its direct effects on the human body."[15]

Its gross effects—"DDT jitters"—were readily apparent in cockroaches and in men.[16] But what of the more subtle effects, with DDT building up in the fatty tissues of liver, heart, brain, and sex glands?

Some scientists were willing to risk comments on those effects at an early date. Among them were a number of medical specialists who appeared before the Delaney Subcommittee in 1950 and 1951. A California physician reported that some of his patients whose fatty tissue contained high levels of DDT showed signs of liver damage in addition to feelings of exhaustion, irritability, and mental dullness.[17] Dr. William Coda Martin, another witness, stressed then and in his introduction to Leonard Wickenden's book based on the hearings that the greater number of hepatitis cases may be caused by DDT residues on foods.[18]

By the time of the Wisconsin hearings, scientists in large numbers had come to share fears about the consequences. Dr. Richard M. Welch, a pharmacologist at Burroughs-Wellcome Research Laboratories in New York, testified that DDT reduced the effectiveness of a number of drugs. Moreover, he pointed out, the stuff could also be affecting man by causing changes in sex hormones. Dr. Robert Risebrough, University of California biology professor, supported the argument that sex hormones are being affected by DDT, which activates enzymes.[19] "No responsible person," he said, "could get up here and say that this constant nibbling away at our steroids is without any physiological effect. It would be irresponsible."[20]

(NACA attorney Louis McLean derided such comments, calling DDT critics "food faddists and/or health nuts, preoccupied with their own sexual potency.")[21]

But testimony about its effects on sex hormones could be dismissed no more easily than evidence to show that it adversely affected liver, spleen, and kidneys, and that it was a cause of cancer in mice and men. Dr. Wilhelm C. Hueper, former director of the National Cancer Institute, who had long been classifying DDT as one of the hundreds of chemical carcinogens in the environment, ad-

vanced pointed evidence to show why. Among studies he
cited was that of the Florida researchers, J. L. Radomski
and William B. Deichmann, which showed "highly significant elevations of pesticide concentrations" in cancer
cases of all types—lung, stomach, rectum, pancreas,
prostate, and urinary bladder—particularly among persons who used large quantities of pesticides in their
homes.[22]

(Dr. Hueper's attitude toward pesticides has not en-
deared him to Washington policy makers who have lion-
ized Dr. Hayes. He told the Ribicoff Subcommittee that
his research had been halted by his superiors, his staff of
sixteen had been immobilized, and he had been excluded
from official meetings because of his work.)[23]

Interestingly enough, less than a month after he and
other experts made a case about the more subtle and
hidden dangers of DDT in Wisconsin, FDA scientists reported that in one experiment in which a "low dosage"
was fed to a monkey, postmortem examination showed
damage to the hypothalamus, an important endocrine
center, which helps to control emotional states, digestive
processes, body temperatures, sex glands, sleep rhythms,
and hunger and thirst.[24]

And DDT is among the *least toxic* pesticides now
widely employed!

Some of its relatives in the chlorinated hydrocarbon
family are far more poisonous. Among them is chlordane.
Dr. A. J. Lehman, then director of the FDA's pharmacology division, told the Delaney Committee that he, personally, "would hesitate to eat food that had any chlordane
residue at all."[25] Yet for the twenty years since he made
that statement Americans have been doing just that. More
than a decade later, Dr. Paul W. Smith of the Federal
Aviation Agency called attention of the Ribicoff Subcom-

mittee to other hazards. Chlordane, he pointed out, was known to cause depression of the bone marrow, reducing the number of red and white blood cells.[26]

(Dr. Smith was understandably troubled. Crop dusting is one of the world's most dangerous occupations. A former duster told me that when he abandoned it, he felt "as if I had rejoined the human race." For the first time he was able to buy life insurance.)

Another member of the family is lindane, which has been implicated in cases of serious blood disorders. Dr. M. M. Hargraves of the Mayo Clinic has been warning against it for years. Cases in point included a young woman who had received twelve blood transfusions without success before seeking help at Mayo. Medical-detective work revealed the cause of her aplastic anemia—an often fatal disease in which blood cells are destroyed. When a lindane vaporizer in her music room, where she practiced for several hours a day, was removed, she improved gradually and recovered. Another case involved a man suffering from fatigue, tremor, loss of appetite, and anemia. Again, medical-detective work revealed lindane as the cause. An exterminator had dusted the underside of his house with the stuff. Some had seeped into a floor furnace, which distributed its fumes through the house. House and furnace were decontaminated immediately; but the man's recovery was a slow process—two and a half years.[27]

Other notorious chlorinated hydrocarbons are heptachlor, endrin, dieldrin, and aldrin, which is converted to dieldrin in man and the environment. Acutely and chronically toxic, like others in the family, they have caused liver damage in experimental animals "in very small doses." The chairman of the President's Science Advisory Committee told the Ribicoff Subcommittee that these pesticides should be scrutinized carefully. Although the number of acute *fatal* poisonings is low, many persons exposed to them, particularly dieldrin, have suffered acute poisoning. Muscle tremors, convulsions, and changes in the pattern of brain activity recur dangerously.[28]

The ultimate consequences of those toxins is still in question. It has long been known that they affect the nervous system—which is unable to tolerate even brief interruptions without serious consequences. They also act on liver, kidneys, brain, bone marrow, and other vital organs and processes. Many experts now agree that they are teratogenic as well as carcinogenic, that is, they cause birth malformations as well as cancer. More recently, it has been suggested that since some of the chlorinated hydrocarbons are converted to epoxides, they affect the structure of the genes, which may result in deformed children. Thus, they are also *mutagenic*.

Not the least of our problems is that some of the most villainous members of the chlorinated hydrocarbon group are almost as toxic when absorbed by the skin or inhaled as when taken orally. Yet it is almost impossible to detect their presence. In his protest against the use of chlordane and dieldrin in 1951, Dr. Lehman pointed out: "The individual has no warning of skin contact since neither of the compounds is irritating to the skin in low concentrations."[29]

England banned many uses of the more toxic members of the DDT family many years ago, with very minimal agricultural losses. We have used them to such extent that by the spring of 1968 "maximum" accepted levels had been reached. Where we are now is anyone's guess, thanks to the determination to wait until *all* the facts have been discovered.

There has been far less question about the dangers of

the other large family of pesticides—the organic phosphates. All of them, from "relatively harmless" malathion to absolutely poisonous TEPP, are related to and function like nerve gasses. (So do the carbamates, the third principal group.)

The "nerve gas" pesticides inhibit the enzyme that transfers messages from the brain to the acting agents. When impulses are sent by the brain commanding our muscles, glands, and fibres to act so that we can talk, walk, breathe, or do anything else, the impulse follows an intricate route. It finally arrives at a "transfer" point, where one nerve fibre connects with another. A substance called acetylcholine is released to excite the proper agent to act. The acetylcholine must be destroyed immediately so that the signal does not jam—as, for example, an automobile horn will continue to bleat until pressure is removed. The removal of "pressure" is accomplished by cholinesterase, which splits acetylcholine into two inactive substances.

Both the organic phosphates and the carbamates unite with cholinesterase in the body and prevent it from destroying and neutralizing acetylcholine. Therefore the signals jam. Army technical manuals provide a concrete description of what happens then. The first symptoms parallel those of relatively harmless irritants: the nose begins to run, vision is blurred. Then nausea sets in, followed by vomiting, excessive sweating, uncontrolled salivation, and urinary incontinence. The heart, which beats rapidly in the early stages, slows thumpingly. Convulsions follow; then, coma and muscular paralysis. Breathing becomes increasingly difficult, finally impossible. Then death.[30]

Because the effects are so horrifying, it was assumed that the organic phosphates would be used sparingly and under rigidly controlled circumstances. Because the symptoms are so obvious, it was assumed that victims could be readily identified and treated.

Neither assumption was warranted. After insects began to develop resistance to formidable doses of DDT, its more toxic relatives and the organic phosphates came to be used with increasing abandon. By 1968 nearly 60 million pounds of parathion and methyl parathion were being produced. When the DDT ban becomes reasonably effective, that figure is expected to soar.

After a series of disasters involving men working in manufacturing and formulating plants and ground sprayers and crop dusters, some states began to require that all such employees be tested frequently to check their cholinesterase level. When it is low, they are taken off the job so that it can build up again. Those who do not recover must take other jobs since even minimal exposure can be fatal.

No such protection, however, was made for farm workers or for the general public who are also exposed. Who among them or us has had a ChE check this year?

The need is great, particularly among farm workers. Symptoms, it now appears, are not all that obvious. For example, when California public health officials were called in to investigate an outbreak of parathion poisoning several years ago after 90 peach pickers in one area had to seek medical aid, they decided to make a further study. Selecting at random 70 other workers who showed no signs at all, health officials found that 50 percent of them had "significant reduction of cholinesterase."[31]

Persons who do show symptoms are in little better shape. Physicians are rarely knowledgeable about pesticide poisoning, even in places where it frequently occurs. A witness told Senator Walter F. Mondale's Subcommittee on Migratory Labor in 1969 that doctors often misdiagnose parathion poisoning as "flu." As a consequence of its "unchecked" spread, worker safety advocate Jerome B. Gordon added, "Uncounted thousands of the nation's migrant farm workers, farmers, and suburban homeowners have been fatally overcome or seriously disabled." He held organic phosphates largely responsible for the more than 100,000 cases of pesticide poisoning that occur each year.[32]

That the number may be even higher was suggested a a few months later during a hearing by the House Subcommittee on Labor. Dr. Lee Mizrahi of a rural clinic in a California farm county said that nearly half of the children he tested during a nutrition study showed signs of organic poisoning: skin rashes, burning eyes, nausea, vomiting, dizziness. "Some of the children, like their parents, had been feeling sick." Since Dr. Mizrahi's patients were not in emergency shape, the discovery was made quite by accident. He indicated his dismay and concern. "To me, it is tragically absurd that in 1969 such a study by an obscure rural doctor should be the first one ever done on children," Dr. Mizrahi told the legislators. "We think this problem is widespread."[33]

Dr. Thomas Milby, chief of the California State Department of Public Health, agreed with Dr. Mizrahi that pesticide poisoning had reached "near-epidemic proportions in some areas"; he also suggested that since organic phosphates account for more injuries and deaths than any other pesticides and since they are being used as replacements for DDT, an in-depth study of their effects should be made.[34] A report compiled by his department in 1969 showed that farm workers are in serious danger. In one county, where 774 workers were tested for pesticide poisoning, 154 of them reported one related symptom; 144, two symptoms; 109, three; 83, four; and 163, five symptoms.[35]

The organic phosphates, like the chlorinated hydrocarbons, have also been known to produce long-range effects. In a report in *The Lancet,* two British medical researchers noted that sixteen persons who had been exposed to those pesticides for between 18 and 24 months had suffered "schizophrenic and depressive reactions, with severe impairment of memory and difficulty in concentration."[36] The organic phosphates and carbamates have been described as carcinogenic and associated with birth abnormalities in test animals.

Other effects are only beginning to come to light. So, too, are the full effects of another group of toxicants—the nitrophenols, which work acutely and cumulatively on cells. Early signs and symptoms of those poisons are easy to ignore—particularly in hot weather since they include excessive sweating, thirst, and a feeling of euphoria followed by fatigue. Yet the lethal dose is small. And according to experts, there is no antidote.[37]

The most recent and one of the most horrifying pesticide problems was called to the attention of the American people in December 1969, when three children of a school janitor in New Mexico were taken to a hospital after eating pork contaminated with a mercury compound. The hog had been fed granary sweepings of seed treated with a commonly used fungicide. The result? A year later, one child was still in a coma; another had the muscular response of a spastic; a third was blind and crippled. There was little likelihood that any would recover.

That mercury is a devastating poison has been known scientifically since Paracelsus, the Swiss physician, wrote a clinical description in 1533.[38] However, it continued to be used for years as a therapeutic, for a wide variety of ills, including syphilis. Inorganic mercury poisoning became an occupational disease after the industrial revolution—to such extent and to such effect in the felt industry, for example, that "mad as a hatter" became the term used to describe the illness. (It worked not only on the brain and nervous system, but less obviously on liver, kidney, and other organs.) And the danger has increased geometrically during the last few decades because of the widespread use of organic mercury compounds in industry and agriculture. They are more readily absorbed than inorganic mercury—taken in through the skin and lungs—to accumulate and lodge in the tissue of brain and other vital organs.[39]

The first protests against methylmercury, one of the highly toxic organic compounds, came from conservationists in Sweden. There farmers had been using it to treat both fungus-infested and healthy seed as routinely as they plowed. Birds were dying, they said, from eating the treated seed or from eating creatures that had eaten the seed. According to one of the Swedish conservationists, Goran Lofroth: "Their charges were dismissed by industrial and agricultural experts."[40]

Charges became impossible to shrug off after 110 persons in Minamata, Japan, were killed or severely disabled between 1953 and 1960. A plastics plant in the area was discharging methylmercury into the waters off the coastal town; people eating the contaminated fish and shellfish were poisoned. So were some of their unborn offspring; one of the more curious aspects of the case was that women who had few or no symptoms gave birth to babies with congenital defects. Further protest arose in Japan in 1965, when 26 people in another coastal town were poisoned, five of whom died.

Japan moved to replace mercury compounds in agriculture as well as in industry. So did Sweden, after it was found that eggs and meat and fish had far higher levels than products of other European countries—amounts magnifying as they moved along the chain from treated seed to grain to hen to egg.[41]

No action was taken here, with mercury compounds becoming best sellers, widely used to treat seeds of wheat, barley, peas, rice, and other grain before planting. Nor does it seem that action is likely to be taken.

Public protest was so great after a National Broadcasting Corporation television program about the hazards of mercury, movingly documenting the plight of the New Mexico children and their family, that the USDA ordered the company selling the compound held responsible to remove the product from the market. The company took the USDA to court, and won its appeal to overturn the suspension—after a USDA official testified that he knew of no permanent injury resulting from the use of the product *per se*.[42] Pesticide testing procedures are not rigorous. Generally, they involve establishing the LD_{50}— lethal dose for half of the test animals. Also, the effects of single and multiple doses over relatively brief periods must be determined, and "safe" and effective use against pests evaluated. (These tests are made exclusively by the manufacturers!)

However, it often takes years for the dangers of weak carcinogens to reveal themselves. Dr. Samuel S. Epstein of Children's Cancer Research Foundation and the Harvard Medical School warned recently that pesticides *"could affect and catastrophically so, as many as 1/10,000 of the population and yet probably escape detection by conventional procedures involving test groups of as few as 50 adult animals for a given dosage."*[43]

Dr. Epstein developed tests for a wide range of pollutants, injecting materials into mice during their first three months of life only. He made startling findings. Trace amounts of urban atmospheric pollution—the amounts inhaled by humans in three or four months—produced "a high incidence" of tumors of the liver, lymphatic system, and lung. Dr. Epstein found that a commonly used herbicide, maleic hydrazide, also induced a high incidence of liver tumors. The amount a person could absorb from potatoes alone within four years (based on FDA tolerances) is comparable to the level that is carcinogenic to mice.

Singly, the poisons and pollutants are bad enough. In combinations they are even more dangerous. They may cancel out some chemicals—neutralize the effects of such drugs as antihistamines, barbiturates, some antibiotics. They may enhance the effects of others. Scientists have been concerned since 1950 about potentiation or synergism—the ability of two or more agents to produce a greater effect when combined than the sum of the individual effects. In that year, the FDA commissioner pointed out that combinations of chlorinated hydrocarbons at "harmless" levels produced perceptible liver damage; yet none of them did when administered alone at the same rate.[44]

Four other investigators reported that the organic phosphate, malathion, which is considered one of the least toxic pesticides in that group, reacted dramatically when animals being tested were also exposed to some of the others. The LD_{50} for malathion was established at 1,400 mg. per kg. for oral dosage; that of EPN, 65 mg. However, the lethal dosage levels when the two were combined plummeted to 167 mg. and 6.6 mg.[45] A later study by Dr. Kenneth P. DuBois, director of the University of Chicago's toxicity laboratory, supported that finding. It indicated that other organic phosphates could also potentiate malathion. For example, he found that when TOTP was injected in rats that had been exposed to malathion, the LD$_{50}$ dropped from 1,000 mg. per kg. to 8.2 mg.[46]

More recently, a study by Dr. Epstein showed that when Piperonyl butoxide (PB), a comparatively inert and nontoxic compound used widely in pesticide formulations, was administered by itself to infant mice it was neither toxic nor carcinogenic. However, when it was administered with other agents (also at nontoxic levels), it induced liver tumors.[47]

Not even sophisticated chemists know what combinations of chemicals they are taking in at any one meal—to say nothing of during any day or any week. Farmers are so anxious to arrive at market with flawless products that they dump on incredible numbers as well as amounts of pesticides. In *The Hidden Assassins,* Booth Mooney cites one instance in which an FDA inspector found that a lettuce grower had used chlordane, endrin, dieldrin, DDT, toxaphene, malathion, cryolite, and rotenone on his crop—only eleven days before harvest.[48] When they were added to the rest of the intake in the body of an unsuspecting consumer. . . . The possible consequences defy imagining.

It is not realistic to imagine that we can wash them off our foods or wait them out. The half-life of some chlorinated hydrocarbons is fifteen years. And the organic phosphates are by no means as quickly degraded as we have been led to believe. The stained jeans mentioned at the beginning of Chapter 2 carried their deadly burden for more than eight months before they almost killed the youngsters who put them on. Several years ago a report from the Mississippi Agricultural Experimental Station indicated the clinging qualities of malathion, which was believed to have a very short life. Commercial broccoli plants, harvested a week after spraying, were blanched, frozen, and stored for seven months. After all those procedures and all that time, they still contained residues.[49]

Concern is growing that if DDT is banned, the replacements may represent a far greater threat to human health. Not so long ago a California public health official warned, "If the use of nonpersistent pesticides increases, experience shows that the number of poisonings among workers, among children accidentally swallowing them, and among fish and animal populations will increase."[50] The same feeling prompted Congressman George E. Brown, Jr., to introduce a "safe pesticides" bill. "It is obvious," he said, "that DDT must undergo strict controls, but I am just as worried that many other pesticide types might pose as much of a danger as DDT. Government must be given enough discretion so that the whole range of pesticides can be given detailed analysis."[51]

Curiously enough, it seems easier to stir people about the poisoning of animals than of their own kind. That is why the major battles against pesticide polluters have been waged not by the Amalgamated People Lovers, but by organizations concerned chiefly with other living things.

4. . . . AND OTHER LIVING THINGS

ONCE UPON A TIME—our time—a group of workers with the World Health Organization went into some remote mountain villages in Borneo. Armed with their DDT sprayers and impelled by their desire to rid the villages of the flies and mosquitoes that carried sickness to the people, making life hard for them, they accomplished "Mission Pesticide" in heroic fashion.

But something went wrong. The cats that ate the lizards that ate the poisoned roaches and flies began to sicken and die. And the rats that feared the cats that had eaten the lizards that had eaten the roaches and flies no longer feared to go into the villages. So they invaded them, bringing diseases that caused serious epidemics in such number that the entire country was threatened. The threat did not subside until the Royal Air Force parachuted a new supply of cats into the village to restore a more equitable balance of nature.

That is no fable for a "Pollution Primer," but an account of a very real "ecological backlash," presented to delegates at a UNESCO meeting in 1969.[1] The story is worth noting because it describes so accurately the ironic manner in which even well-intentioned pesticide programs have gone awry.

What happened in Borneo is being repeated with variations all over the world. Not long ago, a member of the faculty of Tel Aviv University described what happened

there when a powerful pesticide was used to keep mice
from destroying crops. It worked, all right. Too well. As
the poisoned mice moved slowly along the ground seeking
their burrows, they became easy targets for the birds of
prey. Beginning from the fifth day after the thallium bait
was distributed, "paralyzed and dead birds were found
in the fields." Eventually, all of them died, even the
lightly paralyzed ones. The crops were left vulnerable to
attack.[2]

In England, Canada, the United States, Russia, and
other countries, chemical pesticides are also reported to
be breaking down the "first line of defense against pests"
—the predators and parasites that have kept them from
taking over the world. A Russian scientist, Vladimir
Peskov, reported in the spring of 1970 that the abuse of
chemicals on Soviet farms is creating a major agricultural
problem and zoological disaster. Wildlife reserves are
being decimated because of such episodes as two that
occurred on collective farms recently. Directors allowed
poisoned oats to be scattered from crop-dusting planes
on entire fields to kill gophers. One field was "covered
with feathers" after flocks of birds began to nibble the
poisoned grain. In both places, other principal victims
were foxes—the biggest natural consumer of gophers.[3]
Like the Russian scientist, Prince Philip of England commented recently on the irony of hunters being liable to
punishment for what others do every day as a matter of
course:

> Pesticides, insecticides, poison and pollution have
> destroyed more life than man has ever taken, and by
> affecting the capacity to breed and by destructive
> interference in the food chain, whole populations of
> species are being exterminated. What man as a hunter

has failed to do in millions of years, man as a businessman and scientist is achieving in a couple of generations.[4]

As early as 1950 the head of the Agricultural Research Council in England was warning that the "indiscriminate use of DDT has produced some very disturbing effects." The reason, he pointed out, is that the natural enemies of some agricultural pests have proved "more susceptible" to the pesticide than the pests themselves.[5] On this side of the Atlantic, as early as 1963, experts were cautioning that pest insects able to tolerate large doses of chemical killers "can now be counted in the hundreds."[6] The only answer has been to increase the amounts of chemicals and to seek more toxic ones. Even that has failed. While the environment and higher forms of life have been increasingly damaged, insects have developed phenomenal resistance. "Superflies" now resist doses of poison equivalent to 14 pounds of the lethal stuff to a 200-pound man. And the resistance of other insects has become so great that some scientists estimate that by 1980 all present pesticides will be obsolete.[7]

The first intimation that pesticides might backfire came only a year or so after the end of World War II, when entomologists and sanitation and health workers began to report that DDT-resistant flies were thriving from Sweden to the tip of Italy.[8] Mosquitoes followed the pattern. One species, a prime public health danger, is now so impervious to chemical assault that no effective control has been found.[9] The German cockroach, another major disease carrier, is so resistant to both the DDT group and the organic phosphates that it is classified as "indestructible."[10] Farm pests have also developed such immunity that in some areas farmers are spraying seventeen and more times each growing season to protect their crops.[11] And many of them are worrying openly that the spraying is causing more damage than the bugs.

At the same time the Swedish and Italian entomologists were noting the resistance of flies to chemical attack, other scientists were cautioning about the "withering" effects of DDT and the other chlorinated hydrocarbons on birds, fishes, frogs, and other indispensable allies in the continuing struggle to keep pests under control. Fairfield Osborn raised questions about the cure-all in *Our Plundered Planet* in 1948: "This new chemical is deadly to many kinds of insects. . . . But what of the ultimate and net result to the life scheme of the earth?"[12] Few heeded the question, which was being echoed by others. After all, as one observer noted sadly, scientific reports were pretty dry reading compared with the "sensationally successful" reports of DDT's miraculous properties.[13]

So the devastation has continued. The world becomes more ominously quiet as the fable of a "silent spring" becomes reality in many communities. In 1970 Norman Lewis, a British journalist, described the way of things in a center of one of California's great agricultural valleys:

> . . . not a single sparrow twittered in the eaves of Delano. Nor were there lizards on the dry walls, nor snails in damp places, nor frogs in ditches. Even domestic animals were rare. I remember after several days being stopped in the streets by the sight of a wasp crawling out of a hole in a post, which by this time seemed extraordinary.[14]

For years, the full extent of pesticide damage to birds was not known. The robins, sparrows, and other birds plummeting from the sky, acutely poisoned by pesticides picked up in lethal doses from worms and other polluted

sources of food, were considered to be the complete
casualty list. But what was happening to the rarer species
of birds—the Bermuda petrel, the brown pelican, the
peregrine falcon, the golden eagle, the bald eagle, and
others now on the "critical" and "extinct" list? Those
birds were not dying of acute poisoning. They simply
didn't reproduce. They couldn't reproduce. Shells on their
eggs grew thinner over the years—too thin to protect the
embryo. In 1969 the "ultimate" was reached when Audubon Society researchers found an egg with no shell at all
—just a membrane covering around the tiny dead eagle
inside.[15]

How that ultimate came about was described during
the 1969 hearing before the Wisconsin Department of
Natural Resources on appeals to outlaw DDT and other
"hard" pesticides. Dr. Robert Risebrough of the University
of California, Dr. Joseph J. Hickey of the University of
Wisconsin, and Dr. Lucille S. Stickel, pesticide research
coordinator of the Department of Interior's Patuxent
Wildlife Research Center, were among witnesses making
a damaging case against DDT and its principal meta-
bolite, para, para-prime DDE. DDE, a "virtually indestructible" compound, was held directly related to shell
thinning. In one experiment with mallards fed DDE at
"environmental" levels, the ducks broke 24 percent of the
eggs laid. (Controls broke only 4 percent.) Moreover,
eggshells of the DDE-dosed mallards were 13.5 percent
thinner than those of the control ducks. In a unique
experiment with kestrels—the first predatory birds reared
in captivity successfully enough to permit experimentation—Dr. Stickel found that shells of eggs laid by birds
dosed with DDE were approximately 15 percent thinner
than controls. A second generation similarly dosed also
laid eggs with shells of that thickness. "From these

studies," she reported, "it is evident that DDE in minute amounts can cause marked impairment of the reproductive success among at least two major bird groups."[16]

Dr. Charles F. Wurster of the State University of New York, Stony Brook, reported that he and his colleagues had found that DDT and dieldrin had induced enzymes to break down steroid sex hormones in pigeons so that female birds metabolized their own estrogen. When estrogen levels are below normal, calcium production is disturbed. So is its transportation to the oviduct to become part of the eggshell. The result? Thinner shells or no shell at all.[17]

Dr. Wurster has vigorously opposed the massive spray programs in which government agencies have participated, calling them biological experiments of "truly colossal proportions."[18] They have done grievous damage not only to birds of the air, but to every form of aquatic life, from the most minute phytoplankton to the largest sport fish. The acute effects of pesticide poisoning of the waters have been known, and protested, for years.[19]

The classic case that illustrates the hidden and more sinister action of pesticides occurred at Clear Lake, California—an ecological drama which is still being played out. The largest natural fresh-water lake within the state's boundaries, it was treated in 1949 with small amounts of DDD (14 parts per *billion*) to eliminate swarms of non-biting gnats that had come to infest the resort. Control efforts seemed brilliantly successful. Treatments were repeated in 1954 and 1957 because of re-infestations from neighboring lakes. Again, they were deemed successful. But residents and visitors began to wonder and complain about the disappearance of the Western grebe, the lovely waterfowl that had added to the picturesque quality of the lake. After the 1957 application, Clear Lake's grebe population dropped from 1,000 pairs to 20. For five years not a single young grebe survived to adulthood.

Meanwhile, other problems had developed. Although the grebes seemed to be dying like flies, the gnats were back in full buzz. More alarming, sport fish died off; and an abundance of nutrients was choking the lake to death with algae. Beaches were covered with green slime; waters were coated with blue-green scum.

What had happened? A study two years later made that clear: a process called *biological magnification*. Although by that time not even parts-per-billion traces of DDD remained in the water, plankton had concentrations of 5.3 p.p.m.; plant-eating fish, from 40 to 300 p.p.m.; the carnivorous fish at the top of the aquatic chain, 2,500 p.p.m.; the birds, between 1,600 and 2,000 p.p.m.[20]

A University of California entomologist, Dr. Sherburne Cook, Jr., set about reviving Clear Lake in 1961 through restoring a system of natural controls. First step was to halt all DDD applications. During the "emergency," a short-lived pesticide was used to keep down gnats. A few years later, 3,000 Mississippi silverside fish were "planted" in the lake to eat up the algae. That is now down by almost 90 percent.

With the algae cleared out, other fish began to make a comeback. The silversides quickly multiplied to millions, providing an adequate diet for bass and crappie and for the grebes—which began to make a tentative appearance. In 1969, 82 young birds were added to the list of living things at Clear Lake.

Recently, Dr. Robert L. Rudd of the University of California described the comeback of the grebe, along with the lake, as "a phoenix risen from the mud flats."[21]

Unfortunately, not all water stories are ending so happily, as many other incidents recently have suggested.

Many of them have involved DDT and other hard pesticides. After the crab harvest in the San Francisco Bay dropped from nine million to one million pounds a year, a California Fish and Game official urged that new methods of pest control be developed "that don't depend on these long-lasting poisons that pollute our ocean fisheries."[22]

That attitude is shared by Wisconsin's Senator Nelson, who drafted a bill in 1969 to prevent the interstate sale and shipment of DDT. He said, "I know of no other single environmental pollutant which is endangering the quality of life on earth more than DDT and other persistent pesticides of the chlorinated hydrocarbon family."[23] Principal evidence for his case was the seizure a few months earlier of 28,000 pounds of salmon from Lake Michigan, with concentrations of DDT ranging up to 19 p.p.m. and of dieldrin up to .3 p.p.m.—levels far above those considered harmless in other foods.[24] (In the panic that resulted, the FDA was given authority to set tolerances for residues in fish. Waters are so contaminated that the level of 5 p.p.m. was allowed, far higher than that considered harmless in other foods.[25])

Perhaps the most alarming note so far as the waters are concerned was the recent announcement that even at the very lowest level of the chain the existence of the biosphere is being threatened. Seventy percent of the world's supply of oxygen is derived from what scientists call the process of photosynthesis in plankton—the tiny "wandering" single-celled plants in the sea that are linked to all living things. Solar energy captured by their chlorophyll transforms carbon dioxide from air and water into simple sugars. In the process, oxygen is released into the atmosphere. Without this means of restoring oxygen, animals and men would shortly breathe themselves to death. Dr. Wurster's studies have shown that this vital process is also being jeopardized. Concentrations of DDT as low as a few parts per billion in water have been shown to affect photosynthesis of a number of species of phytoplankton.[26]

The water situation was summed up in a homely fashion recently for a friend of mine traveling in Louisiana. Strolling across a field with a farmer, he pointed out a beautiful willow-fringed lake on the man's property. "Your private fishing preserve?" he asked. His host looked at him sourly: "You know better than that. I raise cotton. There isn't a living thing in that lake. Not any more."

The earth itself is being poisoned—man's greatest natural resource that has such profound mythic significance that we regard man as the essence of it.

Science and technology have made possible great achievements: marshes reclaimed for farming, lake beds turned into fields. Deserts have been caused to flower. Sadly, some of the medications developed to revitalize the earth and enhance its fertility are now known to be killing the patient. "Man is exploiting the earth that feeds him much as a parasite multiplies until it kills its host," a scientist warned some years ago.[27]

Soil is not lifeless stuff. Even the desert is alive—a marvelously intricate complex of animate and inanimate things, of dead matter and living organisms bound to each other in a cycle of death and resurrection. At the base of the biotic pyramid, on top of which man rests precariously, are the rock particles. Then there is the organic matter added by dead plants and animals. Finally, there is the community of living plants and animal organisms.[28]

Functioning together in the presence of air, water, and sunshine, they produce all living things and their environment. Each element is indispensable. Even the microscopic entities—molds, bacteria, funguses—play a vital role. Their work is made more effective by insects and earthworms. Those perfect little blending machines mix decomposed organic material with soil particles (up to a depth of six feet) and cast it on the surface as richer soil.[29]

Without worms the earth would be sterile. Yet they are being ruthlessly exterminated by pesticides and synthetic fertilizers. So are the bacteria, funguses, and other micro-organisms being destroyed by agricultural chemicals,[30] as are the creatures at the top of the chain: the herbivorous animals that provide fertilizer and the carnivorous ones that regulate the number of plant eaters as well as nourish the earth.

Pesticides interrupt the chain of life in a number of ways. Some of them stimulate the release of plant nutrients from the soil.[31] Not only do pesticides kill beneficial soil organisms all along the line, they also contaminate food grown in it for long periods. Sometimes they are detected. Consumers have rejected potatoes, carrots, tomatoes, peaches, and plums grown in soil contaminated with benzene hexachloride (BHC) and lindane because of their "funny taste."[32] However, not all pesticides alter flavors; many, therefore, go undetected.

During the past few years herbicides have become even more of a threat to the earth than insecticides. By 1968 they represented nearly 57 percent of all pesticide dollar sales.[33]

No one with any experience in gardening and few without would quarrel with the idea that weeds must be controlled. Farmers damn them with poetic fervor as "insidious thieves" and "crafty enemies without senses, without mercy."[34] According to the USDA, by 1965, annual losses due to them in this country amounted to $2.5 billion; farmers were spending an equal sum to control them. Although those estimates should be regarded with some skepticism, since farmers are notoriously free about calculating losses as compared with profits, weeds are serious pests.[35] They cost nonfarmers a lot, too: money spent for health care, higher prices for foods, contributions to subsidize reclamation and conservation programs.[36]

Chemical controls have been used for centuries: common salt, copper sulphate, carbolic acid, iron sulfate, and others. Arsenicals became popular at the end of the nineteenth century as "total" weed killers. They turned out to be so poisonous and so persistent that their use has been banned in many countries. A single application in an area with little rainfall may *sterilize* the soil for as long as eight years.[37] Their use has continued here, and arsenic poisoning continues to be a problem in many farm communities.

More modern weapons of chemical war against weeds were introduced in the 1930's, after the French workers discovered the herbicidal properties of yellow dye compounds of the dinitro group. Two of them came into wide use in England during World War II: DNOC and dinoseb. War does not encourage nice distinctions. Since the compounds helped to obtain bumper crops, their less attractive qualities were overlooked. For one thing, they are deadly. Yet DNOC continues to be stockpiled in England and in this country in a casual way. Dr. Kenneth Mellanby said recently that "supplies maintained on many farms could each wipe out the whole population of a city the size of Cambridge."[38]

The great "breakthrough" in killing power came after the war, when chemical companies began to market "growth" compounds—substances which have properties similar to hormones, the strange and powerful acids that control man's physical, mental, and emotional behavior. Those *auxin*-type chemicals gave farmers almost supernatural power over the vegetative world. With them, they could increase the size of fruits and vegetables, artificially stimulating ovaries of plants. They could direct plants to take a particular shape and size. They could order trees and plants to produce flowers and fruits of such-and-such a kind, such-and-such an amount and size. Farmers could even command plants to cease functioning or to grow themselves to death.

The effect on the farming and agricultural chemicals industries was electric. By 1949, only four years after the first of these compounds was generally introduced, 2,4-D was being used on 20 million acres of small grains and cereals in the United States.[39] In addition to that herbicide and its analogs, others were developed with different modes of action: nitrogen derivatives and petroleum oils. Gases were marketed to fumigate the soil: methyl bromide, carbon disulfide, and chloropicrin, which had been known during World War I as "vomiting gas."[40] In 1944, farmers had a choice of about 14 herbicides; by 1965, at least 125 basic compounds were available in some 8,000 registered products. Use, particularly of the auxin-type herbicides, has increased enormously. Between 1966 and 1968, production of various kinds rose from 271.933 million pounds to 402.781 million pounds.[41]

Neither their mode of operation nor their consequences were fully understood by scientists. Yet salesmen and other merchandizers encouraged use of the products, praising safety and efficacy. "At the usual rates of application, they do not injure animals, fish, or man," was the refrain.[42] Workers exposed to them were less certain. Shortly after herbicides made their appearance in Puerto Rico, a visiting instructor at the university wrote to a friend of mine about the protests of the workers:

> They can't even keep chickens; they eat the grass with herbicide on and die. The same thing happens to their pigs. They drink the water out of the streams and the herbicide drains into the streams; they're afraid of being poisoned themselves.

After a while, more sophisticated farmers began to worry, too. In 1969 California was forced to ban the use of propanil—fifth most popular herbicide in the United States—in a number of counties. Prune producers, almond growers, and others claimed that the herbicide being used extensively on rice fields was endangering their crops. Drift from sprayed fields caused excessive damage to fruit and blossoms, they said.[43]

However, even though scientists had been cautioning for years that plant regulators were so "potent" they could "cause much damage in the hands of the inexperienced and uninformed," no widespread protest was made by them until information began to leak out of Vietnam about the extent to which the United States was using them in that unfortunate country.[44] Senator Barry Goldwater's promise to defoliate Vietnam contributed importantly to his overwhelming defeat in the Presidential campaign of 1964. So it was with genuine outrage that many Americans learned less than a year later how much had been done to achieve that goal.

"Operation Ranch Hand" was the name of the military game. That euphemism was given to the chemical war because the techniques and weapons used were taken over so directly from agriculture. The "Ranchers," as pilots were called, had a blunter conception of their missions. A plaque hanging in their headquarters ironically proclaimed:

ONLY WE CAN PREVENT FORESTS[45]

The first organized appeal for a halt was made by the Federation of American Scientists in 1964. Members charged that Vietnam was being used as a *proving ground* for chemical war. Former troop carriers, they said, had been turned into massive crop dusters capable of releasing almost 900 gallons of defoliant during a four-minute run— enough to turn a 250-acre field or forest into a lifeless plot.[46] Defense officials rejected the appeal, insisting that the chemicals were "not harmful to people, animals, soil, or water."[47] The Pentagon continued to ignore protests made later by the American Association for the Advancement of Science and an independent group of 5,000— including 22 Nobel Prize winners.

No one, including the United Nations, seemed willing to act. Then the Society for Social Responsibility in Science moved. A relatively small group of scientists, dedicated to "fostering throughout the world a tradition of personal moral responsibility for the consequences to humanity of professional activity," the SSRS raised funds to sponsor a trip by two authorities.

Dr. Egbert W. Pfeiffer of the University of Montana and Dr. Gordon H. Orians of the University of Washington set off on their fact-finding mission on March 17, 1969. In the course of it, they flew under machine-gun fire in Army helicopters and crop dusters. They traveled the waterways of the Rung Sat Peninsula on a Navy patrol vessel. They interviewed U.S. military authorities and Vietnamese scientists. And they amassed evidence for a terrible indictment.

According to their estimates, more than 1.7 million acres of cropland and forest were sprayed during 1967 alone; in 1968, more than 1.384 million acres.[48]

Dr. Pfeiffer and Dr. Orians exposed the fallacy of Defense Department claims that only "safe" amounts of "safe" herbicides were being used in "small areas." The four principal agents—2,4-D, 2,4,5-T, picloram, and cacodylic acid—were all being used "at about ten times the rate of application at which they are used for civilian purposes."[49] At least one of them, 2,4,5-T, has been held by scientists as responsible for thousands of deformed and defective babies in areas in Vietnam where it was used. (That pesticide was temporarily suspended from interstate sale in the United States in 1970 for home use.[50]) Moreover, application was not being limited to "target areas." The scientists said they found "abundant evidence" of moderate-to-severe defoliations in many places far removed from sites of direct application. Pilots did not display much concern about proper weather and temperature conditions, and understandably jettisoned cargo anywhere rather than jeopardize crews and planes.

Antidotes have not been provided or used. Vietnamese scientists were given no information about what is being sprayed. In addition to their assault on humans, the chemicals have seriously damaged all forms of life:

> As a result of their use in Vietnam we saw many miles of forest with not a green leaf remaining. Animal life had almost totally disappeared. We saw damage by chemicals to rubber trees, and were told that if the defoliation program continued that the rubber industry will be destroyed. We saw the destruction of valuable hardwood forests, and learned that two defoliating attacks will kill 50 percent of the commercial forest timber. We learned that the destruction of mature forest trees is allowing bamboo to invade the defoliated areas and the forests that have been defoliated are changing from valuable timber to useless bamboo forests.[51]

Taxpayers are now paying for at least some of the damage. After a closed-door hearing by a Congressional foreign affairs subcommittee in 1970, it was announced that the State Department had authorized payment of $3 million for damage claims in Vietnam. Additionally, the government was also considering a claim for $12 million by the Cambodian government for damaging rubber trees there in a defoliation campaign.[52]

At home, meantime, the defoliants continued to be used by private and public weed warriors. During January and February of 1970, almost 400,000 acres were treated with one or both chemicals. Some weeks later, on April 15, 2,4,5-T was banned—by the Pentagon and the Department of Health, Education, and Welfare. The Pentagon ban took. Herbicide makers had little to worry about, however; a few months later domestic sales were back to normal. Both the Agriculture Department's Pesticide Regulation Division and the FDA were maintaining their record, said Congressman Richard J. McCarthy, of failing to assume their public responsibility and to enforce the law.[53] In Washington, it was business as usual.

5. WHAT PROTECTION? (I)

HOWEVER GREAT OUR admiration for American business—and with reason—none but the most delusionary thinker could imagine that we do not need protection against it. The goal of any *efficient* entrepreneur is to make money. If that can be accomplished by operating in the public interest, as it often can, well and good. If not. . . That eventuality was summed up neatly a century ago by an acknowledged giant: "The public be damned."

A major function of governments at all levels in our democratic society is to shield us from assaults on our persons and property by the profiteers. It has been since 1837, when the U.S. Supreme Court decided that Massachusetts had the right to build a bridge across the Charles River to compete with the privately owned existing span. Commuters should not be entirely at the mercy of the owner/toll collector, it ruled. While property rights are to be "sacredly guarded" by the government, public interest "must always be regarded as the main object."[1] To insure that it is, as business has grown bigger so have the protective powers of government.

Or so we think. Those who are in a position to know are less likely to share the belief that someone, somewhere, is watching out for our welfare. Not long ago California's Chief Deputy Attorney General Charles A. O'Brien commented on the "false sense of security" that exists because of the "pervasive influence of government upon our lives."

People assume that the food they eat, the appliances they buy, the cars they drive, the insecticides they use are safe. "That is the job of government. That's why you pay taxes—so you can live in safety." But the experience of his office during recent years, he said, indicates that, "Often no one is watching the store—and, at worst, the thieves are eyeing the cash register."[2]

Mr. O'Brien made that statement shortly after he announced that the attorney general's office would join the court battle to force state agriculture officials to release pesticide spraying records. He said that his decision to fight the public agency his office officially serves was based on the paradoxical situation that makes it impossible for doctors treating people to gain access to essential information about poisonous pesticides, although that information is available to fish and game researchers. "Surely," Mr. O'Brien said dryly, "human beings deserve the same advantage as striped bass."

How little protection has been afforded people by their *official* protectors has been made clear during the last decade by Rachel Carson, Ralph Nader, and other leaders of the "consumer revolt"—men and women following as private citizens the example set by that remarkable public servant, Dr. Harvey W. Wiley. It was he and the dedicated young members of his "Poison Squad" who, shortly after the turn of the century, forced reluctant legislators to act against poisoners. Food and drug manufacturers were then selling such filthy and toxic products that more casualties were suffered by United States troops in the Spanish-American war from contaminated meat than from enemy bullets. The profiteers were so busy on the home front that sitting down to any meal was like indulging in a game of Russian roulette. Would the diner walk away from the table or not?

Like most protective measures, the basic law of 1906 and its subsequent amendments have been "a poor, unstable compromise between the interests of the food industry and the demands of an aroused public opinion."[3] The built-in weaknesses of all protective laws have been enhanced by failure to provide realistic penalties. I witnessed an ironic illustration of that some years ago during a parole hearing I attended at one of the California state prisons. One man who came before the Adult Authority had spent 18 of his 32 years in "correctional" institutions for thefts, the total value of which had not amounted to $1,000. At the same time, the "gentlemen conspirators" in the electrical industry were serving sentences of less than a month. That was their punishment for having successfully conspired to defraud American taxpayers of nearly $3 billion!

Even if there were penalties, who is to enforce the law? Appropriations for enforcement staffs in the regulatory agencies have been kept miserably low by specially interested legislators. Some of them are working overtime to keep government out of the people's business. For example, when Senator Abraham Ribicoff introduced a bill to give more policing power to the Department of Agriculture—he wanted establishments as well as products to be registered so that inspection could be made at that critical point—another legislator came running to the industry's rescue. Parke C. Brinkley, president of the National Agricultural Chemicals Association, was then able to reassure the membership: "Through the understanding of Congress, and particularly Senator [B. Everett] Jordan of North Carolina [chairman of the subcommittee to which the bill was referred], we have been given some time to see if the situation might be improved without the necessity of federal intervention."[4] That "compromise" turned out to be "entirely acceptable" to the organization. No more was heard of the matter.

Those deficiencies in the protective program are enhanced by venal and incompetent employees and by the empire-building tendencies of agency directors, who struggle furiously with other agency directors to expand their spheres of power. The situation was memorably described not long ago by Lee Loevinger, assistant attorney general for antitrust under President Kennedy and a Federal Communications Commissioner under President Johnson:

> Unfortunately the history of every regulatory agency in the government is that it comes to represent the industry or groups it's supposed to control. All of these agencies were fine when they were first set up, but before long they became infiltrated by the regulatees and are now more or less run by and for them. It's not a question of venality either. More, the agency people consort with this or that representative of some special-interest group and finally they all come to think alike. Every company that's concerned about government control and is big enough to manage hires a man—maybe four or five men—at anywhere from thirty to seventy thousand dollars a year to find out what we're up to. And by God, they find out. They wine and dine agency people and get to be great friends with them. Like a lot of people without much money, some bureaucrats are impressed by being around big shots and the big life. Sooner or later, all of these agencies end up with constituents. And they represent them damn well, too.[5]

A concrete illustration of the Loevinger theory, showing in vivid detail how the regulated-regulator alliance operates against the public interest, was provided recently. *Deficiencies in Administration of Federal Insecticide,*

Fungicide, and Rodenticide Act, both the *Report* and the *Hearings,* merit a place in every citizen's library. Black-humor fans will find them of interest, worthy of a place next to *Catch-22.* Joseph Heller writes better about the Absurd, but for irony, plot-complot, characterization, situation—the nonfictional documents are hard to beat.

The serio-comic story began in September 1968, when the U.S. Comptroller General sent to Congress a report prepared by the Government Accounting Office. The accompanying letter pointed out tersely that the report showed "a need for the Agricultural Research Service of the Department of Agriculture to improve regulatory enforcement procedures involving pesticides."[6]

The ARS, it should be noted, is the agency responsible for enforcing the provisions of the Federal Insecticide, Fungicide, and Rodenticide Act (FIFRA) of 1947, as subsequently amended. That basic law requires that all pesticide products shipped across state lines be registered with ARS before being sold. ARS must determine their safety and effectiveness. It has authority to obtain and test samples, and to remove those which are not in conformity from the market and cancel their registration. Importantly, it is also authorized to report violators to the Department of Justice for prosecution.

The General Accounting Office decided to make its study, since the 60,000 products then registered with ARS affect "virtually . . . every segment of the public."[7]

How was the Agricultural Research Service enforcing the law? GAO investigators reported, with considerable astonishment and indignation, that relations between the agency and the pesticide makers were so amicable that during the thirteen years from February 1955 through February 1968 not a single violator had ever been reported to the Department of Justice for criminal prosecution. Yet major and deliberate violations were frequent. During 1966, for example, ARS tested 2,751 samples of pesticide products—a very small number of the total. But of them, 750 samples were in violation of the law, 562 of them in *major* violation.[8]

The ARS sent notices to 242 shippers that criminal proceedings might be instituted against them. According to the GAO report, they couldn't have cared less. Some sent back "flimsy" explanations; some of them ignored the notices completely. Seventy-seven of them simply continued to violate the law, confident of their immunity and ARS's do-nothing policy. Among the repeaters were two known by ARS to have violated the law on twenty separate occasions during the year.[9]

The few seizures that were made that year—106 in all —were not calculated to allow consumers to rest easier. When samples proved to be unsafe or ineffective, the only thing removed from the market was the stuff at the *one* retail or wholesale outlet where the sample had been collected. In practice, that was about as reasonable as having the Food and Drug Administration confiscate the vials of a contaminated vaccine only at the pharmacy where the sample had been obtained and allowing equally contaminated vials to be sold everywhere else in the country.

In one case, the ARS investigators seized eleven containers of a liquid spray insecticide from an outlet in Santa Fe, New Mexico. The material was contaminated with a toxic ingredient not named on the container. The "please excuse wrong label" from the manufacturer was readily accepted, although the ARS was aware that the mislabeling had resulted in "a very dangerous situation." It did not insist on recalling the products from other points of sale; it did not issue a public warning.[10]

The ARS's solicitude about the well-being of the pesticide industry—as well as the attitude of the criminal businessmen—is responsible for a number of injuries and fatalities. In 1960, for instance, it took off the market one product and limited the content of others containing thallium sulphate—a highly toxic compound used chiefly to control rodents. Deaths and injuries continued to occur. The Public Health Service recorded about 400 cases of children poisoned by thallium during 1962 and 1963. In August 1965 ARS finally bowed to protesting public health workers and canceled the registration of 58 thallium products. Again, it was "So what?" Thallium products continued to be produced and sold. In fact, in January 1968 one GAO staff member located 65 packages of a thallium product when he checked markets in suburban Maryland,[11] a short bus ride from ARS headquarters.

The second and perhaps more humanly interesting part of the story of *Deficiencies* began after a House subcommittee headed by L. H. Fountain of North Carolina decided to get some first-hand information about what, if anything, was going on at ARS. Their concern, aroused by the first report, was intensified by a second. GAO investigators also wanted to know why ARS had continued to register lindane vaporizing devices over the protests of public and private health agencies. The hazards of using vaporizers where food is served, processed, or stored are so great that as early as 1953 at least 14 states and 35 large cities had taken steps to control their sale and use.[12] Another branch of the USDA, the Consumer and Marketing Service, had banned them where meat and poultry were exposed to pesticide vapors.

Congressman Fountain's subcommittee wanted to know why, too. By the time the hearings ended, they wanted answers to a good many other questions about the consequences of the USDA-business *entente*. Some of the questions had such serious implications that they were referred to the Department of Justice for possible prosecution.

Focal point of the hearing was the Shell "No-Pest" strip, one of the most popular and omnipresent devices on the market. The golden cardboard rectangles, dangling from the ceilings of millions of homes, restaurants, and hospital rooms, do not contain lindane, but a highly toxic organic phosphate known as DDVP. The company claims exclusive patent rights to that chemical although, according to the director of the Communicable Disease Center in Savannah, *"It has been determined that the Federal Government is entitled to the entire right, title, and interest in the invention of DDVP."*[13] (Italics added.)

Leading players in the scenes enacted during May and June in Room 2247 of the Rayburn Building were Congressman Fountain, Subcommittee Counsel James R. Naughton, and two ARS officials: Dr. George W. Irving, Jr., administrator, and Dr. Harry W. Hays, director of the Pesticides Regulation Division of ARS.

Enough of the antecedent action of the "No-Pest" drama of the absurd was sketched in, however, to indicate that principal roles had also been taken by three other men: Dr. T. Roy Hansberry, Dr. Mitchell R. Zavon, and John S. Leary, Jr. All three had been associated both with Shell and with the ARS. Dr. Hansberry, an official of Shell Development Company in California, served also on the USDA Task Force, a seven-member group set up in 1965 to study Pesticides Regulation Division procedures for "determining the safety and effectiveness of pesticides offered for federal registration."

Mr. Leary had been chief staff officer for pharmacology at ARS when the "No-Pest" strip was approved for regis-

tration, after he overruled a subordinate's objection. At the
time of the hearing, he was working for Shell Chemical.

Dr. Zavon was multiply identified as consultant to Shell
Chemical Company, consultant to the Pesticides Regulation Division of ARS, assistant health commissioner of
Cincinnati, member of the staff of the University of
Cincinnati's College of Medicine; he was also the author
of a number of reports and scientific studies used by Shell
to support its contention that DDVP is safe.

One of the chief devices for protecting the public from
predators is the basic conflict of interest statute applicable
to federal employees: *18 U.S.C. 208.* That prohibits any
officer or employee, including special employees, from
participating in a judicial or other proceeding if he has
any financial interest in a particular matter; he may not
even render advice. In addition, federal law also prohibits former executive employees, even after they have left
government service, to act as agent or attorney for anyone
other than the United States in any proceeding in which
the United States has a direct and substantial interest.

Since Shell had registered several hundred pesticide
products with PRD, the subcommittee felt it could be
assumed to have considerable interest in USDA proceedings. Subcommittee members were, therefore, curious
about the parts they had played in getting the "Vapona"
(DDVP) device approved. (Vapona is the trade name of
the chemical.)

Questioning in the subcommittee revealed that Mr.
Leary's role in the "No-Pest" affair began when a pharmacologist in his department vetoed the label for the
strip proposed by Shell. He wanted all devices to bear the
word POISON and carry a picture of a skull and crossbones,
since a previously registered Vapona product had been
classified as highly toxic to man. Shell seems to have felt

that would be economically as well as aesthetically undesirable—the sort of thing that might easily discourage
housewives from buying. Mr. Leary was sympathetic to
the Shell position; the day after a visit by a company
representative, he waived the objection and issued the
registration. The U.S. Public Health Service issued a
protest. While its objections were acknowledged to have
"considerable merit from a theoretical viewpoint,"[14] they
were nevertheless rejected. ARS then approved eight
other applications—two made by Shell and six by companies planning to purchase Vapona from Shell and
market similar devices.

USPHS pressed the point. An ad hoc committee in the
fall of 1965 recommended unanimously against the use of
lindane vaporizers and six of the eight members also recommended against the use of DDVP and pyrethrum.
(One of the two dissenters was a representative from
private industry.)

Nearly a year later Dr. Hays bowed—slightly—to
continuing objections from medical experts. He asked
three, who had not been earlier involved in discussions,
to meet with him. Instead of being given the report of the
USPHS ad hoc committee, the medical men were given
copies of a six-page memorandum prepared for the occasion by Mr. Leary.

A few weeks later Mr. Leary resigned from PRD to
accept a position with Shell Chemical Company. Before
departing, he took time to prepare another memorandum.
In it, he said that the ad hoc committee's adverse report
served "no useful purpose" and urged that it "be set aside
as inadequate justification for any changes in the registration status of these methods of pest control."[15]

Protests about the strip and the label continued. A few
months later ARS notified Shell that the latter would have

to carry a warning cautioning against its use in rooms where infants and infirm persons were confined. Shell moved into action. A counter-study was presented, insisting that the strips posed "no hazard to human health." Mr. Leary soon after represented Shell in a meeting on the matter with Dr. Hays, at which, contrary to custom, no minutes were kept.

Dr. Zavon accepted an appointment as consultant to USDA in 1963. At that time, he was also working as a consultant to Shell, and at the same time was chairman of the toxicology committee of the National Agricultural Chemicals Association, which had been formed "to promote the interests of manufacturers and formulators of pest control chemicals in a manner consistent with the public interest." Some persons at USDA called attention to the law and to President Kennedy's conflict of interest memo when Dr. Zavon's reappointment came up in 1964. Reminders were issued again in 1965.

Dr. Zavon's efforts on behalf of Shell had to do largely with conducting scientific studies on the safety of Vapona and making "frequent contacts" with USPHS workers in Georgia and in Washington in relation to the product.[16]

Shell used Dr. Zavon's reports to support the contention that no special warnings about infants and infirm persons were needed. Another study, conducted in an Ohio restaurant for one to two hours, was used to counter reports that residues resulted from the use of Vapona strips around foods.

Dr. Zavon was selective about his roles during trips to Washington for meetings on pesticides. On one occasion, his travel and living expenses were paid by USDA; on another, there was no indication in USDA files that he was acting as a government consultant.[17] He was selective about his titles on other occasions. Although the USPHS ad hoc committee's adverse report had never been made public, he wrote to the Assistant Surgeon General urging that pesticide vaporizers be "re-reviewed." He sent the health director a copy of the report he and some associates had worked up, and he added his endorsement of DDVP—"as a Health Officer." (It was the only endorsement by a health officer in this country known to the subcommittee.) Dr. Zavon's letter made no reference to his relationship with Shell Chemical Company or NACA.[18]

During the hearings the subcommittee members were also curious to know how Dr. Hansberry had obtained conflict of interest clearance for his appointment to the Task Force. That never did become clear beyond the fact that his appointment had been proposed by Dr. Hays. The standard form, SF-68, which Dr. Hansberry was said to have filled out, could not be located; there was no record that his employment had been cleared with the Office of General Counsel. All that could be found was a note—author unknown—saying, "The Agricultural Research Service does not have, or know of, any official business with the persons, firms, or institutions with which Dr. Hansberry has other financial interests as reported on the SF-68 which might constitute a conflict of interest."[19]

None of the 256 products Shell had registered with the ARS could, needless to say, be sold without ARS approval.

Those industry-government relationships were worth exploring in detail, the subcommittee felt. There had to be some explanation why for years, over the very strenuous objections of public health experts, consumers were not warned of the existence of hazards. In 1968 the PRD had taken some action, notifying Shell that the label henceforth must bear a warning: "Do not use in nurseries or rooms where infants, ill or aged persons are confined." But it was not until after the subcommittee hearings that it ordered relabeling of strips currently being marketed without that statement.[20]

It is not that Pesticides Regulation Division cannot act fast—when the occasion warrants. As a matter of fact, the subcommittee wondered just why it had moved so swiftly in the matter of the Aeroseal DDVP product. The only action taken against any Vapona item was instituted in March 1969, when a notice was sent to the Aeroseal company announcing suspension of the registration because information had not been provided to show that the strips were effective or safe when used as directed. "We consider the product to be potentially hazardous to persons exposed," the notice said.

The Aeroseal strip differed from the Shell product *only* in that the chemical was impregnated into paper rather than resin. The active ingredients and instructions were identical. According to the testimony, the Aeroseal registration had covered a Vapona device to be manufactured by Shell and purchased from Shell. Shortly after Aeroseal began to manufacture its own supplies of Vapona, PRD was visited by a Shell representative complaining about the Aeroseal product. That was on March 20, 1969. Four days later—although no report had been made by the laboratory—registration was canceled.[21]

Dr. Hays was pretty vague about the motivation for that action. Indeed, he was pretty vague about much that concerned pesticides.[22] In any event, some of the dialogue between Dr. Hays and committee members bordered on the extravagant. When questioned about the number of pesticide poisonings yearly, he said that 150 to 175 might be considered "a reasonable estimate." Congressman Fountain demanded incredulously: "Is that for the whole nation? 150 to 175 for the whole nation?" Nor was Dr. Hays shaken to learn that USPHS reports indicated that

50,000 might be a more reasonable estimate.[23] (Many experts insist it is at least twice that number.)

When questioned about the confusing, contradictory, and inadequate labeling of pesticides—another responsibility of ARS—Dr. Hays described himself as "fully convinced that they are being screened very carefully." At that point, Congressman Fountain asked the subcommittee counsel to read "pertinent excerpts" from a label accepted by PRD five days before the hearing began. The label on the fly and roach spray produced by Hysan Products Company of Chicago cautioned on one side:

> Close all doors, windows, and transoms. Spray with a fine mist sprayer freely upwards in all directions so that the room is filled with the vapor. If insects have not dropped to the floor in 3 minutes repeat spraying, as quantity sprayed was insufficient. After 10 minutes doors and windows may be opened.

On the other side, the cautions urge:

> Use in well ventilated rooms or areas only. Always spray away from you. Do not stay in room that has been heavily treated. Avoid inhalation.[24]

Of even greater concern to the subcommittee, however, was the unilateral action of ARS and its PRD over the objections of the Department of Health, Education, and Welfare. Dr. Hays and some of his subordinates were questioned sharply about that, despite his efforts to brush off the matter with the statement, "I would say a half dozen in which the Public Health Service has expressed some concern."[25]

He was quite wrong in that estimate, it turned out. Between January 1, 1968, and March 31, 1969, USPHS had objected to 252 product labels.[26] Investigation by the subcommittee also disclosed that during the five-year period ending June 30, 1969, HEW had objected to the proposed registrations of more than 1,600 pesticide products—objections that were almost entirely ignored.[27]

The House Committee on Government Operations concurred with the findings of the subcommittee and the GAO. In its report, it found that the USDA Pesticides Regulation Division had:

1. "Failed almost completely" until mid-1967 to enforce provisions of the act designed to protect the public from hazardous and ineffective products being marketed in violation of it.

2. Approved "numerous" pesticide products over objections of HEW without complying with required procedures for resolving safety questions.

3. Approved pesticide products for uses "which it knew or should have known were practically certain to result in illegal adulteration of food."

4. Failed to insure that pesticide labels clearly warn users against possible hazards.

5. Failed to make effective use of even the limited data available about pesticide poisonings.

6. Failed to act promptly when it had reason to believe a registered product might be ineffective or potentially hazardous.

7. Failed to remove potentially hazardous products from the market after registrations were canceled or suspended.

8. Failed to warn purchasers of potentially hazardous products.

The report also charged the Agricultural Research Service with failing to take "appropriate precautions" against appointing consultants to jobs in which their duties might conflict with the financial interests of their employers.

The only positive note in the findings was a word of praise for Lowell E. Miller, who had been appointed assistant director for enforcement of PRD in 1967. Since his appointment, PRD has begun to request pesticide manufacturers to "voluntarily recall" violative products and to make other "significant improvements."[28]

(Readers cannot help but feel some sympathy for Harold Alford, assistant director of PRD during that trying time. Mr. Alford was so mindful of his public responsibilities that he pointed out to the Task Force that the law prohibited disclosing information about pesticide formulas to interested persons. "This should be thoroughly understood," he warned, "since Dr. Hansberry is an industry representative." For his pains, Mr. Alford was excluded from the second series of meetings held by that body—although he had been appointed its executive secretary by the Secretary of Agriculture himself. When the subcommittee asked Dr. Hays to explain his exclusionist order, he said that he had barred the door to his assistant because he wanted to have "free and open discussions.")[29]

Recently, the USDA has taken some steps to regulate pesticides more realistically. In the summer of 1969 it imposed a brief moratorium on DDT to "study the problem." It stepped up its read-the-label campaign on radio and television as well as in farm publications. In November the Secretary of Agriculture directed that greater emphasis be given to new non-persistent pesticide products as well as those already registered, in order to protect the environment.[30] In December of that year, it finally got around to halting the use of bug-killing shelf papers containing lindane, a pesticide vehicle that organizations like Consumers Union had been protesting for almost a decade.[31]

But it will take firm and persuasive leadership to convert the USDA from what Dr. Paul Ehrlich has called its history of "pushing pesticides." Massive spray programs continue with Department of Defense enthusiasm for unloading defoliants on Vietnam. It has been almost impossible to block them. One of the few successes was reported by Senator Abraham Ribicoff in 1963. During his term of office as governor of Connecticut, the USDA insisted on the need for a statewide spray program to eliminate the gypsy moth. Scientists considered it "outrageous," he said; so did commercial nurserymen, who were threatened with boycott on their shipments. "I recall telling the USDA," he noted, "if this was their attitude, they could get out of the state—we did not need them." At that point, federal officials backed down and agreed to spray only those areas that were considered to be in need of spraying.[32]

Other efforts to modify USDA's pesticide pushing have been less successful. And they may continue to be, if Congressional powers like Representative Jamie L. Whitten of Mississippi continue to control its destiny. For about two decades, the dapper and energetic legislator has exercised almost total control over the agency's budget—$7 billion a year by 1969—and over the conduct and attitudes of its more than one hundred thousand employees. Presidential and Congressional directives may be flouted with impunity, as USDA has done by practically ignoring the order to develop other than chemical pesticides. But not Representative Whitten's directives. His word is even more forceful than law, as Nick Kotz has pointed out in *Let Them Eat Promises: The Politics of Hunger in America*.[33]

The kind of fear he can inspire has not a little to do with the USDA's attitude about pesticides and pesticide makers. Mr. Whitten is pretty keen about pesticides. A lot of cotton is grown in Mississippi, and no one is checking that for residues. He gets impatient with people who do worry about that sort of thing—Rachel Carson, for example, and some FDA people. When some of the latter decided to lower to zero tolerance residues of a number of chemicals considered dangerous, Mr. Whitten had a staff prepare a report objecting to the "direct and indirect losses to pesticide manufacturers and farmers, respectively." The changes were being made "merely" because of FDA's fear that residues "might be injurious to health."[34] He holds that the concern about pesticide residues in foods is "a witch hunt." The staff working on an answer to *Silent Spring* under his direction dutifully agreed, noting in the report:

> The individuals who oppose the use of pesticides claim that pesticides are harmful; whereas the individuals who support the use of pesticides claim that pesticides are harmless. Because no one at the present time can prove who is correct, any discussion of long-term effects of minute traces of pesticides on human beings would be fruitless.[35]

Now there is a thought for any day.

Although the USDA's record of pesticide pushing is hard to surpass, there are plenty of runners-up in Washington and in the various states and counties across the nation.

6. WHAT PROTECTION? (II)

THE U.S. DEPARTMENT of Agriculture is not the only federal agency that disregards its obligations to see that Americans receive even reasonably fair treatment in the marketplace. When President Kennedy delivered the first special consumer message to Congress some time before his death, he had in mind something very different from what has been going on in Washington since then. He spelled out the four basic rights: to choose, to be informed, to be heard, to be safe. Regulatory agencies were advised that the new motto was "Let the Seller Beware." The office of Special Assistant for Consumer Affairs was created to insure that that altruistic slogan would be translated into business practice.

Profiteers, lobbyists, and regulators united to empty the rhetoric of content. The old *caveat emptor* signs were rehung, the special assistant assigned a place below the salt. Operating on a budget smaller than the one she had as Pennsylvania's consumer counsel and pressured by special interests, she soon became more preoccupied with "safe" causes like the fat content in hot dogs than in risky ones like the poisons in them.[1]

Technically, the responsibility for that area lies with the Food and Drug Administration. It has since 1938, when the Federal Food, Drug, and Cosmetics Act was passed, replacing the 1906 law and proscribing the addition of any poisonous substance to foodstuffs except those *absolutely essential* to production. A significant amendment was made in 1954, after the use of pesticides became widespread, which directed the FDA to set "safe and legal" tolerances on raw agricultural products for the economic poisons approved by the USDA. (Residues in processed foods were already covered by the basic law, which included all additives.) The FDA was given that power since the USDA might be reluctant to bar in foods the toxic substances it was advising farmers to use on their crops. The theory was, as two FDA officials noted, the agency "has no conflicting interests or responsibilities in the production or marketing of food and allied products."[2]

The concept of tolerances involves the belief that for all chemicals there is some level of dosage that will not cause harm to persons exposed to them. That "threshold hypothesis" was discarded after scientists working on radiation protection standards found that there was no level at all that did not increase genetic mutations. They believed that was true for many agricultural chemicals and for other toxic materials used in food processing. The Delaney "Anti-Cancer Amendment" of 1958 prohibits any carcinogenic substance in food in any quantity; therefore a zero tolerance was assigned to residues of a number of pesticides.

Chemical, farm, and food processing lobbyists descended on Washington with cries of "unnecessary"and "unfair." Table salt and lots of other familiar substances could induce cancer, they argued. The food industry would be ruined if the purists were allowed to have their way.[3]

Congressman Delaney would not be talked down by industry or FDA officials. He called public attention to instances in which people had been exposed to danger.

An FDA ruling in 1956 allowed fruits and vegetables to be marketed with residues of a pesticide that had induced cancer in test animals. Later tests showed the chemical to be "even more injurious," Representative Delaney told a meeting of the National Health Federation. The FDA had reversed itself.[4]

The attack on zero tolerances continued—understandably, since the stepped-up use of pesticides began to make it increasingly difficult to find any food at all that had not been contaminated. Other tolerances were increased. Between 1954 and 1965, for example, fourteen of the eighteen changes for established tolerances were increases.[5]

On the relatively few occasions when the FDA has acted, it has outdone itself to insure that those who rendered the seized foods "unfit for human consumption" did not suffer the consequences of their actions. Growers in the Northwest who doused their cranberry bogs with aminotriazole, a powerful weedkiller that had induced thyroid tumors in more than half the rats tested, were given an $8.5 million consolation prize for not being allowed to sell contaminated crops in 1959. Sauce and jelly not being eaten that Thanksgiving cost taxpayers a good bit more than they would have cost served up at the table.[6]

(Ironically, the USDA, which had fought the action and which had approved the pesticide for use on cranberries despite the FDA's "no residue order," was hailing the action later as an indication of "the extent of public protection built into the registration review as handled by a conscientious Agriculture Department staff with the assistance of its informal liaison advisers."[7])

Again, in 1963, when FDA seized milk contaminated with dieldrin and heptachlor, dairy associations in the Southeast and Southwest demanded indemnity for members. This time, $8.8 million was written into the "poor people's" Economic Opportunity Act.

Recently the FDA has been priding itself on having reduced tolerances for DDT and some other pesticides. Its enthusiasm about its actions is not universally shared. Public interest may have been involved; so undoubtedly was the 1968 decision of the Council of the European Communities to slash tolerance limits for pesticide residues on and in fruits and vegetables.[8] For example, the DDT tolerance set by that group was 1.0; in the U.S. it was then 7.0. Similar disparities in other cases would have barred exports from this country—a big business.

The FDA has continued to claim that the tolerances— as of 1968, 3,115 on 175 pesticides—are safe.[9] Again, that opinion is not universally shared. One of the most recent cases involved the herbicide 2,4,5-T—banned for use in Vietnam but continued here. Dr. Lee A. DuBridge, White House science adviser, urged that its use for food be canceled by January 1970. In 6 tests conducted for the National Cancer Institute, abnormal fetuses were produced by as many as 90 and 100 percent of the test rats exposed to "relatively large doses" of it; at the lowest dose, 39 percent. No action was taken until mid-April, after another test bore out the hazards and after Arizona residents protested that drift from a U.S. Forest Service spray program had caused stillborn and deformed goats and chickens, excessive vaginal bleeding in women, and destruction of home gardens. Congressman Richard J. Mc Carthy of New York, after a visit to the Arizona area, charged that the FDA had failed to enforce the law by not establishing safe tolerance levels for the chemicals.[10]

Not the least problem is that the FDA is less careful than warranted in considering company claims. Primary responsibility for proving that poisonous residues are fit for human consumption rests with the manufacturer. The FDA then passes judgment on the scientific studies submitted. Most of them are based on short-term animal experiments; many of them have been perhaps unduly concerned with marketing potential. After the first test for the National Cancer Institute revealed the hazards of 2,4,5-T, scientists for one of the major manufacturers insisted that a contaminant rather than the chemicals themselves caused the birth defects in all the mice. That was the claim that carried weight during the two years before a second test by a government agency substantiated the grim findings.[11]

For another thing, how much of even "safe" poisonous substances consumers are actually taking in is a matter of speculation. The FDA sampling is modest; each year thirty diet samples in five geographic regions are studied.[12] They do not take into account that gross differences in pesticide levels may exist in various areas; they do not indicate that food intake is never really standardized. One person may eat five or ten times the "normal" amount of a particular type of food. He may thus absorb five or ten times the amount of DDT, DDE, TDE, endrin, dieldrin, heptachlor epoxide, lindane, BHC, aldrin, toxaphene, and others that follow those ten leaders in the "well balanced" American diet.[13]

Just as the number of diet samples is absurdly small, so is the number of interstate food shipments checked by the agency—less than one percent of the total. If FDA publicists find it encouraging to note that each year 25,000 samples of food shipments are checked, consumers may find it less reassuring to note that more than 2,475,000 go across state lines unchecked. Farmers cannot "afford" to be as scrupulous as they should be or even might wish to be about the misfortunes, accidents, and errors that affect their products—the carrots that have taken up endrin from the contaminated soil, peaches coated with parathion, vegetables laden with benzene hexachloride that

someone had mistaken for fertilizer.[14] Fear of FDA inspection is not the most effective deterrent—not with 99
chances out of a hundred that shipments will not be
examined.

Scrutiny by state and local inspectors is even less of a
threat. In some places, there are no such persons. In
others, procedures are sometimes erratic. A California
official told me that agents looking for residues are
guided by "smell." Sniffs are then followed up by more
scientific tests. When I mentioned that to some friends
who had been vegetable growers before switching to
flowers, they thought it hilarious. "Smell pesticides? Why
the stench at the market where we shipped ours was so
strong a blind stranger would have no trouble finding it
from blocks away. Men handling the deliveries all wore
gloves; lots of them had face masks. The reputation of
some growers for last-minute spraying was so bad that
some of the workers refused to handle their stuff. Lots of
growers don't think a thing of spraying a couple of hours
before crops are harvested."

The FDA does need more money for inspectors. Although it complains regularly about the lack, it has not
done much to press that point—as Senator Ribicoff noted
in 1964.

What is wrong with FDA is not merely lack of enforcement staff and legal authority. As Congressman Fountain
noted sharply, "It appears to me that frequently FDA
has not utilized to best advantage the resources available
to it."[15] Despite cries of "harassment," he had gathered
so much evidence of that that in the spring of 1970 his
government operations subcommittee decided to find out
why.

A number of extremely curious episodes involving FDA
officials in 1969 and 1970 precipitated the decision. First

was the ban on cyclamate, the artificial sweetener linked to cancer in animals, in the fall of 1969 by then HEW Secretary Finch. The *Affaire Cyclamate* had its beginning when Dr. Jacqueline Verrett, a research scientist with the Food and Drug Administration, called attention to their dangers in a television report. Her three-year study showed that 15 percent of the chicken embryos exposed to cyclamates showed deformities: feet attached directly to the hip, toes fused together, "flipper" legs. Understandably dismayed that her report was shelved, Dr. Verrett was able to get across to millions her message: "I don't recommend cyclamate for chicks, and I don't recommend it for people."[16]

Subcommittee members wanted to know why Secretary Finch, who immediately banned the stuff, had earlier apparently reversed recommendations for implementing restrictions and had, in one case, allowed millions of mislabeled soft-drink bottles to remain on the market contrary to the recommendation of FDA scientists.[17]

The next headlined episode occurred a few weeks later when FDA Commissioner Dr. Herbert L. Ley, Jr., was ousted from his post. Although not widely known as a fearless fighter for the public interest, he had invited the hostility of the pharmaceutical and pesticide industries in his three-year term of office. During that time, FDA had acted to remove 300 "ineffective" drugs from the market and to lower tolerances for a number of pesticides. Commenting on his departure from the consumer protection agency, Dr. Ley said rather bitterly: "The FDA is not protecting the public as many people think. . . . What the FDA is doing and what the public think it's doing are as different as night from day."[18]

Two days later, dispatches from Washington carried the news that HEW would eliminate the "blacklist" which had kept hundreds of eminent scientists, including several Nobel Laureates, from serving on advisory committees. When existence of the blacklist had first been made public in *Science* magazine in June, officials categorically denied it. Then reversing themselves, they announced that the list would be destroyed.[19]

The major uproar did not begin until March 1970, when the Associated Press obtained a copy of a report by Dr. Howard L. Richardson, then chief pathologist at FDA. In his words: "On September 10, 1968, I arrived to take over the most demoralized group of individuals I have ever encountered in my lifetime."[20] In a memorandum to Commissioner Ley, shortly before he was ousted, Dr. Richardson charged that agency officials "on occasions too numerous to relate" had tampered with scientific findings that might have modified official government positions on the safety of some food additives and pesticides. For instance, old FDA slides and worksheets revealed what he termed a suspiciously high incidence of cancer in test animals exposed to cyclamates. Yet those findings were not included in FDA's report of the experiment published years earlier because, Dr. Richardson said, the pathologist who had conducted the experiment and signed the report had allowed a nonpathologist superior to write it.[21]

When stories began to circulate, the new FDA Commissioner, Charles C. Edwards, acted. Dr. Richardson was demoted to Number Two man in the Pathology Division. First place was given, at least temporarily, to a man who was not a pathologist.[22]

The bureaucratic bungling and finagling by officials who have not only risen to, but soared beyond the level of their incompetence might be amusing—if anything less serious were involved. While the Richardson case sug-

gests the kind of thing that is going on back at the ranch,
out on the road the publicists are busy about the business
of allaying fears and inspiring confidence.

When an official in the compliance division was asked
by a reporter for the *Wall Street Journal* if the FDA was
not troubled by his disclosure that half of the raw agricultural products sampled during a two-year study contained poisonous residues, he replied brightly: "Our toxicologists aren't at all worried about the problem now.
But we're going to keep watching it."[23] In the fall of
1969 an official of the FDA Bureau of Science found no
due cause to be alarmed that the milk of nursing mothers
contained levels of DDT three to seven times higher than
tolerated for cow's milk. Nor was he disturbed about
cancer or any other damage: "It is not known what
effect accumulated DDT has on public health. It might
have none at all."[24] Another FDA official reassured an
Oregon State University conference that "current levels"
of pesticide residue "are not a threat to world health"
—despite the recent findings of his own branch.[25]

Whenever health hazards have been demonstrated,
the FDA counters with an order for another study.

One rather bizarre illustration of that type of action
began in 1963, after the President's Science Advisory
Committee recommended that chronic effects be studied
further, using both immature and adult animals. The
National Cancer Institute accepted the responsibility, and
it worked out a contract with Bionetics Research Laboratories. The study was to be long term—at least five years
—and impressively comprehensive: it involved the bio-
assay of 130 compounds on more than 20,000 mice.

A preliminary report of the findings was scheduled to
be given by the research director at the annual meeting
of the Society of Toxicology in March 1969. It was widely

publicized as one of the major scientific events of the year and one that would have far-reaching consequences, since it identified some of the most commonly used pesticides as "clearly tumorigenic."[26]

A few days before the meeting, and with fuzzy explanation, the report was canceled.

Unable to get a copy of the paper, I enlisted the aid of Congressman George E. Brown, Jr. He was not able to get the report either. However, a few weeks later he sent me a copy of a statement by Dr. Kenneth M. Endicott, National Cancer Institute director. He said that his institute and other government agencies had decided that the "initial statistical analysis was not sufficiently detailed to be interpreted with any degree of certainty." He added:

> The authors of the preliminary report decided that they should defer presentation of their paper, which even at present would necessarily be incomplete and, therefore, misleading, and report their studies fully at a later date after all the analyses have been completed.[27]

That the authors had reached that belated decision continues to raise eyebrows among persons familiar with scientific meetings. Off-the-top-of-the-head papers are not presented; both writers and their reports are carefully screened months, sometimes years, in advance. Nor is it possible to dismiss a five-year study of such dimensions lightly.

The copy of the letter written in Dr. Endicott's variation of gobbledygook was followed by a copy of a letter from HEW Secretary Finch to Congressman Brown. In that, he stressed the need for further studies "in order not to mislead or alarm the American people."[28] Apparently, to get just such a reassuring study, he appointed a committee of "outside experts" to prepare a report on the health hazards of pesticides within six months.

The outsiders, not surprisingly, numbered a good many whose views on pesticides would not alarm anyone— least of all the manufacturers. Chairman was Dr. Emil M. Mrak, chancellor emeritus of the University of California at Davis. Co-chairman was Dr. William J. Darby of Vanderbilt University, where he was recently joined by Dr. Wayland J. Hayes, Jr., of DDT fame. Dr. Mrak's enthusiasm for pesticides has been widely known since 1960, when he served as chairman of a special committee set up by former Governor Edmund G. Brown to consider "Public Policy Regarding Agricultural Chemicals in California." Dr. Darby's enthusiasm is also widely known, partly as a result of his editorial activities for chemical industry journals. Representatives of Eli Lilly and Dow Chemical were also named to the commission.

As might have been anticipated, the report was bland —in the extreme. It advocated further study even of those substances identified as hazardous for more than a decade. "The health and welfare of the public must be effectively protected," the commission observed the formalities. "However, it is not in the best interest of the public to permit unduly precipitate or excessively restrictive action based only on anxiety."[29]

That is in line with the what-you-don't-know theory of poisoning.

Health hazards were reported in a low key. Additionally, the commission indulged in extracurricular comments about the obligations of government to make life richer and fuller for the chemical industry. "Incentives" should be provided—i.e., money—to "encourage the development of safer chemicals." Rather than there being public ownership of new developments, patents should be assigned to licensees, and the "working life" of patents should be extended.[30] The latter suggestions were pretty remarkable, considering the way industry has appropriated what has been invented or developed at the expense of the tax-payers. Moreover, United States patent laws involving chemicals are among the most industry-oriented in the world. (One of the chief reasons for the high cost of medical care is the effect patent laws and practices have had on drug prices.)

When an "Interim Report" on the work done by Bione-tics for NCI was finally issued, almost no one was listen-ing. The revision went all out to eliminate "anxieties." It stressed the "incompleteness" of the evaluation. It held the probing experiment more relevant to mice than men. Nevertheless, some findings were interesting; 11 of 123 compounds administered orally had induced "a signifi-cantly elevated incidence of tumors."[31]

The findings, however, are the least disturbing thing about the episode. What is far more disturbing is the degree of censorship exercised over science by industry and industry apologists within government.

The record of other agencies, including the United Nations, is scarcely more encouraging than that estab-lished in Washington. The World Health Organization has a vested interest in pesticides because of public health programs. As a consequence, it has consistently minimized their dangers to humans—particularly that of DDT.

It is not altogether surprising that a WHO report on the Safe Use of Pesticides in Public Health echoes in an almost uncanny manner the public relations releases of the chemical companies. Persons named as experts to WHO committees are not likely to be "unfriendlies." For example, the sixteenth report of the WHO experts stressed that:

The concern that has been expressed in recent years about contamination of the environment by this very stable and persistent insecticide should not, in the opinion of the Committee, be considered sufficient reason for substituting other insecticides for indoor residual spraying against mosquitos. The safety record of DDT remains outstanding.[32]

The chairman of that committee was none other than Dr. Wayland J. Hayes, Jr.

WHO opinions are then used as guidelines in this country and everywhere else in the world. They were questioned for the first time at United Nations headquarters in the fall of 1969. Secretary General U Thant issued a report asking pointed questions about annual distribution by the Children's Fund of 12 million pounds of DDT. Acting on WHO advice, UNICEF has been sending DDT to 59 countries and territories in large quantities—about one of every eight pounds being produced. How long, asked the report, can UNICEF continue the practice?[33]

Not everyone at headquarters seemed equally concerned about the need to avoid "such damage to the environment." When I spoke with a WHO information officer about the problem a few months earlier, he launched into a tirade against "people who worry about pesticides." They are "wonderful," he insisted.[34]

Just how much longer the inhabitants of the most heavily deluged countries will continue to regard them as wonderful is another matter. As fleas, ticks, flies, roaches, and other disease carriers become increasingly resistant to DDT and to more toxic poisons used in larger quantities, the acknowledged risks become greater—to people, to animals, and to the crops that are the economic hope of underdeveloped nations.

Not much that is favorable can be said of various

other home-front agencies also involved in protecting people from the poisoners. For decades the Federal Trade Commission tolerated deceptive advertising claims. Lindane vaporizers, for example, were held "safe" in ads long after they were outlawed in many places, and even after the USDA's belated acknowledgment of their dangers.[35] The U.S. Public Health Service and the Department of Interior's Fish and Wildlife Service admittedly have been hampered because they have only "advisory" roles. But they have too often failed to speak out in public about the hazards they have warned of quietly in conference rooms and private reports.

State and local agencies, particularly departments of agriculture, have shown themselves even more industry-oriented than the federal agencies. Some propriety is observed in Washington, where hearing rooms are often peopled by competent reporters. Fewer of them are taking notes in hearing rooms in state capitols and city halls, where off-the-record sessions are more frequent and bureaucrats and legislators are more openly held to be *private* servants.

I had a chance to see at close range how closely knotted are the ties that bind local government officials and pesticide interests in 1969 at a court hearing in Bakersfield, California. The AFL-CIO United Farm Workers Organizing Committee, headed by Cesar Chavez, was seeking to gain access to pesticide spraying records. Workers charged that they were being sent into sprayed fields before the legal waiting period had elapsed; some protested having been sprayed while working with crops.[36]

Although the records are *public records,* an order had been issued six months earlier—a "temporary" order— restraining the county agricultural commissioner from allowing UFWOC to see them. (He is required by law to keep for inspection records of the commercial pest control operators: the date of treatment, material and dosage used, the number of units treated, and other pertinent items. Individual farmers, even corporate ones, are not required to keep or file records.)

Action to check the records had begun on an August afternoon, when UFWOC chief counsel Jerome Cohen called at the office of Commissioner C. Seldon Morley. The visit, to judge by courtroom recollections, was not a particularly sociable affair. Commissioner Morley rejected the request; the records, he insisted, had been given to him "in confidence." Mr. Cohen was equally insistent on his right to have that "vital public information."

One way of gauging the size of a town is the speed with which word gets around that established practices are being questioned. Although Bakersfield, the seat of oil-rich and crop-rich Kern County, has about 75,000 inhabitants, it must be among the smallest of towns. Within two hours after the union attorney had left the commissioner's office, three crop-dusting corporations, acting on behalf of all members of the local Agricultural Chemicals Association, had managed to get the restraining order. Mr. Morley, the "defendant," was thus legally enjoined from opening the files. The judge had signed the order with remarkable promptness, considering that the attorney for the trade association admitted that "in the very limited time available . . . we have not found direct authority on the point. . . ." Superior Court hearing on UFWOC's petition, delayed at the request of trade association attorney Stephen E. Wall and County Counsel Ralph Jordan, was finally slated for January 29.

Great changes have occurred since the days of the Joads in Kern County, which lies at the southern end of the San Joaquin Valley: probably the world's most fertile region. U.S. 99, twisting down from the Tehachapi Mountains and leveling north past Arvin, Weedpatch, and other towns on the migrants' route, is now a broad highway. Nondescript public buildings in Bakersfield have been replaced by glittering steel and glass rectangles of ultra-modern design. The "Okies" and "Arkies" who survived the great hunger have adopted the attitudes and manners of California farm folk, even to snarling "union" just like the Establishmentarians.

But once inside the handsome paneled courtroom where the hearings were scheduled, changes seemed less fundamental. The old issues were still *the* issues, dividing the courtroom and the case right down the center: human values vs. business license; philosophy vs. technology; concept vs. coin.

In the spectators' seats to the right of the entrance sat the crop dusters: technological experts who defy the laws of gravity by their ability to fly "right on the deck" and who challenge the laws of biology as they wage chemical war in the fields. Their workday confrontations with nature had given them arrogance, bound them firmly to the Now. On the other side of the barrier were their spokesmen: Mr. Wall, a rather handsome man who seemed confident that the law would come to terms with him and was irritated about having to go through the formalities; County Counsel Jordan, modeled along the lines of Nero Wolfe, but less urbane; and Commissioner Morley—a "real life" portrait by Grant Wood, American Gothic to the marrow.

In the spectators' seats to the left were the farm workers. They, too, had been stamped by their work. Their faces, more varied in structure and richer in hue, had the settled patience of persons who regard nature as process rather than enemy and for whom there is past as well as present—and the hope of tomorrow. Their spokesmen were Jerry Cohen, sandy-haired, freckled, young; and darker, heavier, blunter, younger David Averbuck. Representative of the many well-educated and totally involved young persons for whom Delano and Cesar Chavez had become the center and symbol of meaningful protest, they also characterized the "new breed" of lawyers who had rejected the professional notion that law is an abstract game for the affluent. They are determined it shall serve as a vehicle for delivering justice to all the people.

Beyond the two factions, on the raised bench under the golden seal of state, sat Judge George A. Brown. Courteous, grave, keenly interested, he indicated himself a man deeply appreciative of the dignity and proprieties of the law. Although the issue he was to rule upon seemed simple enough and immediate, it was really of far-reaching consequence: to what extent could and would the law curb the agricultural and chemical entrepreneurs?

The union received strong support in its claim that farm workers and the general public need protection. Some of the health hazards due to casual practices and secretiveness were described by state health officers and the owner of laboratories in the area which provide ChE tests for crop dusters and formulators.[37] Dr. Thomas Milby, chief of the California Department of Public Health, sharply attacked the policy of secrecy. "It is unthinkable that any worker should be enjoined from finding out the potentially lethal substances to which he might be exposed." It was his position that replacing DDT and other hard pesticides with the organic phosphates made full disclosure of their presence imperative. The organic phosphates account for more injuries and deaths than any other pesticides, he said.[38]

The witness who revealed most clearly the nature and extent of economic and environmental hazards was Dr. Robert Van den Bosch, professor of economic entomology at the University of California. An outgoing, Hobbitt-like man who is an internationally recognized expert, he held that California farmers are being heavily penalized by the "overkill" program. Because broad-spectrum chemicals have killed off "good" insects as well as "bad," many species of pests have been given license to explode. By preserving the complex of predators and parasites that exercise natural control, by promoting intelligent farming practices, by using highly selective pesticides, farmers could realize enormous savings in money, land, and men's health and lives. Dr. Van den Bosch pointed out that there were moral as well as economic and biological reasons for substituting an ecological approach for the unilateral war. "What we are talking about," he said, "is a philosophy."

That was not what some people in the courtroom were talking about. From the standpoint of the pest control operators, the duty of the law was clear—to sanction business as usual. Mr. Wall based his case chiefly on the escape clause in the California Code. Although that holds that access to information about the people's business is "a fundamental and necessary right of every citizen of this state," it also precludes disclosures of records of law enforcement agencies and—of obvious interest to businesses—records possessed by other agencies if they contain trade secrets or certain reports "obtained in confidence."

The records of pesticide applications contain trade secrets, Mr. Wall held; they had been given to Commissioner Morley in confidence.

County Counsel Jordan also argued forcefully on the

"trade secrets" and "confidentiality" points. It is novel in
a courtroom to see attorneys for plaintiff and defendant
on the same side of the table, sharing the same witnesses,
citing the same precedents, making the same appeals. And
the alliance between public officials and private operators
in this instance was rendered more ironic by another
"chemical case" going on. At one point, the hearing was
recessed so that a jury could bring in its verdict and Judge
Brown could pass sentence on two rather frayed young
women; one very blonde, one very brunette. While working at a place called the Hillbilly Ranch, they had sold
—according to the felony charges for which they were
sentenced—six dollars worth of Seconal and amphetamine
tablets to a police informer. The prosecuting attorneys,
like the jurors, wore expressions of outrage over the violations of public health and safety—to say nothing of
public morality.

Mr. Jordan expressed even greater outrage about the
union's appeal to see the records. In his zeal to protect
the trade secrets of Mr. Wall's clients, he questioned Dr.
Van den Bosch in such a fierce manner that Judge Brown
was once forced to ask him to "stand back a little, please."
The county counsel scoffed about the "somewhat ethereal
question of whether the public interest of disclosure
outweighs the public interest of confidentiality." He dismissed affidavits of injured workers as "a pile of garbage."

Commissioner Morley was so solicitous about the applicators' trade secrets that he could have been mistaken
for Mr. Wall's confidential clerk. Animation is not one
of that public official's distinguishing characteristics. But
one of the occasions when he seemed more person than
portrait occurred in the corridor outside the courtroom
after Dr. John E. Swift had testified. Another University
of California entomologist and a consultant to the California Department of Agriculture, he had been sum-

moned, it seemed clear, chiefly to counter the testimony of his colleague. The commissioner was delighted with Dr. Swift's performance. "They were trying to put you on the spot," he thwacked the expert on the shoulder heartily, "but you came through fine, fella."

Considering how vividly those words and gestures summed up the policy and attitudes of the "regulators," it was not hard to understand the passion in Mr. Cohen's voice when he talked about UFWOC's role as "public defender." "I think it is inefficient to rely on government agencies," he retorted sharply to a comment by Mr. Wall. "We don't trust government agencies. We rely on ourselves, and we would rather rely on public law."[39]

In that case the law did not provide much relief. Early in the spring Judge Brown handed down an order instructing Commissioner Morley to keep the records secret. Disclosure, he decided, "would seriously hamper the essential cooperation existing between all segments of the pesticide industry and the farmers on the one hand with the commissioner on the other."

Judge Brown was right about that. The point he missed and the point missed in another case that year is that pesticides are no longer anyone's *private* business.

Curiously enough, that point was first acknowledged by a California grape grower. On September 18, 1969, officials of A. Perelli-Minetti and Sons Vineyard signed a contract with UFWOC. In addition to guaranteeing field workers some of the highest wages and best protection of any persons employed in American agriculture, the company pledged itself to work closely with the union health and safety committee to prevent pesticide poisonings.

Henceforth workers will be informed about what is being sprayed at the Perelli-Minetti ranch and when. Some substances have been ruled out entirely. DDT, aldrin, diel-

drin, and endrin have been eliminated, and no other
chlorinated hydrocarbons are to be applied "without the
necessary precautions." When organic phosphates are used,
the Health and Safety Committee shall recommend the
length of time fields shall be closed to workers after
application. Baseline cholinesterase tests paid for by the
company shall be given to all workers involved in their
application—just as they are, by state law, to crop dusters
and workers in pesticide manufacturing and formulating
companies.[40]

Jerry W. Fielder, state agriculture director who had
established the secrecy policy for all the county com-
missioners, continued to scoff at the "crusade" against
pesticides for some weeks after. In a speech before the
agricultural committee of the state senate, which was considering a measure to halt the use of hard pesticides, he
said, "It's simply not true that pesticides are used indiscriminately without concern for people, animals, property,
or the total environment."[41] (Precisely how he knew this
was not made clear; at the hearing in Bakersfield one of
his subordinates had said: "We do not make tests of our
own. We take the word of the chemical companies.")

At any rate, a few months later, quite unexpectedly,
Mr. Fielder experienced what seems to have been a near
complete conversion. Shortly before Christmas he announced that the use of 91 pesticides on farm crops would
be prohibited as of January 1970; new restrictions would
be placed on 120 others. In the accompanying statement
Mr. Fielder said: "We are taking a much broader view
of pesticide usage. The boundaries of concern are no
longer the farmers' fences."[42]

They never should have been. They might not have been
if scientists and academicians had not played the game
of "grantsmanship" at public expense.

7. HIRE EDUCATION

THE "SCIENTIFIC MIND" is a soaring achievement: flexible, fastidious, fearless. Ranging macro- and microcosmically, it has liberated the power locked up in the atom, precisely located an undiscovered planet; it has mastered the forces of the universe we inhabit and allowed us to transcend its earthly bonds. When the mind is housed in the body of an academician . . . well, there is the mind we trust. For one of the few surviving educational myths is that the scientist-professor is of a community of gentlemanly scholars who serenely pursue the truths of their various disciplines in order to lead the rest of us from the cave into the radiant reality.

"Nothing," as a former university president said some time ago, "could be further from the truth."

Since before the days of Chaucer, the role of academicians had been to "gladly learn" and "gladly teach." That has been abandoned in recent years as outmoded. The typical college *professional* is a jet-hopping performer on the corporate circuit, putting on shows of expertise for the highest bidders, safely removed from the chores and bores of classroom life.

Success in *academe*—particularly for scientists—is measured not by traditional standards of teaching, research, and learned publications, but by the size of the grants a man has promoted from government agencies and

foundations and by the number of positions he has negotiated with business enterprises.[1]

Colleges and universities have become convenient bases
from which to operate. The rewards are various, their
extent unknown—the prestige of the institution and the
specialists involved often being determining factors. As
consultants, professors receive about $100 a day from
government agencies and between $50 and $500 from
private industry. Special assignments bring higher returns.
An economist testifying before a legislative committee
investigating drug pricing in 1967 was paid $10,250 by
the Pharmaceutical Manufacturers Association for his
services; another received $4,500.[2] Research grants are
equally varied—ranging from a couple of bags of fertilizer up to millions of dollars: enough to set up departments within departments, schools within schools, and
even to organize the spin-off companies flourishing around
almost every large institution of higher learning. Commercial editorial work may also pay well. And for the
lucky few, there is the possibility of becoming a director
of a major corporation at $10,000 to $20,000 a year, plus
expenses and fees for attending board meetings.

Two representative "success stories" chronicled at two
ends of the country in 1969 may serve as illustrations.
Writing in *The New York Times*, Robert Reinhold described the life of a 33-year-old research physician, a
specialist in endocrinology. He had gone far in his two
years as an associate professor at Massachusetts Institute
of Technology. There he taught one course a semester
and supervised the work of six graduate students. But he
was by no means idle. A member of the editorial board
of three scientific journals, he also worked as consultant to
the National Aeronautics and Space Administration, the
National Institutes of Health, a drug company, and a light

bulb manufacturing company. He had, moreover, found time to do research that "produced" thirty papers and to give about fifty lectures away from the school.[3]

Another scientist at the University of California at Riverside, according to Los Angeles *Times* staff writer William Trombley, had been able to perform the same kind of juggling act. A 48-year-old professor of chemistry, he receives about $24,000 a year for his modest school duties—teaching a freshman chemistry class and a graduate seminar, and supervising the work of five post-doctoral students. He, too, receives additional income as consultant to state and federal agencies and two major corporations: American Cyanamid and Bell & Howell. He is also founder, former president, and chairman of the board of Environmental Resources, Inc.—a company that prospers by offering advice on environmental problems to the National Air Pollution Control Administration and assorted public and private groups.[4]

Both scientists defend the manner in which they have sailed over the barriers separating the town and the gown to forge a business-government-education alliance. The MIT specialist says his outside jobs bring him into contact with "the real world." His California colleague glows: "When I come back to the classroom, I can relate the real world to my students."

It can be questioned whether an institution of higher learning is the natural habitat of persons capable of such clichés. "The real world" . . . shades of George F. Babbitt! What cannot be questioned is the effect of absentee teaching on students and the conflicts of interest that arise, although most deny that they do. The California chemistry professor told Mr. Trombley: "The hardest part about being a consultant is that you have to compartmentalize your mind. When I hear things at Cyanamid I have to be really careful that I don't later reveal things that are proprietary . . . but I'm not about to sell the State of California down the river for $200 a day."

"*Sell*" is a strong word. No doubt there are those who receive funds and maintain their integrity, who, like Sir Francis Bacon, could accept gratuities from pleaders and remain "the justest judge in England." But we are unwilling to take such a risk with our chief justices; nor should we permit others to be so tempted. "The real issue," as Professor Louis Kampf at MIT has stated pointedly, "is where your loyalties lie."[5]

Like students these days in the "Multiversity," professors tend to identify less with the total community and more with subgroups that lie outside the walls—particularly a subgroup that showers him with honors and gifts, refers to him respectfully as "Professor" and "Doctor," entertains him at conventions, and makes up to him and his wife for their scrimping during years of postgraduate study. Dr. Robert M. Hutchins, former president of the University of Chicago, was biblically blunt about the need to halt the alliance: "Where a man's treasure is, there will his heart be also."[6] More to the point perhaps is that where a man's treasure is, there will his expertise be.

Stunning demonstrations of that have been called to public attention recently. In April 1969, more than two months after one of Union Oil Company's wells blew out off the coast of California, *the California Attorney General's office had not been able to get the help of a single university expert in preparing the $500 million damage claim against the company and the $500 million damage claim against the Federal government.* In order to prove that negligence had been responsible for contaminating more than 20 miles of beach and destroying sea life in intertidal regions for 50 miles, a "mountain of evidence" was needed—the kind only experts could provide.[7]

After Chief Deputy Charles A. O'Brien had filed suit, he began to call engineering and oil geology specialists at universities in California. He realized quickly that "roadblocks had been thrown in the path of the state." All seemed to be working on grants from the oil industry, he said. "There is an atmosphere of fear. These experts are afraid that if they assist us in our case on behalf of the people of California, they will lose their oil industry grants."[8]

When I spoke with him four months later, he was still without expert advice and still shaken by what he considered the clear betrayal of public trust. An old friend, an oil company executive, denied that his company or others had ever told educators not to appear. "I believe him," Mr. O'Brien said with some bitterness. "But these guys are so alert to self-interest that they don't need orders."

By contrast, there was no dearth of academic experts when the oil industry pressed to resume off-shore drilling, which had been called off by the government, partly in response to demands by political leaders and conservationist groups and partly in response to the more than 100,000 signatures collected on petitions.[9]

On June 1 a White House panel astounded the public, conservationists, and concerned politicians alike by recommending that Union Oil Company be allowed to develop the well that had blown out and 50 others. Even though the drilling was being done in earthquake territory, the panel said it would be less hazardous to continue than to seal off the site.[10]

Qualifications of some of the eleven members seemed impeccable. In addition to oil industry representatives, an assortment of university men were appointed: Dr. John C. Calhoun, Jr. (chairman), vice-president of Texas A & M University; Dr. Henry W. Menard of Scripps Institution

of Oceanography; Dr. Gordon MacDonald, vice-chancellor
for research and graduate affairs at the University of
California at Santa Barbara; Dr. Lee A. DuBridge, former
president of California Institute of Technology and science
adviser to President Nixon.

Yet the performance of the panel was denounced as
"casual" and "superficial." Senator Alan Cranston of California and Senator Edmund S. Muskie of Maine said that
at a two-day meeting in Los Angeles it had heard only
from representatives of Union, Gulf, Mobil, and Texaco
and from one government official, the director of the
Geological Survey of the Department of Interior. (According to a later report, Dr. Calhoun and two other
panel members, Professor Hamilton M. Johnson and Professor Murray F. Hawkins, were chairmen of science or
geology departments that had received grants from Union,
Texaco, Gulf, and Mobil totaling $179,000 over the past
five years.[11])

"It is not the mark of experts to substitute their general
expertise and background for a specific, detailed, and
independent study of the problem," the senators said. "It
is neither scientific nor professional to make recommendations based solely on testimony by proponents of one
specific solution—especially when those proponents have
a vested interest in continuing the drilling and production
and were the same people who decided to do the drilling
that led to the oil spill in the first place."[12]

Apparently the standards governing scientific evidence
—that it be adequate, accurate, objective—had been lost
on the way to the forum.

What incensed Mr. O'Brien particularly was that the
state university had refused to make its experts as available to the state as to private industry. It would be hard
to find an institution in the country today that is *private*

in the strictest sense, because of the billions in tax dollars poured into all colleges and universities in the form of buildings, equipment, scholarships, research contracts, government grants, and the special tax privileges all enjoy. Nevertheless, some schools are more public than others. Among them are the nation's 70 land-grant colleges and universities established since 1862, when Abraham Lincoln signed the Morrill Act to extend the benefit of higher education to "the people."

Some of those public institutions have, at one time or another, achieved distinguished records of public service. One, as Clark Kerr noted in *Uses of the University*, was the "Idea of Wisconsin" during the Progressive era before World War I. "It entered the legislative halls in Madison with reform programs, supported the trade union movement, . . . developed agricultural and urban extension programs as never before. The university served the whole state."[13]

Most, including the University of California, over which Mr. Kerr once presided, have rendered more limited service. A report by Ann and Hal Draper several years ago charged that university studies, research projects, and statements are so contorted that they are little more than a gigantic whitewash for California agribusiness—"a super-exploitive industry whose main crop is (worker) poverty."[14] Even the *Wall Street Journal* has described the agriculture division and extension services as "a tax-paid clinic for a major industry."[15]

That public institutions have so aligned themselves is due largely to the politically appointed boards of trustees and regents. Drawn chiefly from business, banking, commercial, and industrial upper echelons, they have looked upon public education in terms of private service. Administrators, teachers, and students who have refused to equate it with the policies, practices, and personnel needs of Sludge Motors and the First National Piggy Bank have been regarded as campus radicals in the trouble-making tradition of Thorstein Veblen.

Many of our problems—and almost all of the problems of pollution—are not technological ones, but social. But efforts to encourage students to relate social responsibility to science and technology are frowned on as vigorously here as they are reported to be at the University of Moscow. Not long ago, a state college physics instructor in California departed from standard practices in his exams. A former physicist in the aerospace industry, he believes it "unfortunate" that scientists often simply solve problems without considering the possible effect on society. He asked on a test such questions as: "How much energy would it take to orbit a botulism bomb capable of eliminating the human race 10 times over?" "Compute the rotor revolutions of a helicopter macing the people of Berkeley." "With what velocity would the body of a student recoil if he were killed by a shotgun blast to the stomach?"

Governor Ronald Reagan's adviser on education called the examination "a stinking, lousy production." Not surprisingly, the physicist's colleagues also registered "official disapproval."[16]

From World War II until very recently there has been little town-gown conflict within the educational establishment. During the war the country made incredible gains in every scientific and technological field by marshaling abstract thinkers to work out concrete answers to practical problems. Business and industry decided that what was good for the country was good for them, if not necessarily in that order. And General Motors, General Electric, General Dynamics, General Foods, and General General invaded campuses—"buying" brains. If the brains were also working for government agencies, so much the better. It is nice to have a friend at court when specifications are being written, standards are being set, laws are being formulated, contracts are being awarded.

Because insecticides and other agricultural chemicals were a major breakthrough, agricultural schools and science departments were natural magnets. Before World War II, entomologists ranked with traveling salesmen as a butt for jokes—eccentrics who consorted with butterflies and bugs. DDT and the rest of the arsenal suddenly made giants of them.

Bill Knee, a staff writer for the University of Wisconsin *Daily Cardinal* reported recently on what happened at that school: "Insecticide salesmen and industry officials beat a path to the doors of the bug experts. Since entomologists were responsible for recommending specific insecticide brands for crop pests, each company was naturally eager that its product should get the nod. Entomologists were treated to dinner; grants from the insecticide industry began to flow in."[17]

He listed among the insecticide manufacturers granting money to the Wisconsin Department of Entomology since 1967: Shell Chemical Company, Union Carbide Corporation, American Cyanamid Corporation, Chemagro Corporation, Dow Chemical Company, Velsicol, Niagara Chemical Company, Allied Chemical, Stauffer Chemical, Chevron Chemical, Geigy Agricultural. Most of the grants were modest (the Federal government gives more, but seems to get less in return); however, some were large enough to enable entomologists to make "fine careers . . . out of hard pesticides."[18]

Not everyone has been enthusiastic about the game of Corporations on Campus. Some students and some diehard teachers in science and the humanities have been troubled about the new morality and fearful about the ability to "compartmentalize" adequately.

Such concern is not unreasonable. The assortment of potential identities can make it very difficult for even the most honorable and best-intentioned to separate one "self" from another. And a spectator can be totally confused—as members of the Congressional subcommittee looking into the charges of the General Accounting Office themselves confessed to being perplexed by the multiple faces of Dr. Zavon: one week in Washington as representative of Shell, another as consultant to the USDA; writing letters signed variously as Shell representative, as health officer of Cincinnati, as professor of medicine. And in all roles, he was involved with the same pesticide issue.

Answers must be provided for a number of pertinent questions.

Is the witness before the Congressional Committee or legislative body testifying as a disinterested member of the academic community or as a consultant of Effervescent Enterprises?

The late Senator Estes Kefauver was curious to know this when a veritable academic parade was presented by the Pharmaceutical Manufacturers Association seeking to stave off legislation. By the time Eugene V. Rostow, dean of the Yale Law School, was reverently introduced, the senator's patience was wearing thin. "Of course," he commented, "I don't blame the PMA for trying to get somebody from Yale." Then, after Dean Rostow clearly stated that he was appearing as an individual, Senator Kefauver drew an admission that he had been *employed* by the PMA or the law firm representing them to make a presentation before the committee.[19]

During the 1967 investigation of the drug industry by Senator Nelson's subcommittee, there was also speculation about which professorial identity was speaking. James Ridgeway, in *The Closed Corporation,* cited the testimony of Dr. Alfred Gilman of the Albert Einstein College of Medicine at Yeshiva University in New York City. Dr. Gilman began the long "scholarly" letter to support the case for brand names by identifying himself as a "pharmacologist, educator, and co-author of a well-known text." What he failed to mention was that he was also consultant to three drug companies and "had been asked to write the letter by the president of PMA."[20]

Money is not the only thing special interests have to offer. There is the publicity—giving credit where and when credit is due. The press releases ground out by the "Industry Task Force for DDT" of the National Agricultural Chemicals Association during the 1969 Wisconsin hearings provided all the "instant fame" that any generally unsung member of the academic community could hope for.

Among the academicians whose opinions were widely disseminated were a number from the University of Wisconsin, Rutgers, Vanderbilt, and other schools. Dr. R. Keith Chapman, professor of entomology at Wisconsin and a member of the state Insect Control Recommendations Committee, said that there were "no feasible substitutes for DDT" on some vegetable crops; it "gives absolutely maximum results." Dr. Frank Cherms, a professor of poultry science at the same school, denied that DDT caused changes in reproduction rates of birds.[21] Professor Bailey B. Pepper, entomologist at Rutgers University, another industry witness, told the hearing examiner that "if agriculture is to remain competitive, it is vital to have DDT included in the insecticide arsenal."[22] (Another Rutgers scientist went even further later in the year, telling 300 agricultural officials at a meeting in South Carolina that opponents of DDT were an "irresponsible minority" and that to ban it is "tantamount to genocide of millions of humans."[23])

The most famous among the industry witnesses was Dr. Wayland J. Hayes, Jr., former chief of toxicology of the U.S. Public Health Service, then a professor at Vanderbilt University. Dr. Hayes continued to hold firm in his 20-year stand that a ban on DDT would be "disastrous." He considers the pesticide "safe."[24]

Is the government panelist drafting standards and legislation performing his job as scholar-scientist or as a loyal member of the "team" at Universal Polluters?

The incredibly bad conditions of air, water, earth—all suggest that the team members were in there pitching when standards were being set. Although the health hazards of smog, of pesticides, fertilizers, and other chemicals contaminating the food supply have been known to scientists for years, local and national legislators have been repeatedly assured by some "scholars" that poisons are really good for the country.

When scholar-writers and scholar-editors are busy about their publishing labors, are they being purely scientific or thinking of the future of Special Interests, Inc.?

That is not easy to tell. For example, Dr. William J. Darby of the Vanderbilt University's school of medicine —whose name crops up frequently on commissions and committees appointed to examine the health hazards of pesticides—responded in a highly emotional manner to *Silent Spring*. "Silence Miss Carson" was the title of his review of the book in *Chemical and Engineering News*[25] —a concept scarcely in keeping with the freedoms of thought and speech so valued in the academic community. More recently, Dr. Darby has expressed strong disapproval of "irresponsible" criticism of the chemical additives in food. Additives may improve nutrition, he thinks.[26]

That view is shared by Dr. Frederick J. Stare, chairman of the Department of Nutrition at Harvard's School of Public Health. Dr. Stare's journalistic efforts, which appear on the food pages of papers all across the country, along with the grocery ads, are scarcely characterized by restraint. During the truth-in-packaging controversy, for instance, he dismissed studies showing how even well-educated women were grossly deceived when they shopped. The proposal, advocated by almost every consumer expert in the country, "would be bad for the consumer," Dr. Stare said.[27] In the spring of 1970 Dr. Stare, who is also a board member of the Continental Can Company, defended MSG and other chemicals in foods: "As a physician and a student of nutrition for the last 30 years, I am convinced that food additives are far safer in actual use than the basic natural foods themselves."[28]

Over the years, Dr. Stare has made invaluable contributions to pesticide makers. Two of his testimonials which have been frequently used to defend their uncontrolled use are:

> As a physician and student of nutrition for the past twenty-five years, let me state categorically that I do not know, nor have I ever heard, of one single case of ill health in man to be due to adding approved chemicals to food. . . .[29]

and

> One irrefutable fact that the critics of pesticides have
> been unable to answer is this true statement: there is
> not one medically documented instance of ill health
> in man, not to mention death, that can be attributed
> to the proper use of pesticides, or even to their im-
> proper use as far as ill health from residues on
> food. . . .[30]

In addition to the literary exercises of Dr. Stare, Dr.
Darby, and other notables, there are more modest produc-
tions by lesser known writer-scientist-teachers. When it
became known at the state college where I work that I
was doing some research on pesticides, members of the
agriculture department provided me with a steady stream
of articles—all vigorous defenses and many of them
sounding curiously like materials I had been given by the
information director of the National Agricultural Chemicals Association in Washington. People concerned about
residues were held to be "playing a numbers game";[31]
prohibiting any pesticide, even DDT, would greatly alter
our eating habits and lower our standard of living.[32]

Quality is not the primary objective of the publications.
As Leonard Wickenden noted, "Some professors of agriculture do not think it beneath them to write advertisements for chemical fertilizers."[33]

Many of the testimonials are undoubtedly heartfelt;
some of them are undoubtedly motivated by the desire to
get ahead. In the publish-or-perish jungle, it is no secret
that "right thinking" articles more readily find a home
than those that will not please sponsors and advertisers.

Also, there is the problem of who is going to pay to
have the articles published. Many agricultural and scientific journals, like the vanity press, *charge writers to print*

their works. A scientist at my school told me he had paid
$40 a page for his last article.
Still other questions remain.

*When the scholar-teacher sets a handful of graduate
students on a research project, is it one he considers vital
or one that was suggested by a public relations director
of Cesspools Unlimited? In the classroom is he speaking
as a scientist or a friend of Benighted Consolidated? Will
the administration and members of a department tolerate
anyone in their midst who is not a member of the Friends
of Industry Association?*

The answers are not entirely reassuring. Some research
is no research at all. James Ridgeway cited an interesting
example of alleged pesticide research carried on by scientists at the University of California, which is the official
state adviser on pesticides. A university extension agent
in Fresno, he said, received a $70,000 grant from four
chemical companies that wanted to test new compounds
for combatting principal cotton pests. The actual research
in the field, which consisted of counting the bugs before
and after spraying, was done by chemical company workers. Their findings appeared in a university report. Thus,
Mr. Ridgeway pointed out, the company "used the university as a facade behind which they tested and marketed
their new products."[34]

The air of secrecy surrounding defense projects at universities carries over to private industry. Commenting on
activities at the Russell Laboratories of the Department
of Entomology at the University of Wisconsin, Bill Knee
wrote:

> The working atmosphere there reminds one of "The
> Double Helix." Technicians and graduate students

are under strict orders not to discuss any details of
the lab's research [on pesticides] with anyone not in
the group. Even other students in the entomology
department are not welcome in room 839 and Professor [E. Paul] Lichtenstein asks them to leave if he
catches them.[35]

The ways in which schools respond to outside demands
to keep things under control are varied—easing out "difficult" faculty, suppressing "inconvenient" reports, fixing
patterns of instruction.

Dr. William E. Smith told a Congressional subcommittee several years ago that scientists who advocated caution in approving unproven food additives "are apt to
wind up without a job." Dr. Smith, who has gained international reputation for his work in determining environmental carcinogens, reported that his appointment as
associate professor of industrial medicine at New York
University was not renewed after he had shown a superior
there certain data indicating a cancer hazard in an industry that "had retained him [the superior] as a consultant."
His own experience and the experience of a medical director for a large chemical company who was "too" interested
in cancer-causing chemicals were not unusual, Dr. Smith
said. "Government, university, and industrial research in
this field has been obstructed, while apologists for carcinogens are in great demand."[36] His experience was not
unique. Frank Graham, Jr., reported in Since Silent Spring
that Dr. Robert Rudd of the University of California "paid
the price usually exacted of academics who hit hard at
the system."[37] His classic Pesticides and the Living Landscape cost him a promotion and led to his dismissal "without notice or cause" from the California Experiment
Station.[38]

Universities respond in less direct ways. Victor J. Yannacone, Jr., reported that a 10-year-old recommendation against using DDT in gypsy moth control programs "left the privileged sanctuary of a Cornell file cabinet" only after court action was instituted.[39] Biological controls offer a highly promising solution to pest problems. Yet, thanks to industry pressures, schools have generally ignored or sabotaged research in that field.

Pandering to special interests is not consistent with the "uses" of the university. Among administrators speaking up recently about this is Daniel G. Aldrich of the University of California at Irvine, who said in an address in 1969:

> Furthermore, I do not believe that agribusiness or any other industry gains in the long run by bending the university to purposes it could as well do for itself or through some other private or public agency. The university, alone, is uniquely suited to the pursuit of new knowledge—and the transmission of that knowledge—for its own sake. Its diversion from this central mission not only fails to serve society at large, it is detrimental to the extent that society's dynamo for progress—the search for new knowledge—is dimmed.[40]

They are brave words. Whether they will prevail is another matter—if the merchandisers continue to have their way.

8. MERCHANDISING DEATH

"PEST CONTROL, AS it exists today, is largely a matter of merchandising."[1] That recent appraisal by an internationally known authority, Dr. Robert Van den Bosch, is accurate. The reasons why are not hard to discover—the need to control pests and the creation of a "pesticide mentality."

Agriculture, man's oldest civilized activity, is a very new science—if it is really one at all. Wide gulfs between theories and their practical application have been made even wider by the recent economic demand to turn fields into factories. Outside help was sought to bridge the gulfs, to make agricultural science work with even reasonable certainty and to give authority to the scientists. Pesticides promised to perform that trick. The early results and the subsequent selling job convinced them and the farmers and the public, alike.

It can be said that the greatest agricultural "scientists" were the prehistoric hunters and scavengers who first discovered that grains could be planted, cultivated, harvested, and stored. But thousands of years passed before magic gave way to methodology, before ritual and myth evolved into technological and scientific skills. In many parts of the world today ancient patterns persist. I have been in villages only a few kilometers from the modern capital of Mexico where men and women till the soil with wooden plows (steel will "chill the earth and kill the seeds"), bury images, and sacrifice animals in the field on "sacred" planting days.

In 1700, all over the Western world, farming retained its biblical quality: plowmen scratched the land or smashed it, broadcast seed over the roughened soil or dropped it into little furrows, prayed that nature would be kind. During the eighteenth century, which marks a turning point in man's efforts to bend the earth to his own wishes for his own benefit, important changes came about. Sometimes they resulted from bizarre, but effective theorizing. One such theorist was Jethro Tull, whose *Horse-hoeing Husbandry* was a best seller on both sides of the Atlantic after its publication in 1733, influencing such farming enthusiasts as George Washington. Tull's belief that plant roots had "sucking mouths" through which they took into their "guts" tiny particles of earth led to the use of horse-drawn hoes, breaking plows, and cultivators.[2] Other notable Englishmen followed him: Stephen Hales, cleric and physiologist, whose experiments led to the discovery of capillary action, the curious force that causes sap to rise through the stems of plants and trees; Arthur Young, whose initial farming failures led him to seek out and compile widely circulated reports of successful practices; Sir John Lawes, who developed and marketed over the horrified protests of his family "J. B. Lawes' Patent Manures." Easily the most famous British name in agriculture is that of Charles Darwin, who discovered the breeding system of hybridization while looking for ways to improve grain.

Other eighteenth and nineteenth century notables emerged in other countries: Carolus Linnaeus, the Swedish botanist; Antoine Laurent Lavoisier, who laid the foundations for modern chemistry and set up model farms for studying agricultural problems before he was beheaded during "the Terror"; Nicolas de Saussure, Swiss physiologist, whose experiments showed how plants used the minerals they absorbed and revealed the process of photosynthesis.[3]

Americans played an important role, in agricultural technology as well as science. Eli Whitney developed the cotton gin within a year of his graduation from Yale in 1792. Cyrus McCormick in 1831 invented the reaper—the first major departure from harvesting grain with sickle and scythe. Luther Burbank, Edward M. East . . . the list is very long.

But every gain brought with it new problems. Each time man increased his ability to farm profitably, he disrupted the balance of nature, encouraging pests to defeat his efforts. Before man became a farmer, as Dr. Kenneth Mellanby has pointed out, "most weeds were rare plants."[4] Insects and funguses that had never caused trouble exploded disastrously after their natural enemies had been driven off by "unnatural" practices, like the extensive cultivation of alien crops.

For every forward step, farmers seemed to take one backward, causing a frustration that was intensified by the economics of American farming. In most parts of the country, agriculture left off being a way of life and became a big business. The Jeffersonian dream of a nation of small farmers died a few decades ago; by 1969 their number had dwindled to only 2 million. Another one million "big" commercial farmers were turning out 90 percent of the nation's farm output.[5]

Land ceased to be a living thing to the owners; it became a mine to be exploited. Corporate farmers have concerns other than maintaining natural balance and harmony. Farm subsidies have enhanced destructive practices. Originally conceived as a means of insuring the existence of the small farmer, they have prompted the agribusinessmen to transform agriculture into the *violent science*. Eager to get the rich rewards the government offers for keeping land out of production, they exploit the rest of their holdings for maximum profits. Soil depletion? Throw on more chemicals. Outbreaks of pests? Bring in new killers.

By the 1940's pests had become such a problem that something drastic had to be done about them. Older botanical pesticides were cut off by the war. The arsenicals were useless. The codling moth had acquired such resistance to lead arsenate in the Pacific Northwest that by 1943 Washington farmers were using 17 million pounds a year to protect their apple crops—more than enough to kill 2 billion people.[6]

Farmers' need for control measures coincided with the desire of the manufacturers of the new "wartime products" to find a civilian market for pesticides.

Farmers are notoriously resistant to new-fangled ideas. But the chemical companies were convinced that the selling job could be accomplished. They unleashed a barrage —which has continued—of advertisements and publicity releases of high-powered persuasiveness. Pesticide advertising revenues transformed farm journals from the poor relations of the publishing business to slick products in full color. Scientific, household, and gardening magazines were also showered with largesse. What editor would be churl enough to question the hand that was feeding him so lavishly?

Very few, it turned out. Uncertainties, uncomfortable questions were set aside.

In 1946, for example, farmers were being assured that DDT was the answer to all prayers. It was bringing aphids under control in Maine, ridding livestock of flies and other insects in Florida, Kansas, Texas, Arizona. It was killing off greenbugs in Oklahoma, wiping out corn borers in Iowa, saving peaches from fruit moths in California and Georgia. If some was good, a whole lot more was better. And never mind the cost—that could be passed along to the consumers.

When the first glow began to fade, chemical companies had new answers. Two years after the public relations department of E. I. du Pont de Nemours & Company, Inc., was hailing the effectiveness of DDT for just about everything, it was touting "Marlate" to farmers for crops "intolerant of DDT." And farmers were urged not to be chintzy about it, but to use as much as 100 pounds to an acre.[7]

The chemical industry had found the perfect open-ended market. A chemical that cost as little as 1.6 cents to produce could be sold to farmers for 51 cents.[8] As pests grew more resistant, farmers had to use more and more of the old standbys or turn to new and more poisonous substances. There was no question of rebelling; advertising had so perfectly engineered consent in farming circles that to protest pesticides was to indicate disbelief in God and motherhood.

Flaming ads were creating a similar "pesticide mentality" among householders:

MAKE YOUR HOME SAFE. . . . KILL BUGS DEADER THAN DEAD. . . . PROTECT YOUR CHILDREN WHILE THEY SLEEP. . . . NO MORE ROACHES. . . . BUGS AWAY. . . .

The advertising barrage was constant and confusing. Often the image dreamed up in an advertising agency was dangerously at odds with that revealed in technical journals. Dieldrin, chlordane, lindane, and other powerful chlorinated hydrocarbons were recommended for household use, as well as deadly organic phosphates, with no indication of the hazards involved. Ads in reliable publications, particularly those with "seals" of approval, contributed to the delusion that pesticides are harmless.[9]

It is not surprising that warnings have gone unheeded. Have not pesticides resulted in a higher standard of living, bigger farm profits, better foods, and healthier people?

That's what the propaganda says. And far more significant than the advertising has been the publicity and public relations campaign. While there are still some people who question ads, many—perhaps most—feel that the articles they read in newspapers and magazines they trust are reliable, disinterested reports. It would not occur to them that what appears as editorial material had been written in the offices of industry flacks.

The National Agricultural Chemicals Association took understandable pride in its record for that sort of thing during 1968. In the annual report for that year, it noted that editors of more than 11,000 daily and weekly newspapers in cities and towns of the United States with populations of 50,000 or less had received on the average of once a month "a carefully prepared article on pesticide chemicals"—an article framed as an editorial! *The pesticide articles have been used by some 500 of these newspaper editors as their own comment and editorial each time they have been published.*[10] (Italics added.)

The NACA also provides cartoons, "which newspaper editors and publishers have been glad to use." The sample in the report showed a grain sack representing World Food Production, wearing boxing gloves labeled "pesticide" and "protection" and giving a knockdown blow to a wretched looking insect. It was a highly sophisticated and very effective piece of journalistic art.

During the year, the NACA distributed to more than

3,400 newspaper editors in smaller towns and suburban areas stories described as "most helpful in carrying information about the industry to the general public." It carried on a special program in Michigan to head off efforts of conservationists and sportsmen to halt the use of persistent pesticides. That program was so successful, the NACA editorialized proudly, that a bill to set up a state committee on pesticide control under the direction of the Director of Conservation was tabled.[11]

It would be interesting to know where many of the opponents thought they had gotten their ideas. And from whom.

Responsible journalism requires that special pleaders be identified. Some newspapers and magazines make an effort to do that. Thus, not long ago when a letter of protest appeared in the Los Angeles *Times* about a cartoon unfavorably depicting DDT, the editor took the trouble to identify the writer as "plants manager for a chemical corporation."[12] When Dr. Stare's tribute to food additives appeared in *Life,* he was identified not only as the head of the Harvard University School of Nutrition, but as a board member of Continental Can Company—an association that was noted by at least a few readers.[13]

This is not to suggest that all persons who defend the uncontrolled use of pesticides are associated with or employed by chemical companies. But it is socially responsible to make such connections known. So would it be responsible for scientists writing for journals that demand payment for publication to indicate who footed the bill. And readers of all publications might be able to appraise material more intelligently if they had some knowledge of the source of the publication's advertising revenues.

In the pesticide industry it is considered ultimate treachery to depart from the party line, for one company to downgrade another's product or fail to give moral support to a company under attack. When one member of the industry uttered critical comments in 1970 about another's product, he was brought up sharply by the editor of *Farm Chemicals* soon after in the June issue of the magazine:

> We have come to expect "the press" (a term covering the newspapers, the "Huntleys and Brinkleys" and other media) to give us trouble. But when *their words* are used by one of "us" to promote one pesticide over another, we have truly reached an inept state in pesticide merchandising.

As a consequence, whatever private reservations they may have, individual companies work just as heroically as the NACA to keep the public "informed" about the advantages of all pesticides. In times of stress, ranks are closed and the issuance of publicity releases stepped up. Some are stunningly effective. Perhaps the most widely distributed single piece of pro-pesticide literature is one written by the public relations officer of the Industrial Pest Control Association of London. An "answer" to *Silent Spring*, "The Desolate Year" portrays in vivid imagery the horrors of a world without pesticides: "The bugs were everywhere. Unseen. Unheard. Incredibly universal." They converted strawberry patches into jungles; turned potatoes into "black slime." "What, at the end of such a year, would be the fate of the United States of America?" it wound up. If this unanswered question were not chilling enough, the final turn of the screw was provided by an accompanying note saying that all the events were true— "NOT FICTION . . . FACT"—even if they all did not take place together.[14]

Farmers, of course, have been principal beneficiaries of

the effusions of professional publicists and of non-industry advocates. They have been bombarded through the handsome leaders, like *Farm Quarterly,* and more pedestrian periodicals with information showing how pesticides have increased yields, cut labor costs, eradicated animal and plant diseases, eliminated plagues. Much of the prose clearly echoes the "briefing papers" put out by the NACA.[15]

USDA yearbooks and bulletins have also stressed the benefits of pesticides to farmers, warning that without them livestock population would drop by 25 percent, crops by 30 percent, while food prices would rise by 50 to 70 percent.

Growers have been urged to ignore unfavorable studies and pin their faith on those holding pesticides man's greatest boon. Recommendations are sometimes absurdly at odds with the evidence presented. For example, cotton growers were told by one publication that recent findings indicate the bollworm is not as destructive a pest as it has been made out to be. It attacks squares chiefly during the early season: "The early square loss is of no economic importance since a cotton plant produces about twice as many squares as can be set." Yet on the very same page, they were also told:

> And you can't be too careful about insect control during the period when the squares are forming. . . . This is a critical time when insect damage can seriously affect the crop.[16]

Nonfarmers are also informed constantly about the advantages of pesticides. That is scarcely surprising since the market is so large. Lawns are, in terms of acres involved, the largest "crop" in the country. Add to this the amount of pesticides used on gardens, flower beds, foun-

dation plantings, and inside houses. In 1969 a Michigan
State University entomologist advanced the theory that
urban and suburban centers rather than farms might be
the major sources of pesticide contamination of streams.[17]

As protests about pesticides have increased, so have the
defenses—in both volume and tone. *Barron's,* the widely
circulated business and financial weekly, warned in a recent editorial about the "liberal folklore" notion that man's
use of chemical poisons is harming the environment. Under the title of "Up With People and Down With the
Venomous Foes of Chemical Pesticides," it put down
Rachel Carson, members of the Environmental Defense
Fund, and other objectors as mischievous myth-makers of
left-wing or anti-business bias. They are, it said, of the
same "radical persuasion" as the defenders of Sacco and
Vanzetti and those who believe that "automation destroys
jobs."[18]

In addition to thousands of articles in magazines and
newspapers, popular books have encouraged the belief
that without pesticides all would be lost. Two of the most
frequently cited are Congressman Jamie L. Whitten's *That
We May Live* and Wheeler McMillen's *Bugs or People?*
Mr. Whitten's, chiefly an attack on *Silent Spring,* cites the
familiar arguments of Dr. Darby, Dr. Hayes, Dr. Stare. In
an appendix it provides an honor roll of the 185 scientists
and 23 physicians interviewed when Mr. Whitten's staff
was preparing its "anti-Carson" report.[19] Mr. McMillen's
rather more effective defense of pesticides (curiously
enough considering the attitude of novelist Louis Bromfield, a conservationist and founder of Malabar Farm) won
the Bromfield Gold Medal award in 1965 for its author's
"services to conservation."

In addition to posing a false dilemma in the title and
thus obscuring the issues, Wheeler McMillen made ex-

tensive use of the testimony of industry witnesses before state and national legislative committees. Four pages are devoted to the testimony of Mabry Anderson at a USDA hearing on pesticides in Memphis in 1964. Mr. Anderson, described as an "enthusiastic conservationist, fisherman, hunter, and outdoor writer," had spread insecticides over 150,000 acres each season for a decade in his job as crop duster. The crop-dusting conservationist denied that pesticides like parathion, endrin, and DDT had any adverse effects on fish and game, even when applied fourteen times during a season.[20] He classified the protests about insecticide use as a "witch hunt."[21]

(Many crop dusters who were not quoted take a different view. A groundsman at the state college where I work told me recently that his decades in that business had persuaded him that no one without a special license should be allowed to even handle pesticides. A few hours before talking with me he had taken spray equipment from one of the student workers. "The kid didn't know what he was doing. He had already gotten some of the stuff on his shoes. I told him to get them off right away. He did, and his feet were already covered with blisters.")

Other recent popular books that minimize the hazards of pesticides are Henry Still's *The Dirty Animal*[22] and P. L. White's *Let's Talk About Food*, a book prepared for the American Medical Association. Infinitely more skillful is Bill Ballantine's *Nobody Loves a Cockroach*.[23] This sprightly tour through the chambers of horrors occupied by rats, flies, spiders, roaches, and other hateful pests ends up with a fulsome account of the author's visit to the headquarters of J. R. Geigy, A. G. in Basel, Switzerland. The oldest chemical firm in that city, its scientists worked to develop the insecticidal properties of DDT during World War II—which in traditional neutral and business-like fashion were offered to the opposing sides. The book is larded with protests against pesticide critics, chiefly Miss Carson.[24]

Ballantine describes the "fuss" as unwarranted since only one piece of legislation resulted from the Ribicoff Subcommittee hearings: "So it seems that we were not as unprotected by our government agencies as *Silent Spring* had led us to believe."[25] While it is true that the only legislation was to prohibit pesticide makers from selling products "under protest" (an incredibly dangerous situation since *anything* could be so marketed), Mr. Ballantine has failed to distinguish between need and how need is met by industry-pressured legislators. It may be that the view from Geigy headquarters in Basel was not as clear as Swiss views can be.

Books for general consumption have been supplemented by "educational" treatises for amateur gardeners. Some of them advocate pesticides only in response to public demand. Reasonably typical of that group is the generally excellent *The Gardener's Bug Book* by Cynthia Westcott. In the 1956 edition (the 1946 book makes little mention of chemical controls), the author devotes several chapters to cautioning readers that they can do "more harm in 10 thoughtless minutes than the bugs can do in a whole season." She prefaces instructions to use them as follows:

> If you don't know *what* you are doing and *why* you are doing it, don't do anything in the line of chemicals. Stick to sanitary and cultural measures and encourage beneficial insects and birds to work for you.[26]

Many, perhaps most garden advisers, have gone far beyond her subsequent recommendations for spray campaigns. For example, the author of *The Green Thumb Garden Handbook*, whose column has appeared in hundreds of newspapers, urges:

> It's best to apply a pesticide before trouble begins. That means keeping a residue of spray on the foliage at all times by renewal doses every ten days.[27]

That advice is comparable to advising people to keep well by dosing themselves with antibiotics before any sign of illness appears. Perhaps a penicillin tablet a day will keep the doctor away, but no one except a mad drug salesman would advocate that. Unfortunately, a good many amateur bug bombers as well as professionals follow it. Exterminating companies estimate that about 90 percent of their work is *preventive*.[28]

Insecticide mentality—pest hallucinations—has resulted from the very good press chemical killing compounds have received and the very bad one accorded bugs. For example, news that the Russians were coming could not have precipitated more hysteria than front-page scare stories in 1969 about the discovery of a South African spider in a small town in California. People were worried as far away as New England; there was pandemonium in the California town of El Monte. People by the hundreds had been showing up—"trembling"—at the city hall at all hours. Some called at 3:00 A.M. demanding immediate identification of harmless water and garden spiders. One family, a mother, father, and six children, abandoned their home and demanded sanctuary. A police officer noted that the same persons rarely became upset by rattlesnakes that make their way into the community in search of water.[29]

Many farmers exhibit the same paranoid reaction to insects, calling for full-scale chemical war at the sight of

a bug. Many do not even need that to launch an all-out
blitzkrieg. They spray according to the calendar rather
than according to need.

That approach to pest control is the result of a cradle-
to-grave indoctrination. The crusade to sell pesticides
begins in the home offices of the major agricultural chemicals companies. Some of them are very large. Geigy, for
example, which is considered "Number One," fans out
through affiliate corporations that operate in more than
100 countries.

Pesticide salesmen, after training, take to the road to
educate wholesale and retail distributors, wining and
dining them and encouraging them to share the rich rewards of overkill. Some companies are carrying the educational campaign all the way to the users. Geigy, a
pioneer in that, organized a "corn clinic" conducted by its
salesmen. According to a recent report[30] more than 125,000
corn growers had been reached through "these sensitive
training programs," which start early in December and
continue right up to planting time. Salesmen are rigor-
ously trained for the "clinic craze, which . . . really takes
the Midwest and Northeast by storm every year." Results
are impressive. Geigy is a leader in corn insecticides and
herbicides—selling in a recent year, according to USDA
figures, 2,310,000 pounds of Diazinon (a broad-spectrum
insecticide) and 10,255,000 pounds of Atrazine.[31]

Geigy does not neglect junior farmers. The president of
the United States affiliate was recently appointed chairman of the Agricultural Chemical Campaign of the
National 4-H Foundation to organize support for 4-H
programs. Like other pesticide giants, the company "believes strongly in the Extension Service and has built a
reputation with university researchers and administrators."[32]

That sort of reputation pays and pays, since farmers depend heavily on recommendations of university researchers and county farm agents. Most are vigorous advocates of pesticides. As a result, the more "education" a farmer has the more likely he is to be a heavy user.

The government-industry-education alliance is cemented during conferences and conventions, at which farmers, educators, and salesmen are constantly exhorted to "get the message across." Reasonably typical was a recent meeting of the Southeast Pesticide Formulators Association. A USDA official did a brilliant job of urging listeners to "do a better job" of telling "the good story" of pesticides. "We live in an era," he warned, "in which everything seems to be suspect." That should not be allowed to interfere with pesticide promotion: *"We must be ahead of those who are looking for instances where they can show that we are in any way harming our environment by their use."*[33] (Italics added.) A few months earlier, academicians and government scientists in Canada had received similar instructions from an industry representative. In a rousing sales talk, Louis A. McLean hailed chemical pesticides as the greatest single boon in the history of agriculture and asked his audience to "make educational efforts about pesticides your avocation—your mission." His blueprint:

> Speak to farming-connected groups to start. But devote major efforts to informing urban groups, who know little of the necessity, value, and safety of pesticides. Answer the many false stories that have been repeated, even though you may be accused of thereby contributing to controversy. No consent by silent compromise with false accusation has yet contributed to understanding. And direct some of your educa-

tional efforts to informing your colleagues who teach subjects not connected with agriculture.[34]

Pesticide publicists, incidentally, have plenty of latitude to get their message across to scientists, both in person and in print. For example, in 1967 the American Institute of Biological Sciences allowed Mr. McLean the forum of its official publication *BioScience* for his extended attack on the "compulsive types" who oppose pesticides, whom he characterized as "neurotics, driven by primitive sub-conscious fears to the point that they see more reality in what they imagine than in fact."[35] And more recently, Robert E. Hamman of Geigy had opened to him the pages of the prestigious *Bulletin of the Entomological Society of America* to present a stirring appeal for weakening the Delaney Clause in the Food Additives Law, which now prohibits carcinogenic substances. Condemning "vocal" critics, he urged his readers to remember that their image is being tarnished by "sensational and unscientific" reports.[36]

The circular self-reinforcing process continues—in business, in the colleges and universities, in the field. University extension agents are such notorious pesticide advocates that even growers have been questioning their advice recently. In an article about California wine makers, John D. Weaver described such a reaction. Being shown the Livermore winery by Karl L. Wente, president and general manager, Mr. Weaver was taken to a vineyard that had been turned over to the fieldmen from the state university's extension division. The "weed boys" were convinced they had the answer to morning glories—a nuisance in the fields—in a chemical spray. Mr. Wente vetoed their solution, telling Mr. Weaver that the spray caused too much damage to the vines. His answer? Water.

His reason was simple: "It allows the grapevine to get so big that it shades the morning glory out and it gives up the ghost for lack of sunshine."[37]

Such simple, safe, and effective solutions are frowned upon as not in keeping with the chemical age, at least so far as many university associates are concerned.

A manufacturer of a device that controls pests without the use of chemicals told me that at a demonstration he had organized to show tobacco farmers how effective and inexpensive crop production could be, he was interrupted and insulted by agricultural extension agents. They warned farmers that they would be "ruined" if they heeded him. He was vindicated a few years later, when tobacco farmers were notified that they would be ruined if they continued to use chemicals in such quantities.[38]

When customary "educational" programs fail, business and government agencies and representatives are not above wrist-twisting. An internationally known organic farmer who told a television audience that he did not use insecticides because of their relationship to cancer was immediately beset by banks demanding loan payments and packing house officials demanding control of his grove prior to picking. "Under pretext that his failure to use insecticide was poor management, they placed guards upon his ranch and threatened to spray all his trees," reported Laura Tallian in *The Pesticide Jungle*.[39]

Opposition to government spray campaigns has generally been fruitless. One of the rare successes was scored in 1969 in Texas. The state, the federal water pollution control agency, and private conservationists united to keep the USDA and the Air Force from covering four square miles at Kelley Air Force Base with a 10 percent dieldrin compound at the rate of 30 pounds an acre. The objective was to control insects brought in on planes from other countries, particularly Vietnam. No one had any quarrel with that. They did, however, with the method. "This is like chopping off a child's head because it has dandruff," said Dr. Clarence Cottam, director of the Wilder Wildlife Foundation. "It's ridiculous."[40] After the state director of parks and wildlife said that if any fish kill occurred suit would be filed against the individual who made the application (a federal agency could not be sued), and after the public was thoroughly aroused, a stop order was issued.[41]

There are many names for the kind of merchandising that has been carried on by the government agencies and the chemical industry. One is murder. The public, which is forced to pay, can make its choice.

9. A SPECIAL PROBLEM

THE CHEMICAL FERTILIZER industry is another legacy of World War II whose destructive force is being trained against our environment and our persons. Gaily wrapped and stacked in grocery stores, garden supply centers, and farm wholesale houses, and glowingly advertised as "life forces" through singing commercials and slick magazine ads, those synthetics are now helping to kill our rivers and lakes, to sterilize the soil they are supposed to revitalize, and to pose such health hazards that residents of many United States communities are warned against drinking tap water.

That annual sales are now exceeding the $2 billion mark is due to American farming as well as economic malpractice. In older cultures, the need to nourish the soil—"that thin film that is all that stands between man and extinction"[1]—has always been recognized. Three thousand years ago Homer told of how Ulysses' thralls fertilized the land with manure. Some centuries later Theophrastus, a Greek philosopher, categorized animal wastes in their order of values from human to horse. Vergil, a sophisticated farmer as well as a great poet, urged fellow Romans to use legumes as "green manure"— advice that has been widely followed since.

It was not until well into the last century that scientists began to understand the elements essential for plant growth: carbon, hydrogen, and oxygen drawn from the air; nitrogen, phosphorus, potassium, and ten other elements extracted from the soil. The first three make up more than 90 percent of the plant; of the remaining thirteen, nitrogen is the most important because it is considered to be "so sensitive an indicator of the quality of life."[2] Although nitrogen gas makes up about 80 percent of the air, plants must get their supplies from the soil, where it is released by bacteria from humus and decaying organic wastes. If the soil is undisturbed or farmed properly, the nitrogen supply is in balance. Only small amounts leach into surface waters or are converted into nitrogen gas, ammonia, or nitrogen oxides.

This continent was almost incredibly fertile when the first settlers arrived, because much of it was undisturbed and because Indians respected the life-death-decay-life cycle. Every school child knows that Squanto showed the "saints and strangers" how to plant and cultivate the corn that enabled them to survive—dropping a dead fish into the earth beside the seeds.

Whatever reverence for earth the English settlers had when they arrived (precious little, since all things not of the kingdom of God were suspect), it was lost after a few New England winters. It became man against nature. To the death.

The same attitude characterized many later immigrants. If and when the land they farmed died, they moved on to the seemingly inexhaustible West. In the 1800's the brutal theories of the Industrial Revolution were translated to farming; human needs were not respected, neither were the needs of earth. In the twentieth century vast areas of grassland were placed under intensive cultivation —"ripped open by the plow and wheat was cultivated on them by a process which is better described as mining than agriculture."[3] Factory farms were developed: "farm-

ers" planted and went away until it was time for the
crops to be harvested.

It took some years for catastrophe to overtake the
rich earth left unprotected between mining operations.
The sun baked it; winds swept over it; one-crop plantings sucked it dry. John Steinbeck in *The Grapes of
Wrath* describes what came after:

> The dawn came, but no day. In the gray sky a red
> sun appeared, a dim red circle that gave a little
> light, like dusk; and as that day advanced, the dusk
> skipped back toward darkness, and the wind cried
> and whimpered over the fallen corn . . . When the
> night came it was black night, for the stars could not
> pierce the dust to get down, and the window lights
> could not even spread beyond their own yards. . . .[4]

A kind of judgment day had come upon the land—if
not the sort that fundamentalist preachers were referring
to in their doomsday sermons. The U.S. Soil Conservation
Service reported in 1935 that over 100 million acres of
the best cropland had been irremediably ruined.[5]

Soil bank reserves, diminishing for a couple of centuries,
were dangerously overdrawn. New deposits would have to
be made.

The chemical industry obligingly stepped forward at
the end of World War II with an offer to make up the
deficit. Synthetic nitrogen plants built to turn out ex-
plosives were converted to fertilizer factories. Demand
for chemical fertilizers, which had been used in modest
quantities for years, was enhanced by postwar prosperity.
Farm subsidies increased it. By 1964, farmers in this
country were spending more than $1.7 billion for artificial
fertilizers—an increase in consumption termed "fantastic."[6] Sales have been going up at the rate of 9 percent
a year since.

Small existing companies were overshadowed by chemical giants like W. R. Grace, Monsanto, Allied, Du Pont, and Olin Mathieson. Major oil companies invaded the market: Gulf, Socony, Mobil. Cities Service began to buy up smaller fertilizer companies, using them as marketing arms for petrochemical by-products. Natural gas companies, prime sources of anhydrous ammonia, a key ingredient in nitrogen fertilizers, got into the business. Even meat packers, like Armour and Swift, which had produced animal fertilizers, diversified into chemicals.[7] Because of the vast natural gas reserves, phosphate rock, potassium, sulphur, copper, iron, manganese, and other elements, the United States rapidly became the world's prime supplier of fertilizers. And prime consumer.

In reaching those heights, it has been helped by one of the world's most aggressive advertising campaigns. Farm journals and garden magazines waxed fat on the advertising revenues. The glories of fertilizer were preached on television and radio. Novel approaches have been used. One of the more striking incentives to buy was developed by Olin Mathieson, which operates what is said to be the world's biggest fertilizer plant just outside Houston. Test plots were staked out along heavily trafficked highways in farm areas. "When the corn [in a fertilized plot] is twice as high as the corn growing next to it by the Fourth of July, people can easily see what a difference fertilizer makes," the company's marketing director told a *Time* reporter.[8]

National and state departments of agriculture got into the act, pushing fertilizers with all the ardor with which they have pushed pesticides. The universities and colleges helped to carry on the public relations and merchandising programs. Consider, for example, the course of study worked out by the Center for Research and Leadership Development in Vocational and Technical Education at

Ohio State University under a grant from the U.S. Office of Education. That has as its "major teaching objective" to "develop personal qualities and effective abilities needed for entry and advancement by technicians in chemical fertilizer occupations."[9] Teachers are instructed to have students emphasize that high yields, economical returns, and low-cost food are "dependent" on chemical fertilizers and their proper use.[10] The bibliography that accompanies the instruction manual contains numerous references to publications of individual companies and the various trade associations. Instructional materials suggest the use of "fertilizer company publications."

Students are encouraged about the future: "As potential fertilizer salesmen, you will be happy to know, and should tell all customers, that fertilizer is today's best buy."[11] And they are taught to believe that in some places 75 percent of all farm production is due to fertilizers.[12]

Some agricultural scientists would question that figure. So, too, they might question that fertilizers are one of the "best ways to reduce the cost per unit of production." Profits in the fertilizer business are very high, despite the claims of industry spokesmen that farmers are "literally stealing" the stuff.[13] Some farmers are being forced out of farming. That includes the 32 members of a cloistered order of Carmelite nuns. "The rising cost of water and fertilizer" forced them to emerge from seclusion to go job-hunting outside the walls; for one nun, it was her first departure from the convent in 36 years.[14]

Such dazzling promises are held out to farmers that a man would be a fool not to buy fertilizers in large carload lots. For example, the Ohio University sales training program provides a chart showing that if 100 pounds were applied to an acre at a cost of $4.00, corn yields would be 45 bushels an acre; 228 pounds at $9.12 would yield 51.3

bushels; 700 pounds—"recommended"—at $28.00 an acre would get a yield of 76.5 bushels. If corn were selling at $1.30 a bushel, returns on the investment would increase from $58.50 to $66.69 to $99.45.[15]

Inducements for amateurs are equally beguiling. They are offered plant "foods" for every purpose, boxed, bagged, bottled, canned. By 1960 about 1,600 grades were being sold under a bewildering assortment of numbers and letters. (According to laws in the United States, fertilizers must be labeled to show the percentage of the primary nutrients. Thus, 5-10-15 on the label means that the package contains 5 percent nitrogen (N), 10 percent available phosphate (P), and 15 percent water-soluble potash or potassium (K).

Considering the manner in which claims are made, it would behoove both amateur and commercial growers to beware—or at least to be wary. A good many of the promises are as empty of content as those nonexistent fertilizer tanks Billie Sol Estes is said to have offered as security for loans.[16] Soils are not all alike, and the indiscriminate use of a fertilizer may have a devasting effect on the soil, on the crops, and ultimately on people.

If soil is overwhelmed with chemical fertilizer, its quality may decline. There is a vast difference between chemical and natural fertilizers, since the former may lower rather than increase productivity. A 50-year-study in Missouri showed that "the organic matter content and the physical condition of the soil on the chemically treated plots have declined rapidly."[17] More recent studies in Illinois have supported those findings, showing that the nitrate that could not be absorbed by the root systems left the soil, breaking the cycle.

Crops in overfertilized soil are frequently lacking in nutritive values. For example, one early experiment showed that almost twice as much hay was produced on plots given nitrogen than those left unfertilized—3,200 pounds an acre as contrasted with 1,700. But when fed to rabbits, a pound of the nitrogen-fertilized hay produced less rabbit meat per pound than the unfertilized hay. The nitrogen had forced the growth of the hay, but the soil had not been able to supply enough of the other minerals to keep pace with it.[18]

Other studies have resulted in similar findings, since an excess of one nutrient may prevent others from being absorbed and utilized.[19]

Two special hazards of nitrogen fertilizers have recently come to light—to the environment and to human health.

According to Dr. Barry Commoner, we have "massively stressed" the nitrogen cycle in the soil by the introduction of inorganic fertilizer. And, consequently, that "may stress to the breaking point the self-purifying aqueous systems upon which we depend for our urban waste disposal."[20]

The plant nutrients in inorganic fertilizers—phosphorus, potassium, and, particularly, nitrogen—have been making their way into rivers and waters, polluting and overfertilizing those valuable resources . . . "growing" them to death.

Dr. Commoner cites Lake Erie as a striking illustration. For years, conservationists have been concerned about the abuse of the lake, which is forced to cope with the organic wastes generated by about 10 million inhabitants of the basin, pollutants contributed by thousands of industries. Consternation did not become general until 1964, when it became apparent that the lake was *dying*. The reason? Overfeeding from farmland fertilizer runoff. (That problem has been greatly aggravated by phosphates in detergents.)

The nitrogen contributed by the fertilizers, like that originating in sewage, was stimulating the growth of algae, creating huge "blooms," which give the lake the appearance and consistency of pea soup. The massive blooms were unsightly, discoloring vast reaches of lake waters. They were also destructive, Dr. Commoner pointed out, since they die off rapidly and "sinking into the lake, foul it with algal organic matter."

Advanced treatment methods, he says, would make it possible to remove inorganic nutrients from municipal and industrial waste systems, but what of those from farmland runoff? That, Dr. Commoner warns, "will eventually require the limitation of the current high rate of use of inorganic nitrogen fertilizer."[21]

That may come sooner than farmers and fertilizer salesmen care to acknowledge. High levels of nitrates in food and water are now held to be directly endangering the health and lives of humans, particularly infants.

For more than a quarter of a century medical scientists and public officials have had cause for alarm because of a curious, sometimes fatal disease among infants. Methemoglobinemia was first linked with nitrates in drinking water in the United States in 1945, when it was established that certain bacteria were able to convert nitrate to toxic nitrite. If nitrite passes into the bloodstream, it reacts with hemoglobin to form methemoglobin—a substance that interferes with the blood's capacity to carry oxygen. Breathing becomes labored; in severe cases, infants suffocate.[22]

In contrast to the two cases reported in 1945, in 1950 an article in the *Journal of the American Water Works Association* revealed that during a three-year period in Minnesota, 139 cases had been identified; 14 of them fatal. The following year 278 cases were reported during an eighteen-state survey. Thirty-nine children died. "In all of these cases the concentration of nitrates in water supplies was in excess of 45 parts per million," the report stated.[23]

As the use of chemical fertilizers has increased, so has incidence of the disease—to such extent that in 1962 the Public Health Service recommended that when drinking water reached the 45 p.p.m. level, public warnings be issued and parents urged to substitute bottled water for tap water[24]—an item not in the budget of many farm workers.

No effort, however, was made to curb or to discourage the use of chemical fertilizers. As a result, in California and other agricultural states the levels soared. In a number of places, nitrate levels in water were 100 percent over allowable maximums.[25] Scientific studies showed that food as well as water could be dangerously contaminated; that conversion of nitrate to nitrite could take place outside the body as well as in.[26]

Again, the role of government agencies as people protectors proved less than encouraging. For example, Dr. Commoner wrote in 1968 that Montreal health officials became sufficiently alarmed by his comments about nitrate in baby food to make a survey. Some foods, particularly spinach and beet preparations, had levels higher than the 45 p.p.m. set for water. After the Montreal Department of Public Health announced the findings, the Canadian Food and Drug Directorate pooh-poohed the dangers. "No cases of toxicity from nitrates in foods have been reported," it reassured. "While it is well known that a high level of nitrate in drinking water, where large quantities may be consumed, may be harmful to infants, the same dangers do not apply to nitrates in solid foods."[27]

Both claims, Dr. Commoner answered, were "incorrect." Explicit cases of infant methemoglobinemia due to nitrate-

rich spinach have been reported for years in pediatric
literature. The evidence showed that medical difficulties
arose *only* when spinach was grown with intensive use
of nitrogen fertilizer. Additionally, it is not the amount of
nitrate that is dangerous, but its conversion to *toxic nitrite*
in the presence of certain kinds of bacteria.[28]

Health agencies in this country have also brushed aside
the problem. For example, in 1968 the State Water Resources Board in California reported that nitrates in
ground water around Delano were higher than the limit
set by the U.S. Public Health Service. A memo was
issued to local health officers telling them *not* to notify the
public of high nitrate levels. They were to advise only
local physicians[29]—presumably so that people would not
be unduly alarmed about what was happening to their
infants.

The next year, when a study showed that most of the
wells in one community were in excess of the 45 p.p.m.
level and some were in excess of 100 p.p.m., an attorney
with the United Farm Workers Organizing Committee
accused city officials of participating in a "conspiracy of
silence" with growers to minimize dangers and keep
people ignorant of hazards.

At a meeting of the Delano City Council, Attorney
Paul Driscoll urged that the city ask growers to use
nonpolluting substances to fertilize crops. The response
to the suggestion was typical. The mayor insisted: "This
is a state problem. . . . Let's leave this to the experts. . . .
We're doing all we can do." That, Mr. Driscoll noted
sourly, includes telling people that the water *is* fit to
drink.[30]

That people should be concerned was emphasized a few
months earlier by Dr. Samuel S. Epstein. The British-
born chief of environmental toxicology and carcinogenesis

of the Children's Cancer Research Foundation revealed new implications of high levels of nitrates in water.[31]

He told reporters at an American Cancer Society conference that nitrates can undergo chemical changes in the intestinal tract which produce compounds called nitrosamines. Nitrosamines can cause cancer not only in infants but in all persons. Dr. Epstein pointed out that the high incidence of stomach cancer in Japan, Iceland, and Chile may be due to the large quantities of fish eaten in those countries—contaminated fish. He urged that studies be made in the United States to determine the relationship between certain kinds of cancer and water with high nitrate levels.[32]

Scientists are studying other effects of nitrates. Several years ago a Purdue. University animal expert pointed out that nitrate-nitrite poisoning "has been recognized as a potential hazard to livestock production and human life by the medical and veterinary professions for more than 100 years."[33] The problem has been intensified since World War II. He held that the two important considerations for the livestock industry were nitrate toxicity and the effect of subtoxic levels of nitrates, particularly on the metabolism of carotene and Vitamin A.

What animal scientists are urged to consider, medical scientists should also heed. The relationship between high levels of nitrite in the system and depressed thyroid activity carries serious implications.[34] An active thyroid is essential to the conversion of carotene from plants into Vitamin A. That, in turn, relates to our ability to synthesize ribonucleic acid—that substance that tells individual cells how to perform so that they maintain function, health, and life.

The long-term effects of chemical fertilizers on the nutritional value of foods cannot be dismissed. The Food and Drug Administration denies categorically that chemical fertilizers have depleted the nutritional content of food crops: "If plants grow at all they will have the vitamins and minerals you need." And it considers the idea that organic fertilizers are superior a "falsehood."[35] In the same publication, the FDA stresses that it "makes sure" the amount of pesticide residue in foods is safe for consumers.

Since that FDA fact sheet was issued, the tolerances on many have been lowered, in the interests of safety. And current findings by nutritionists and soil scientists suggest that the position on chemical fertilizers might well be modified.

The FDA holds that the theory "you are what you eat" is a false claim of health food nuts and extremists. It is not, according to recent findings. Every aspect of health and well-being is related to nutrition, which is determined by the kinds and quality of foods people eat. Nutritional deficiencies have been linked with many obstetrical and pediatric problems: prematurity, low birth weight, low resistance to infection, and mental retardation.[36] Oldsters also suffer mental as well as physical effects from poor nutrition. A study at the Philadelphia State Hospital showed that 93 percent of Medicare patients hospitalized for abnormal behavior were able to function normally after about six weeks on a decent diet.[37] Scientists are now speculating that food quality can retard the aging process.

The poor condition of the soil has long been known to be related to the use of chemical fertilizers.[38] The excessive use of one chemical may destroy or render another unavailable, making it necessary to add quantities of that, which in turn. . . .

The fertilizer market has been as open-ended as the pesticide market.

Balance cannot be restored merely by dumping on more chemicals, any more than balance can be restored in a nutritionally deficient person by stepping up the intake of vitamin pills. What is needed is a truly scientific approach to agriculture instead of the chemical sales approach—one that works with nature rather than wars against it.

PART TWO
ALTERNATIVES

10. FOR EMERGENCY ONLY

CHEMICAL PESTICIDES ARE here to stay.

And they should be. No rational person in the twentieth century would do away with them any more than he would eliminate the chemotherapeutics that have revolutionized the practice of medicine. Both, used wisely, have infinite power for good. They can help to make life longer for millions of persons; they can help to make living better. However, both medical and farm drugs, when misused and overused, have infinite capacity for harm. When their killing power is unleashed indiscriminately, our environment and our persons are damaged.

Like "wonder drugs," agricultural chemicals of all kinds, insecticides, herbicides, fungicides, miticides, growth regulators, fertilizers, nematodicides, are emergency measures to be used only when emergencies dictate.

The presence of a few pests is not a signal for a drastic prescription—any more than a common cold is reason to reach for an antibiotic, or a sleepless night is reason to take a drug like thalidomide that may cause irreversible nerve damage and turn a normal embryo into a monstrous shape.

While the "insecticide mentality" may be so rigid in some persons that psychotherapy is required, for most, a genuinely informative educational program would lead to rational action. That is the sort of education that has *not* been provided by the merchandisers in and out of school. As a consequence, professional and amateur chemical warriors believe that bombing and spraying are patriotic and virtuous. On the farm, the assault begins at planting time and continues until after the food is packed. Around the house, every day is D-Day in the never-ending campaign—small wonder, with householders flattered and cajoled into taking up arms. The USDA's 1965 *Yearbook of Agriculture*, dedicated to "thoughtful and discerning" consumers, recommends some fifty chemical treatments for controlling lawn insects and diseases, and an almost equal number for dominating weeds around the house.[1]

Because the "education" has been so thorough, the re-education will take more time than can be allowed. Consequently, meaningful ground rules must be laid down to guard against pesticides' being employed wantonly on a large scale. There is no reason why all persons engaged in commercial farming should not be forced to obtain licenses and permits to spray—as commercial applicators now do. There is no reason why economic and people poisons should not be sold in a more discriminating way so that housewives and amateur gardeners would realize they are dealing with extremely dangerous substances.

Nonselective, broad-spectrum pesticides like DDT should be banned or rigidly limited. All must be subject to new regulations governing dosage, methods of application, timing, and proper formulations. And the regulations should be enforced.

No one should be permitted to spray on a large scale without making public—and posting warning signs—what, where, how much, how toxic. The right to know what poisons one is exposed to is critical—a matter of life and death.

Methods of application must be improved and some eliminated. In spite of their boasts of up-to-the-minute planes and ground rigs, some commercial application is so crude that less than 10 percent of the poisons reach the target.[2] Householders, too, have a dismal record of misses. Spray from a "bug bomb" can fill a room, a house, a neighborhood with poisonous fog, which settles down to contaminate objects and inhabitants while the flies and roaches buzz and scuttle undisturbed.

Some progress has been made in localizing chemicals more precisely to the area needing treatment. But there are still too many instances like the one Rachel Carson described that took place in Michigan in 1959, when planes dumped aldrin pellets in a man-made toxic hailstorm over 27,000 acres. Although its effect on the Japanese beetle, which had been a minor pest in the area for at least thirty years, was questionable, its effect on birds, cats, and some humans was devastating.[3]

Saner policies could prevail in more areas if chemical warfare were better directed. Some farmers, motivated as much by pocketbook economics as by a concern for public health, are now using chemicals to treat seeds at planting time rather than spraying and dusting the plants after they have begun to grow. Lindane and dieldrin have been used in that way. The reductions in the amounts used have been significant—only 0.25 ounces per acre as contrasted with the 2 pounds employed in broadcast application.[4] The problems of residue and environmental pollution as well as finances have been equally minimized by careful timing. It is cheaper and safer to control mosquito larvae than to try to control the adult population.

Pesticides applied to control vertebrate pests have always been localized. Pests have been lured to their own destruction by food attractants—cheese in the trap, chunks of meat stuffed with arsenic and other poisons. Now agricultural scientists have begun to refine such procedures.

They have, for example, produced a grain capable of killing field mice and ground squirrels, but because the concentration of strychnine has been so carefully regulated, the feed is not lethal to quail, pheasants, or domestic poultry. Those seed-eating birds which might be affected are kept from eating it because the grain used is of a shape and color they shun.[5]

The same kind of ingenuity was exercised in producing the world's first birth control pill for pigeons—pests in a good many cities. According to a spokesman for G. D. Searle, the pigeon pill, ornitrol, works by inhibiting egg production. Desirable species are protected, since the coating is so large that smaller birds cannot swallow it.[6]

Pastes and syrups, long used to undo hungry ants, beetles, and other unwanted insects in the house, have been adapted to cope with large-scale infestations. During the late 1950's agricultural scientists decided to employ poisoned food lures in Hawaii against the imported fire ant, which was causing serious damage. A brew was concocted of mirex, a very slow-acting poison, and soya bean oil. Corncob grits were soaked in the stuff and scattered at infested sites; as anticipated, the highly social creatures carried the granules to their nests and shared them with the rest of their colonies. According to the researchers, within two days the colonies were wiped out. Control of 96 to 100 percent was obtained by using less than five grams of an insecticide, and without the contamination of milk or any other food products.[7]

More exotic than the use of food lures has been that of sex attractants. Recently discovered to be less specific in action than formerly believed—an important quality since whole groups could be controlled—natural and synthetic sex scents have been highly effective, luring pests to a trap or localized pesticide which finishes them off. Here is real "perfume power" far more devastating than envisioned by the most uninhibited Madison Avenue copywriter.

Appropriately enough, a French naturalist was the first to notice that the aroma of some female insects entrances males. Jean Henri Fabre, during a walk, captured a female peacock moth. He took the rare creature home and imprisoned it in a gauze tent. That night his laboratory was invaded by male moths, flying through the open windows and heading unerringly for the tiny tent. He knew that the presence of the males—most of them had come from miles away—had nothing to do with sight or sound signals. They had been led to the female by something more subtle, not obvious to any other creatures in the vicinity. *Scent* was his brilliant and accurate deduction.

Entomologists recognized that the discovery was significant, but they made only sporadic efforts to identify and use sex-scent attractants to help control insect infestations. During World War II efforts were stepped up, when both Allied and Axis powers launched crash programs to solve one of the most terrible hazards of war—diseases carried by insects.

Working with the gypsy moth, some scientists found that soon after the female emerges from pupation it emits an odor which lures males to it for mating. After mating, the odor disappears. It took twenty years to obtain enough of the erotic substance to identify and synthesize it. Scientists found that nothing would do but the pure essence contained in the last two abdominal sections of virgin females. *Half a million of them were needed to obtain a single drop of pure sex lure.*

That was enough. The first successful experiment was made in England in 1960, where traps baited with a microscopal quantity yielded large numbers of dead males.

Once its chemistry had been identified, scientists were able to synthesize a closely related substance from commercially available ricinoleyl alcohol. Gyplure, named either by a punster or a stolidly unimaginative scientist, has been used widely since then. In New England it was daubed on 50,000 traps set out annually. According to Dr. Morton Beroza, research chemist with the USDA Agricultural Research Service, it prevented the further spread of the gypsy moth in that area "for at least twenty years."[8]

Because of the remarkable improvement in chemical instrumentation, hundreds of other sex attractants have been identified and synthesized. Many of them have been effective and economical. An $11 million campaign to wipe out the Mediterranean fruit fly in Florida a decade ago with broad-spectrum pesticides turned out to be a failure. In a short time the state was reinfested in large numbers. A powerful attractant called trimedlure was more effective. Within the year, the creatures were under control. The expense was modest by contrast with ordinary spray treatments; officials estimate that the government saved at least $9 million in eradication costs.[9]

Another relatively early dramatic triumph for "perfume power" occurred on the island of Rota in the Pacific, which had been plagued by infestations of the oriental fruit fly. Instead of a blanket spray treatment, another strategy was used. Small absorbent boards were impregnated with a combination of methyl-eugenol, a powerful lure for the male flies, and naled, a potent insecticide. They were dropped by airplane over the 33-square-mile island. Responsive males, attracted and poisoned, died as proverbial flies are wont to die. According to Dr. Beroza, they were eradicated in several months. The cost for ridding the island of the pest was only 50 cents an acre—

including the distribution by plane. "You can see the advantages of this approach even aside from the low cost," he reported. "Only the offending insect is attacked. Wildlife is not affected; insecticides are not spread needlessly."[10]

Recently, sex attractants have been used successfully to control the cabbage looper moth and the fall armyworm moth, two very serious economic pests in the United States.[11] A sex pheromone extracted from virgin females of the Pacific Coast wireworm, another problem, has also proved successful. Laboratory tests made in 1968 indicated how responsive males were to minute amounts. Researchers placed rods treated with the pheromone into containers holding male beetles. Their response was "immediate." They climbed the rod and caressed it with their antennae. They remained excited for some time—a condition in which they were noted to "mount any small object that is encountered and perform copulatory actions." Scientists reported that field tests with the synthetic attractant gave "quite exciting" demonstrations of its ability to compete with the natural pheromone.[12]

Sex attractants have been used in unconventional ways. In one experiment, "Operation Confusion," gyplure was spread over a large area in order to "jam" the odor signals. The theory was that with the sex aroma everywhere, males would become completely disoriented in seeking females. Moreover, it was hoped that with the sex attractant everywhere, they might even lose interest in their instincts. Instincts proved stronger. At any rate, enough of the males mated to make "Operation Confusion" something less than the hoped-for success.[13] Others have failed, too; yet often the failures have been rewarding since they have opened new paths to investigators.

Efforts are being made to extend the principle of

"perfume power" to other than food and sex pheromones —to develop additional odorous substances of insect origin that control or affect different aspects of behavior and development. Many of the potent lures are so nonspecific that they can be used against more than one species. However, the argument that money spent to further investigations in attractants is well spent is convincing, since once found and properly used, the pheromone is "available for all future time" and "may provide a means of safe pest control."[14]

Manufacturers and merchandisers have, unfortunately, ignored such appeals and emphasized all-purpose pesticides rather than highly selective ones. The definition of an insecticide as an "agent for destroying insects" clearly implies selectivity of action, as Dr. Robert L. Metcalf noted wryly some years ago, "since the human user certainly does not intend to share with his intended arthropod victims in the hazards of unrestricted chemical warfare."[15] Nor does he intend that his trees and plants and livestock will be damaged. Nor that the intended victim will develop such resistance that he will be forced to continue and step up his attacks for the rest of his life.

Yet most users continued to demand a "bigger bang for a buck." They seem unable to appreciate, thanks to their "education," that broad-spectrum blunderbusses ultimately cost more than small-bore rifles.

Genuinely sophisticated insecticides zero in on target pests without encouraging widespread resistance, without harming beneficial creatures, without jeopardizing man and higher animals, and without permanently contaminating the environment.

Highly specific pesticides are available and have been widely used for years in many countries in Western Europe. Many farmers there are less responsive to the siren songs of chemical salesmen, apparently. For example, Isolane, a narrow-range pesticide produced in the 1950's by Geigy, the company that developed and patented DDT, has been popular for years in Switzerland, Italy, Holland, and Belgium. According to one explanation, the reason that more primitive pesticides are used in the United States is that "in most cases the market for a specific is too small to warrant large-scale production."[16]

Other effective substitutes are available. For example, methoxychlor, which has been known since 1944, has generally the same physical and chemical properties as DDT, yet it is far less toxic to higher animals and may be used on forage and food crops with little residue hazard. According to Dr. Metcalf, a study made with human volunteers indicated that it was safe even when consumed at 200 times the maximum permissible dietary level.[17]

Although he and other scientists were stating flatly years ago that methoxychlor "should be the preferred material in any application where storage in animal tissues is a factor," DDT continued to be used in dairy cattle country and in other places where it has jeopardized humans and nonpest creatures.

Many scientists are concerned that the ban on DDT may be a mixed blessing, since other substitutes are even more dangerous—to people and to the environment. Commenting on the demand to prohibit it without guaranteeing safe replacements, a California public health official, Dr. Alice Ottoboni, said: "If we permit this to be the extent of our thinking, we will have learned nothing from our experience with DDT, nor will we be in a position to prevent a future 'DDT' from occurring."[18] Many of the short-lived pesticides, particularly the organic phosphates and the carbamates, are infinitely more toxic to man and to fish and animals. Some of them are changed into more toxic substances as they degrade— substances which could contaminate the environment even more than DDT and other persistent chemicals.[19]

That danger could readily be minimized if the industry and the regulatory agencies elected to do so. As Dr. Metcalf pointed out some years ago: "Chemists and toxicologists are now capable of tailoring insecticidal molecules, incorporating almost any combination of desirably selective properties."[20] Schrader, the genius whose discovery of parathion in 1944 marked a turning point in chemical warfare, also discovered that he could increase insect selectivity by making relatively simple changes in parathion's composition.[21] Some years later a group of Japanese scientists produced a compound, Sumithion, by incorporating an *ortho* methyl group with methyl parathion. That was far safer than its "parent" since mammals are able to detoxify themselves more readily.

Further manipulations of the molecule have made it less poisonous to lower creatures of desirable species. For example, isopropyl parathion, a close-relative of the broad-spectrum substance, is considered to be virtually nontoxic to the honey bee although highly toxic to the house fly. According to Dr. Metcalf, from the simple, basic structure for toxic action that was described by Schrader "at least" 25 million potential insecticides can be fabricated.[22] Within that wide range of possibilities, surely pesticides could be turned out that would take care of almost any emergency without the devasting effects that are now so common.

The carbamates could also be tailored to produce safe and selective action. Like the organic phosphates, they are inhibitors of cholinesterase; however, they are less toxic and can act selectively.[23]

A promising group are the systemic insecticides. Absorbed by the plant, either through the root or leaves, they remain in the sap until some unwary pest begins to suck it. Exit pest.

The principle involved is one that occurs in nature. For example, some of the gray shale soils of the Dakotas contain selenium, an insecticide which controls many pests when plants pick it up from the soil. (That is done through the roots, from which it goes to other parts of the plant.) Unfortunately, its action is not specific; it is toxic to animals as well as insects.[24] Some of the man-made systemics are also highly toxic to beneficial creatures as well as pests. Azodrin, for example, was considered very promising when it was first used in California in 1966 to control cotton pests. Later, however, it turned out to be so indiscriminately destructive that, after a four-year trial, the university removed it from the recommended list. Dr. Van den Bosch said that in some experiments it engendered "more serious pest problems than it controlled." Moreover, it had a "devasting effect" on birds and animals.[25] Azodrin is very popular in many parts of the country and is even used in California by persons who ignore university recommendations.

Ideally, the systemics could solve another major problem—insure that the application be localized. Some of them are now applied to the seeds directly. Some are introduced to the plant roots in combination with fertilizers. Some, however, are simply sprayed on in the manner best calculated to contaminate very wide areas.

The problem of application has not been completely solved by the new ultra-low-volume (ULV) formulations which are replacing water-diluted formulations. A recent study showed that drift continues to contaminate the environment even when planes are flying only five feet above the target.[26]

For more than a decade, one report after another has stressed the need to explore other avenues of pest control. All have cited the "immeasurable benefits" of chemical pesticides; but all have indicated the need to go beyond what presently exists. Following the lengthy hearings, the Ribicoff Subcommittee specifically recommended that the chemical industry be encouraged to develop safer chemical pesticides; it also urged that steps be taken outside the industry to "accelerate the development of nonchemical pest-control methods."[27]

A major advance seemed to have occurred two years before in 1964, when a symposium took place in Montreal to "consider the opportunities for controlling pests of all kinds without creating undue risks to man and his environment."[28] The meeting, sponsored by the agriculture section of the American Association for the Advancement of Science in cooperation with the U.S. and Canadian Departments of Agriculture, the U.S. Department of Interior, the University of Western Ontario, and state universities and industry, was an exciting one. It brought together experts in various fields and presented a summary of the work being done in all areas—chemical, biological, genetic, and physical—to cope with the major pests. The reports were promising, indicating what could be done if money and manpower were channeled into further research.

But the significant recommendations were drowned by the cacophony from chemical advocates. Money, public as well as private, continued to be spent on chemical research almost exclusively. Recently, only about 30 percent of the USDA budget was being spent on nonchemical controls.[29] The record of most college and university research departments is even worse.

A policy memorandum in 1969, signed by Secretary of

Agriculture Clifford M. Hardin, asserted that the department will "practice and encourage the use of those means of effective pest control which provide the least potential hazard to man, his animals, wildlife, and other components of the natural environment."[30]

The question is, was anybody listening?

Most USDA officials, like most of the rest of us, have been so victimized by the "insecticide mentalities" that they believe that any and all problems can be solved by getting another chemical pesticide if the one being used doesn't work. There are many other answers, simple and complex. A hope is that they will be explored—in the interests of survival.

11. FIRST BASIC STEPS

IN NATURE THERE is no pest problem. Man has created that evil by his efforts to exercise absolute control over his environment.

Scientists generally agree with Dr. Kenneth Mellanby that: "It is difficult to find a satisfactory definition of a pest other than to describe it as a plant or animal living where man does not want it to live."[1] And, it should be added, living where a few have decreed it shall live, out of range of the natural enemies and the conditions that kept it in equilibrium.

Carelessness, stupidity, greed, uncleanliness have caused pest problems. Although the problems will continue until those attitudes and practices are changed, some control measures can be, and should be, taken immediately.

An obvious one is to impose stricter controls on migration. About half—123—of the insect species that cause serious damage in this country are immigrants.[2] Laws to bar them have existed since 1905, when Congress enacted the first prohibition. But the casual disregard for them is indicated by the continuing arrivals: some of the most dangerous and destructive are among the most recent. One year plant pest quarantine inspectors at various ports of entry made more than 32,000 separate interceptions.[3] How many got through is anyone's guess, with professionals using high-powered smuggling techniques to bring in exotic plants and animals to sell at exotic prices, and with amateurs employing ingenious tricks to carry home little "souvenirs" for Aunt Gertrude.

The cost in human life and suffering that could be averted by vigilant inspection and quarantine is great— as Europe discovered after three spice-laden ships refused to wait to unload their cargo in 1348. The Black Death, carried all over the continent by the infected rats, claimed millions of lives; in some places more than half the population succumbed in successive attacks.[4] In a similar way, "Rocky Mountain Fever" and other plagues that have killed hundreds of persons have come to this country.

The financial costs of quarantine dodging are also great. A notable example began in 1946, when a Mexican rancher decided to import some Brahma bulls for breeding purposes. Impatient over delay—every day the animals spent in quarantine meant a loss of stud fees—he bribed an inspector to release them early. The foot-and-mouth disease they carried began to ravage Mexican cattle. To prevent its crossing the 2,000-mile international boundary, U.S. ranchers enlisted the aid of this government. Before the seven-year war was won, more than 135 million American tax dollars were spent to cancel out the "mistake." In the process, incalculable damage was done to the Good Neighbor policy. Communists had a field day over the "invasion" of Mexican soil by *gringo* search-and-destroy missions. Farmers were united in their hatred of "those of the north" who decreed the killing of animals that in many cases represented the sum total of family wealth and pride.[5]

The animal quarantine system in the United States had its beginning when a New York milkman, looking for a "good deal," bought a sick cow from a British sea captain. His bargain set off an outbreak of lung sickness that quickly spread and destroyed valuable herds. Other cut-rate imports spread the disease to other parts of the country to such an extent that by 1880 European nations were halting the import of American cattle. To protect both herds and traders, Congress acted four years later, passing the first animal quarantine law and delegating authority for its enforcement to the USDA.[6]

Since then, quarantine inspectors have become as much concerned with contaminated meat products—home-canned, partially cured, or improperly cooked—as with diseased animals on the hoof.[7] International mail and travelers' baggage are now being carefully scrutinized. With planes and ships carrying about 200 million Americans and foreigners to this country each year from all parts of the globe, plant and insect pest imports have become a problem of magnitude.[8]

Although Western men pride themselves on their high degree of civilization, they continue to be among the dirtiest creatures in the world. When the *conquistadores* arrived in this hemisphere, they marveled at the cleanliness as well as the splendor of the great cities in Mexico and South America. And well they might have. European cities in the fifteenth and sixteenth centuries were cesspools, whose filth invited pestilence. Many have continued so. According to one British scientist, as recently as 1940 the majority of young women in industrial cities there had head lice.[9] England, of course, is one of the neatest and cleanest of countries. And the appalling figures on the number of children being gnawed by rats in New York and other great metropolitan centers in the United States in 1970 mock our boast of regarding cleanliness as next to godliness.

The first insects that developed resistance to pesticides —fleas, flies, mosquitoes, roaches—are all major carriers

of disease and are *all subject to control by sanitary measures*. Perhaps the most impressive job of pest control in
history was done in the Panama Canal Zone early in this
century under the direction of Colonel William C. Gorgas
of the U.S. Army Medical Department. Marshes, the
breeding grounds of mosquitoes that transmitted malaria
and yellow fever, were drained and oiled. Sewage and
water supply systems were built for Panama and Colon.
Thus, uncounted lives were saved when the canal was
built.

Sanitation practices are effective in protecting plants as
well as persons. In South Texas, farmers are required by
law to destroy stalks of cotton plants after harvest. A
similar law went into effect in New Mexico in 1968 as a
result of the success experienced in Texas.[10] That practice
is not news to even amateur gardeners, who have long
known that by burning or destroying diseased rose cut-
tings and fruit they can protect their plants from further
infestations.

Eliminating or minimizing the food supply makes it
possible to exercise control at almost every link in the
chain of being. When large supplies of food are made
available, population explosions occur. That has been the
case with herring gulls, now a serious pest because they
plunder crops, pollute domestic water supplies, compete
with more desirable species of birds, and collide with air-
planes. Inspecting Logan International Airport in Boston
after the major plane disaster in 1960, one scientist called
it "the most extraordinary example" he had ever seen of
the lack of biotic control. It was "virtually a wildlife
sanctuary": with ponds, tidal flats, lush borders, and, "of
course," a garbage dump.[11]

For all the talk about the great gains in agricultural
science, much of what is called farming in this country is

no different from the primitive farming carried on by
ignorant peasants—a despoilation of the land.

It has long been known that pest control can be exercised by such simple measures as timing, crop rotation,
and planting certain combinations.

Timing is very important. If winter wheat, for example,
is planted late in the season, the Hessian fly, one of its
principal pests, will be without board and room during its
highly active period. If various types of squash and melon
are planted early, they will be beyond the seedling stage
and therefore less attractive to borers when they are busy
in mid-July.

Crop rotation is also effective. If pests' homes are taken
away for a season, they will have no reason for staying on.
With their food supply cut off at the source, they will die.
At Malabar Farm, the model project started by the novelist Louis Bromfield, the rotation of plants, along with
improvement in soil structure, has been held responsible
for the garden's not having been seriously affected by
vegetable pests during its long history.[12]

Even when crop rotation is not practical, as on large
specialty farms, strip-cropping and other methods of
planting other growing things in combination can radically
reduce pest populations. Beans near potatoes will protect
the latter against Colorado beetles. Potatoes near beans
will protect the latter against some types of bean beetles.
Soybeans near corn are considered insurance against
chinch bugs and Japanese beetles. Some types of gerani-
ums will protect roses and grapes against Japanese beetles;
chives and garlic will shield lettuce and peas against
aphids.[13] Large-scale experiments indicate that such gardening practices can be extended. One of the most promising plant insurance policies is the marigold—which
Mexicans refer to as the "flower of death." One variety of

Mexican marigolds, *Tagetes minuta,* is being planted widely in England and other countries to curb pests that resist chemical attack. Its leaves have insecticidal properties. They are boiled in water, soaked overnight, strained, and used as a spray by some farmers against codling moths, aphids, and weevil eggs. Also, the roots of the plant exude substances that are powerful inhibitors of underground slugs, wireworms, and nematodes.[14] African marigolds are also being used to attack nematodes that afflict commercially valuable flowers and fruits.[15]

Actually, botanical pesticides have been used for centuries. From the time of the Romans until World War II, they were the chief means of controlling pests. Most important have been white hellebore, pyrethrum, nicotine, and rotenone. White hellebore is perhaps the oldest of the group, well known to the ancient Greeks, who mixed it with milk to kill flies. Pyrethrum has been the most popular. Made of the powdered flowers of some chrysanthemums, it may have originated in China about two thousand years ago. Considered to be "probably the safest of all insecticides for use on a food plant,"[16] it was widely used in this country until World War II halted Japanese imports, but it has been staging a major comeback. In 1968 almost a million pounds of dried flower heads and extract were imported, mostly from Kenya, Tanzania, and Ecuador.[17] (Recently, scientists have discovered a new synthetic, "pyrethrin," which is considered almost identical with the natural product.)

Nicotine has been used since the seventeenth century as a spray and a dust; it is highly toxic for both mammals and insects, but it degrades rapidly. Rotenone, which comes from the roots of different species of Peruvian and Brazilian trees, has long been used as a fish poison by primitive hunters. It is widely praised as a "safe" pesticide since it is relatively nontoxic to man and other warm-blooded animals, although deadly to cold-blooded ones.[18]

How effectively a botanical, properly applied, can protect both public health and the ecosystem was demonstrated to me in the fall of 1970 by Commander Edsel M. Fussell, officer in charge of the U.S. Navy Disease Vector Control Center in Alameda, California. As a medical entomologist, Commander Fussell's primary job is to protect troops from disease-bearing pests. However, he is also deeply concerned with environmental protection.

For some years he and colleagues at the Naval Air Station in Alameda have been conducting experiments to achieve both goals. They have evolved new methods and new concepts that constitute an important breakthrough —particularly in controlling flies and mosquitoes.

Although those principal health menaces have become almost impervious to very persistent and dangerously toxic chemicals, Commander Fussell and his fellow workers felt that they could be controlled even with pyrethrum, if direct hits were scored during application. They rarely are, in conventional application, since the large droplets loosed to fall in poison storms only occasionally zero in on target. To correct that, the navy scientists developed an aerosol generator so light it could be operated from a military jeep which dispenses incredibly small droplets— less than 10 microns in a diameter—to seek out pests. Unlike most ultra-low-volume applications, however, the pesticide is distributed in very low concentrations. Thus, using only a 5 percent concentrate of pyrethrum, the scientists achieved a 100 percent kill of mosquitoes in two hours at 1,500 feet and a 100 percent kill of houseflies.

They have worked out other measures to enhance environmental protection—using vegetable oils as diluents instead of toxic petroleum products, and timing the application so that beneficial insects are not likely to be exposed to them.

In addition to the botanicals, other "natural" methods of cutting down on pests have been developed—methods that are also designed to increase the fertility of the soil. Organic and Bio-dynamic farming and gardening are among them. Although there are undoubtedly fanatics in both movements, most practitioners are far from being the crackpots and cultists they are held to be in scientific and pseudo-scientific circles. The sensible premise of both groups is that one must work in harmony with nature.

Dr. Paul B. Sears, former dean of the Yale School of Conservation, pointed out in his introduction to Leonard Wickenden's excellent *Gardening with Nature:*

> . . . I am convinced that the primary task of applied biology is to understand, respect, and—so far as possible—stimulate the balance of nature in our patterns of land use. . . . This, as I read it, is the intuitive truth of the idea of gardening with nature.[19]

While there is a tendency among natural gardeners to make sweeping claims that pests and diseases *never* attack healthy plants grown in healthy soil, as Dr. Sears noted, the theories of organic gardening have been impressively supported by scientific experiments.

Both the organic and Bio-dynamic advocates believe that the compost heap is the key to successful gardening on any scale. Using natural plant food to develop a fertile, pest-free soil is not new. Roman farmers did it long before the Christian era; Chinese farmers thousands of years ago became known as compost builders. However, composting as a "science" seems to have been originated in this century by Sir Albert Howard. A scientist who served England

at home and in India for many years, he was convinced
that humus composed of animal and plant wastes would
solve pest problems and promote animal and human health.

As Wickenden describes it, the "why" of the method Sir
Albert developed is based on the notion that the mineral
content of all soils is adequate; indeed, in "worn-out soils"
it may rise to 90 times the organic content. The minerals
are useless, however, unless they are rendered available to
plants by acids that are produced bacterially from organic
matter. A contrary position is taken by chemical advocates, who say that fertile soil depends upon the addition
of such essentials as potassium, phosphorus, calcium, nitrate, and others. In a rather amusing footnote to his book,
Leonard Wickenden cites an example of the chemical
mentality at work. He sent a soil sample to the state agricultural experiment station. The soil had not been given
an ounce of chemical fertilizer in the seven years he had
owned the property, although "when it came into my
possession it was so lacking in fertility that it would yield
only the most miserable of crops." The report was excellent, particularly the ratings given to the essential minerals:
"nitrate nitrogen, medium; phosphorus, high; potassium,
high; calcium, very high; magnesium, high."

In spite of those ratings, the report carried a recommendation that the next spring he add a mixture of potassium,
phosphorus, calcium, and nitrogen—in an amount equivalent to approximately 1,300 pounds an acre![20]

The "what" of the method is compost, which builds up
the organic content of soils: "When you put compost on
your soil you put life into it." The reasoning is that compost is a culture bed for micro-organisms of many kinds
that secrete antibiotics. They protect plants against disease
and fix nitrogen trapped from the air. Compost improves
the texture of the soil and its water-holding properties;

acids formed during its decomposition make available to plants some of the store of minerals in the subsoil. Many organic gardeners believe that there is something beyond that—the value not yet known.

Although the mystique of composting is not shared by the undedicated, what is known about it might well encourage amateurs and professionals to build their own heaps.

On large farms, sheet-composting is the alternative used by some and recommended almost universally for others. In *Farming with Nature*, Joseph A. Cocannouer stresses its ability to enhance the kind as well as amount of foodstuffs. Compost, he says, "will improve the land to the point where the produce harvested from that land is uniformly quality produce."[21] By way of a test, the government could pay farmers for putting soil into condition instead of paying them for taking it out of production. If a crop of "green manure" were grown on land for which a subsidy is being received, no more food would be on the market—the bizarre reason for paying subsidies in a starving world!—and the land would be aided. The crop turned under would be the base of the compost "heap." Even if farmers were not subsidized for taking fields out of production for half a year (the time needed to complete the process), Cocannouer thinks it should be done anyhow. A dangerously high percentage of American soils are in "dire" need of this natural soil treatment, he said.[22]

The organic gardeners have become an impressive force in the country. More than 100,000 belong to a club, which draws members from commercial farms as well as business and professional circles. One of the most articulate practitioners is Eddie Albert, widely known as the star of (appropriately) *Green Acres*. A man whose life offstage provides reassurance that the celluloid world is inhabited by genuine human beings, he is concerned with the philosophical as well as physical benefits of a life style that is in harmony with nature. "Our survival depends upon it," he told me recently.

Food stores, books, magazines, supply houses serving the movement have been growing vigorously. The pages of *Organic Gardening and Farming*, an excellent journal published monthly by the Rodale Press,[23] indicate the serious purpose of the movement and the valuable contribution it has been making to combat various forms of pollution.

Like the organic gardeners, the Bio-dynamic people base their practices on a belief in the need for rich humus. The movement was started by a biochemist, Dr. Ehrenfried Pfeiffer of Spring Valley, New York. A highly competent soil scientist, he developed "starters"—active bacteria supported by enzymes and hormones to stimulate the natural processing.[24] That group is also dedicated, various, and enlightened. A woman I know in it—a widow, a grandmother, and former educational director of a consumer cooperative in Palo Alto, California—trusted the theory enough a decade ago to take on a 100-acre farm and woodland in Oregon. Mildred Cowger is well satisfied with the results: Bio-dynamics, she says, has enabled her to provide all her own fruit, meat, and vegetables and to earn enough from the surplus to live comfortably. A few years ago she took a leave of absence from her farm to become the first grandmother to serve with the Peace Corps in Latin America—teaching villagers in Bolivia how to organize credit unions and other co-ops and how to farm profitably.[25]

A far more complex, but highly promising solution to pest problems has been the development of resistant strains: the genetic approach. One of the first successes was scored after the Irish potato famine in the 1840's. The fungus that destroyed successive crops is estimated to have taken a toll of at least 2.5 million Irish people during the years of "The Great Hunger."[26] Unable to develop effective fungicides, scientists answered the problem by developing strains of potatoes that were impervious to the disease.

Another landmark occurred at the end of the nineteenth century, after a fungus—*Fusarium oxysporum*—made disastrous attacks on a wide range of crops in this country.[27] A USDA scientist conceived the idea of breeding the plants that had been able to survive on the wilt-infested soil. What made his success more remarkable was that the principles of Mendelian inheritance and pure-line selection were not then known. First cotton, then flax crops were saved by the resistant selections. According to one expert: "Today, the cabbage, pea, tomato, and melon growing industries in many areas owe their existence to the development of fusarium wilt-resistant varieties."[28]

Another early success involved the sugarcane mosaic, which seems to have been introduced into the South from Asia in about 1914. Within twelve years it had spread so rapidly that losses amounted to $100 million a year. A USDA experiment produced highly resistant and more productive varieties by crossing wild sugarcane with commercial strains . . . the increased productivity being a special bonus.[29] Resistant strains of onion, cotton, pepper, peach, soybean, alfalfa, rice, strawberry, and sweet potato plants have since been developed.

Investment in research on resistant strains has been modest in contrast with gains. In Kansas alone, a few years ago, farmers were harvesting an extra five million bushels annually of a strain of wheat that resisted the Hessian fly. They were also saving money on chemicals since, as one entomologist at Kansas State University pointed out, the effect of a resistant variety "is cumulative and persistent, whereas that of an insecticide is sudden and decreasing in effectiveness unless reapplied."[30]

In spite of the great promise of all those means—cultural, sanitary, genetic, and simple ingenuity—they have been overlooked and often dismissed by many agricultural scientists. One can understand their chagrin at having to acknowledge that water is sometimes a far more effective pesticide than a toxic chemical and that stale beer may be vastly more successful in curbing some troublesome pests than highly touted insecticides.[31]

But understanding wasteful and dangerous practices and allowing them to continue are two different things.

Polluters and their apologists have successfully taken the line that their way is the cheapest way—that the costs of cleaning up the environment would be prohibitive. Experience suggests that the reverse would be true—if researchers would spend less time trying to discover ways to contaminate the planet and more time discovering ways to clean it up.

There is big money to be made in cleaning the environment—as some have come to realize. A few enlightened cities, for instance, are realizing multi-million dollar profits from converting the waste materials fouling the waterways into fertilizers that do not harm the soil. Milwaukee, alone, makes more than $3 million a year from processing activated sludge and selling it through lawn and garden retail outlets.[32]

That sort of economy should be extended to other types of pollution and involve private enterprise. One hopeful sign is that pollution-control companies are now being touted as good investment possibilities by some of the largest corporations in the country. Business magazines like *Fortune* are alerting readers that while economists were predicting "a serious recession" for the economy as a whole, "shares of the anti-pollution companies led the stock market upward."[33]

There is no reason why business and government should not work together in the public interest instead of against it, as they are now, too often, doing.

Government agencies, ever at the ready to take up arms when and where business feels threatened, have spent an inordinate amount of time and effort attacking proponents of alternative methods of pest control. While pesticide pushers have been permitted to operate with flagrant disregard for the public interest, advocates of organic farming, for example, have been treated as enemies of the state.

Perhaps the most telling single instance is the experience of Hugh MacDonald, which was touched on briefly in a previous chapter.

The first part of his story, detailed by Beatrice Trum Hunter in *Gardening without Poisons,* began in 1955 when he took over a "barren wasteland" at the southern tip of the Imperial Valley. Within seven years Mr. MacDonald had transformed the 555-acre "Border Ranch" into an internationally known showplace—and a profitable one, with yearly production up from 20,000 boxes of low grade fruit to 125,000 boxes of prime quality citrus.

He restored and revived it swiftly and without the aid of synthetic fertilizers or pesticides. Cover crops of Espana, wild mustard, vetch, and maize were planted and disked under; thousands of tons of manure, received under a barter arrangement from a nearby beef-fattening ranch, were spread. Dead trees were uprooted; new stock planted. He set aside five acres of land to raise and improve citrus stock—replanting some, selling off the surplus. He encouraged brush and small trees to grow again in the deep canyons as havens for quail, doves, and rabbits. He installed two apiaries of a hundred hives to help pollinate the fruit, and imported pest-eating beetles to keep down the undesirable insects attacking citrus groves.[34]

Mr. MacDonald's victory was turned into near defeat. After he publicly disavowed pesticides because of their relationship to cancer, he was almost ruined. According to the sequel, chronicled by Laura Tallian in *The Pesticide Jungle*, he was set upon by banks and by the packing house through which he shipped his crops. He managed to save his ranch only by "frantic efforts."[35]

Others, including the publishers of *Organic Gardening and Farming*, have been subjected to what might be described as harassment. Two cases were made, unsuccessfully, against them by the federal agency which did nothing to halt the continued advertising of highly dangerous pesticides in clear violation of the law.

While public money has gone to subsidize the developing and marketing of chemical controls, it has been used against or withheld from those working on alternatives, none of which is more promising than the use of *pests' pests* to curb economic and health menaces—biological controls.

12. LIVING PESTICIDES

ONE OF THE MORE memorable sights in Salt Lake City is the seagull monument, a sixteen-foot Doric column surmounted by a sphere with two gilded birds. The statue is striking not because of its lines or sculptural dynamics, but for the gratitude it symbolizes.

In 1848 the band of Mormon settlers, who had been so confident of having found the promised land, faced disaster. Their crops—"all up and looking grand," a journalist among them wrote—were first threatened on July 4 by a frost, "which took beans, corn and wheat and nearly every living thing."[1] Then, to complete what the diabolic ministry had wrought, crickets came by the "thousands of tons." The diary of Priddy Meeks tells what happened:

> Now everything did look gloomy. . . . At that instant [in Sunday meeting], I heard the voice of fowels [sic] flying overhead that I was not acquainted with. I looked up and saw a flock of seven gulls. Then more and more "until the heavens were darkened with them" and they would eat crickets and throw them up again.[2]

The crickets left, and the Mormons were saved. Whether the coming of the gulls is held to be a miracle or a bit of good fortune is largely a matter of religious persuasion. What cannot be questioned about the episode is that, in

principle, it was a remarkable instance of natural biological control.

The knowledge that "good" animals and insects can be
used to keep down "bad" ones is ancient folk wisdom, pre-
dating history itself. One of the earliest examples cited occurred in China, where thousands of years ago citrus
growers used to buy predaceous ants from traveling vend-
ers. They colonized them and put them in orange trees to
control foliage-feeding insects. The growers helped their
little "slaves" to move from one tree to another by building narrow bridges of bamboo rods.

The Yemenites, among other early users of biological
controls, discovered in the mountains rising above the fertile plains a species of ant that preyed on other ants that
destroyed date palms. It became part of their farming
chores to make an annual journey to the mountains to
gather a supply of the former so that the trees would be
kept productive.[3]

Even American children, who are trained to regard
almost every small living thing as "ugh," are still taught
to pick up ladybeetles carefully and blow the bright little
creatures to freedom, chanting: "Ladybug, ladybug, fly
away home. Your house is on fire; your children will burn."

The history of admiration behind that song is lengthy.
In France during the medieval era, the creatures were
considered such a blessing that they were named "Virgin's cattle." In England they were first called "Our Lady's
birds." For centuries, women and children in the southern
counties have earned pin money by gathering the creatures and selling them to hop growers to insure a good
harvest.

Other creatures have also been regarded as lucky and
desirable. Long before the causes of the Black Plague
were known, city and country dwellers kept cats to pro-

tect them from rats and mice. In parts of the world where flies abound, it is still held "bad luck" to kill a spider in the house.

It was not, however, until the eighteenth century that efforts were made to apply natural biological controls in a scientific way. In 1792, British colonists in Mauritius, an island in the Indian Ocean, were so dismayed by the depredations of the red locust that they imported mynah birds to keep the pests under control. The success of that effort encouraged scientists to think of systematically manipulating the populations of parasites and predators to reduce the density of pests below the level of economic injury— the science of applied biological control.

According to the noted entomologist Dr. Richard L. Doutt, the first truly scientific demonstration did not take place until more than a century later.[4]

Inspired by the possibilities, Charles V. Riley gave biological control a brief try in Missouri. He had noticed that the weevil was kept under control in one area by a parasite and he decided to ship the parasites to other parts of the state where the pest was causing trouble. Results were promising, but the researcher did not get his main chance to test out his theories until he was made chief of the Division of Entomology of the USDA.

In 1887 he arrived in California, answering an appeal from the members of the Fruit Growers Association. Their new industry, they said, was threatened by the cottony cushion scale, a pest that had arrived from Australia on some shipments of acacia trees. In less than twenty years it had made such inroads that some orchards on a summer day looked as though they had been standing in a snowstorm. (A tiny reddish-brown sap-sucking insect, the scale derives its name from the formation of its egg mass—a large, white "cushion" holding 600 to 800 eggs, attached to twigs.)

Supremely convinced of the power of living insecticides, Riley promised the growers that he could protect their investment if he could raise $1,500 or $2,000 to send his protégé, Albert Koebele, to Australia to find "the natural enemy." Riley knew that he could not promote the money from Congress. His interest in bugs and his enthusiasm for their abilities had become the subject of Washington jokes. If the request came from him, Riley told his audience, "it would be more apt to cause laughter and ridicule on the part of the average committee in Congress than serious and earnest consideration."[5]

The growers in California were too hard pressed to reject any suggestion. They passed a resolution favoring the idea and pressed their representatives to get an appropriation.

The money came and Koebele went. The rest has become scientific history. Of the possible enemies, Koebele selected a parasitic fly and the now famous Vedalia beetle. He sent back 129 of the latter in three shipments in January 1888. Riley's field agent in California, D. W. Coquillet, threw a gauze tent over a heavily infested orange tree. He placed the beetles in the tent and allowed them to breed unmolested until April.

Spectators at the "grand opening" were dazzled when one side of the tent was pulled aside. Hardly a scale remained on the tree, and the beetles, in enormous number, were taking off for nearby infested trees to continue their work.

New colonies were established in other tented trees. They multiplied so rapidly and worked so hard that Coquillet distributed supplies to 228 orchardists in mid-June. A few weeks later, one citrus grower wrote that from the small colony he had received, "every one of my 3,200 orchard trees is literally swarming with them. All of my ornamental trees, shrubs, and vines which were infested with white scale are practically cleansed by this wonderful parasite."[6] He, in turn, distributed "starter" supplies of beetles to 130 persons.

California fruit growers were so delighted with results that they presented Koebele with a gold watch and his wife with diamond earrings.

Not averse to material rewards, he took off for Hawaii a few years later. In 1902 Koebele received a major challenge there, which allowed him to prove that weeds and vegetative pests could be biologically controlled. A Central American shrub, *Lantana camara* L., which had been transported to the islands for ornamental planting, escaped cultivation and took over thousands of acres of valuable range land. Koebele took off for Latin America and sent back a number of the plant's foes. They worked well, but the lantana had made such headway that it took years to do the job.[7]

Perhaps the most dramatic example of the ability of insects to control plant pests took place in Australia. The prickly pear, *Opuntia*—a useful and ubiquitous plant in Central and South America—arrived in Australia during the nineteenth century. To say that it spread like wildfire is an inadequate description. By 1900 it had taken over about 10 million acres of range land; by 1925, 60 million acres.

In that year, entomologists sent to Australia from Argentina 2,750 eggs of the *Cactoblastis moth*. The larvae thrived; by the second generation the moths had produced more than 2.5 million eggs, most of which were released in twenty locations. The following year another 9 million were released. Between 1927 and 1929, 3 billion eggs from field collections were distributed. Within a year larvae had destroyed huge stands of cactus, returning millions of acres to useful agriculture.[8] No other forms of cactus were attacked.[9]

Other major successes were scored. Among them was the control of a plant known in various parts of the world as St. John's Wort, goat weed, and Klamath weed. Valued by many Europeans for its "magical" properties, it is anathema to ranchers, since it seriously affects the mouths and hides of cattle. By 1944 it was causing major consternation in northern California, occupying about 2 million acres of range land and forcing ranchers out of business.[10]

Chemical controls were too expensive; its natural enemies in Europe could not be obtained because of the war. However, some scientists remembered that the weed had been controlled in Australia after it had been imported to that country by a German immigrant. USDA and University of California scientists studied the feasibility of bringing from Australia the *Chrysolina* beetles that had curbed the weed there. Finding that the beetle rejected as food all commercially valuable crops, they gave the "all clear" signal. The Air Transport Command flew in the first batch in October 1944. The beetles multiplied so rapidly and did the job so efficiently that the Klamath weed was taken off the list of noxious weeds within a few years. Grateful farmers in one county erected a monument to it, after the example of the Mormons celebrating the seagull.

Theoretically, nothing could be simpler than using natural enemies to control pests. After all, as scientists have pointed out, "the greatest single factor in keeping plant-feeding insects from overwhelming the rest of the world is that they are fed on by other insects."[11] Practically, however, it is a difficult and demanding science that presently engages the full-time attention of fewer than a hundred researchers around the world.

Among them is Dr. Paul DeBach, professor of biological control at the University of California-Riverside. Author-editor of the classic *Biological Control of Insect Pests and Weeds,* Dr. DeBach was recently named to head the worldwide organization now devoted to that goal.[12] In August 1970, he and Professor Carl Huffaker of the Berkeley campus were named directors of the university's new International Center for Biological Control.

A tall, rangy man with a cheerful grin and an enthusiasm for pitching horseshoes and playing poker during his lunch break, Dr. DeBach first became "excited" about bugs when he was working on a Boy Scout merit badge more than forty years ago. As an undergraduate at the University of California-Los Angeles, he learned about biological control from Professor Harry Smith, one of the pioneers in the field. "I thought then that was for me," he remembers.[13] He became convinced of that during 1946 and 1947, when he worked on the first major DDT "upset" in California. Although the Vedalia beetle had just about eliminated the cottony cushion scale, widespread spraying with DDT wiped out the beetles. Within a year the scale had staged such a comeback that groves "looked as though they had been struck by a blizzard." Cure was effected only after sprayers were persuaded to curb their activities and after new supplies of beetles were distributed.

Since then, DeBach has devoted himself to tracking down allies in the war against pests and insuring the survival of troops in the field. Since most serious pests are immigrants, finding their natural enemies involves travel. Consequently, when he is not in his laboratory in an old building on the edge of the campus, he is bug detecting on a global scale. During the last two decades he has logged more than 200,000 miles in his search for the "good" foes of threatened plants and trees.

His travels are not on the Hilton circuit. DeBach stalks his prey—some so tiny they cannot be seen with 20-20 vision—in jungles, deserts, mountain villages, city parks, and backyards in Central and South America, Africa, Asia,

Australia, and islands in the Pacific and Caribbean. He travels light; his most important item of "apparel" is a binoscope, which he wears entomologist-fashion perched on top of his forehead when he is not "viewing." His most valued pieces of equipment are the aspirator, with which he sucks up parasites from infested plants, and the "banks" in which the creatures are stored for the trip to the United States.

Prying into hidden corners for bugs is more hazardous than ordinary travel. In addition to the natural dangers of storms, sickness, and landslides—all of which he has experienced—he has also had people problems. During a trip to Burma, a local leader insisted on providing him with a military jeep for his trip to the jungle near the Chinese border. Less welcome was the man's gift of company—an assortment of relatives and three armed guards. Since the guerrillas were looking for likely candidates for ransom, his traveling companions "complicated matters." Nevertheless, DeBach managed to track down some parasitic wasps he was seeking. They have since saved California growers an estimated $200 million. Enormous sums have also been saved by some of the forty other species of friendly warriors he and colleagues have introduced.

"Outstanding successes" have been realized in other countries—Australia, New Zealand, Israel, Tasmania, Barbados, Cuba, Guam, Puerto Rico, Portuguese West Africa, Japan, Mexico.[14] Some efforts have been only partial successes. Predaceous insects have done a reasonable job of controlling the pear psylla in California, British Columbia, and some parts of Oregon; curiously, in the state of Washington, the predators have not been able to reduce adequately the pest that damages the fruit trees.[15]

Some of the experiments have failed totally—not surprising, since the science of biological control is still in its infancy. Very little is really known about the biologies of the more than 700,000 insects—any one of which might become a pest when transported to an alien environment or when natural balance is upset. Very little is even known about the small number now labeled pests and their possible enemies. That is what makes the hunt for effective predators and parasites so exciting to scientists like Paul DeBach. "When you're looking for diamonds," is his way of putting it, "you have to know the right place to look."

The first phase in biological control programs is the importation of likely candidates. The second begins when researchers settle down to study seriously the insects that may be drafted for war duty. Insurance must be given that the draftee is host specific, that he will not join the opposing army of pests. Careful screening tests are made to determine the food needs, the site on or in which eggs are laid, the egg-laying capacity, and longevity.

Candidates that pass those tests are colonized in the insectary at the university's Riverside campus, the largest breeding laboratory of its kind in the world. Then they are given trial runs in the field. If they meet that challenge, they are offered to growers for use on farms and ranches and to commercial breeders of parasites and predators.[16]

Bug raising is now beginning to become a sizable business. Recently, the *Wall Street Journal* announced that as a result of the concern over chemicals, business had begun to "boom." One industry leader cited was Jack Gothard of Texas, who raises *Trichogramma* wasps to combat crop-eating moths. By 1968 he was producing a billion of the tiny creatures a year, whose lethal talents were expected to yield him $200,000. Eugene Mincemoyer, a former tree surgeon, was identified as the "praying mantis king" by reporter Neil Ulman. Even small operators were cheerful about prospects. "Demand is really starting to take hold," Melvin R. Hanson, a Tacoma bug breeder, viewed the future optimistically.[17]

For the research scientists, the crucial struggle comes after the "beneficials" are liberated. Will they survive the assault by chemical weapons?

"Good" visitors as well as natives have and continue to fall beneath the onslaught—ironically, as Dr. DeBach points out, since they are the best possible insurance that farmers and gardeners could have. Natural controls protect crops at least 90 percent of the time—sometimes, as with avocado crops, 99 percent. Similarly, most gardens are under very good natural biological control—or would be if sensibly cultivated.

Yet amateurs and commercial growers alike indulge in what can only be considered the mad "killing game"— canceling their insurance and creating pest problems. Two notable examples cited by Dr. DeBach were the pesticide-induced outbreaks in 1946 and 1947, when DDT almost completely wiped out the Vedalia beetles, and a growing disaster in the 1950's, when the introduction and reckless use of organic phosphates transformed the red mite from a minor pest into the citrus industry's "Number One Enemy."

Like many other knowledgeable persons, Dr. DeBach is extremely wary of chemical weapons: "Personally, I am afraid of many of those poisons and of their effects on the environment."

He and others in the biological control field have confidence that "living pesticides" will be able to do a large part of the job. These include pathogens as well as predators and parasites.

It has been known for centuries that insects, like animals and humans, are susceptible to diseases, although not the same ones. During the nineteenth century an Italian scientist demonstrated that a microbe could cause infectious diseases in silkworms; and following up on the work, a United States scientist urged that diseases as pest controls be explored. The first real breakthrough occurred in 1933, when Dr. R. S. Dutky isolated the bacterium that caused the "milky spore disease" in Japanese beetles. By using the creatures as living culture mediums, he was able to produce spore dusts on a large scale. Government officials, hard pressed to curb the pest that was seriously damaging vegetables, fruit, and forage, decided to give it a try. A massive control program was launched in fourteen states and the District of Columbia; it resulted in permanent control of the Japanese beetle in many treated areas within three years.[18]

Lately much attention has been focused on another pathogen, *Bacillus thuringiensis*. A spore-forming microorganism, it was first isolated from diseased larvae of the Mediterranean flour moth in Europe decades ago. Since then a very large number of insects—at least 110 species of moths and 8 species of flies—have proved to be susceptible to it. Since it was first produced commercially in 1956, it has been used widely across the country against the alfalfa caterpillar, the cabbage worm, and the European corn borer. Curiously, the disease does not harm ladybugs, honeybees, parasitic wasps, or other beneficial insects; and it is so harmless to humans and other warmblooded animals that it has been ruled exempt from tolerance by the FDA.

Experiments have been going on for the last few years with viruses. They are considered promising because they are so highly specific, attacking only the target and harmless to other forms of life. Although high production costs and technical problems involved in culturing them have made widespread use of viruses as control agents seem unlikely, "this state of helplessness is almost over," it has been reported.[19] However, the United States government was withholding approval for their commercial production for "reasons unapparent" to a number of scientists.

One successful experiment was made in Canada a few years ago. After pathologists identified the disease that killed European spruce sawflies—pests that have devastated thousands of acres of forest on both sides of the border—it was found that the virus could be produced and applied easily. The artificially induced epidemic killed off 99 percent of the pests.[20] And it was done at very low cost. Four infected larvae, finely ground, added to one gallon of water was enough to spray an acre effectively. (That formulation allowed some pests to survive—enough to insure the perpetuation of the disease.)

Using a somewhat different vehicle, researchers achieved a 90 percent kill of corn borers in Iowa a few years ago. *Bacillus thuringiensis* was incorporated in little time pills, capsules similar to those people use for all-day cold relief. The bacteria was uniformly released over a period of three days—at the end of which time it proved to be quite as effective as chemical pesticides used on comparable plots.[21]

Other pathogens than *Bacillus thuringiensis* should be on the market soon. At the 1969 meeting of the American Chemical Society, a USDA official reported that the first virus pesticide was being considered for registration.[22] Dr. Arthur M. Heimpel of the Insect Pathology Laboratory in Maryland said that the virus, which had been tested for more than five years, has been effective in inducing a fatal disease in the corn earworm, a pest which attacks at least 22 commercially valuable plants in this country. "All the evidence from numerous tests show the virus to be harmless for humans, other animals, and plants," however. As evidence of his own confidence in it, Dr. Heimpel ate a "helping" of the virus.

Because of our horror about the use of virulent "germs" against fellow humans in the kind of biological-chemical warfare that militaristic minds have been able to conceive and militaristic consciences have been able to propose, the idea of using them to control vertebrate pests is startling. It has been officially opposed in England, where farmers have used a disease to control rabbits.

Myxomatosis, which had been used in France for that purpose, was carried across the Channel in 1953 by an infected mosquito. It spread so wildly that by 1955 the number of rabbits in England had been reduced by about 90 percent. Farmers were delighted. The disease was so specific that no other living things were harmed. It was an economic boon. Rabbits had been costing farmers and gardeners more than £50 million a year. However, animal lovers were so outraged that they demanded laws that made it illegal to spread the disease deliberately. According to recent reports, the ban has been flouted: "black markets" in myxomatosis have flourished, with farmers risking prosecution by buying infected rabbits in order to start an epizootic on their grounds.[23] In countries where animal lovers have been less successful in exerting pressure —as in Australia—the disease is used widely and legally to curb oversupplies of foraging rabbits.

The use of "germ warfare" against lower forms of life does not provoke the same emotions. And the use is growing. Although careful investigation must continue to be made of the potential hazards, there is no indication that pathogens constitute the same kind of danger to man, wildlife, and beneficial insects that is posed by chemicals.[24]

The various forms of biological control have already demonstrated their value. Yet, in spite of the urgings of the President's Science Advisory Committee in 1963, too little has been done in the United States to further their use. According to the director of Canada's Department of Agriculture Research Institute, China and the Soviet Union have encouraged their development. So have some of the free countries, including Canada. It recognized years ago "the importance and potential value of parasites, predators, and other biological controls and developed and supported study of them."[25] The ratio of expenditures on biological controls to chemical controls in the United States is very low—*much* less than 1 to 100.

Those living pesticides which have been employed with success have proved their superiority over chemicals in almost every way. They are far safer: almost invariably they have demonstrated themselves to be host specific, harming only the target. They do not kill or injure people or other living things, nor do they contaminate the earth.

Their effects are permanent. When parasites and predators do their work effectively, pests are kept scarce. Pests virtually never build up resistance to them; and they don't stay around in the manner of unwanted chemicals. They decrease as the pests decrease. If a new outbreak starts, their numbers increase similarly to take care of it. Chemicals cannot and do not have that kind of built-in regulator.

Another advantage is that biological controls are cheaper. The relatively small sums spent on them in California alone are estimated to have saved agriculture in the state more than $100 million in less than ten years. The cost of chemical protection increases year after year. As Dr. DeBach has pointed out, "with some crops, financially, a point of no return has been passed."[26]

Like many other scientists, he believes that restrictive laws are needed. "If you can't legally regulate the use of chemicals, you will never solve the problem." He has worked with groups like the Environmental Defense Fund to obtain them.

However, he is also aware that legislation alone will not suffice. "The growers who are affected will raise too much fuss." They must be helped to solve pest problems in other ways—particularly, he thinks, through the use of biological controls. Pressures to prevent that are constant and powerful. Although economic entomologists have given lip service to the need for more emphasis on biological control, most have not allowed its potential to divert them from their chemical pursuits. Chemicals, of course, are where the money is.

Like others in his field, Professor DeBach values chemicals when wisely and carefully used. At this point, he says, the hope lies with "integrated control"—scientifically determined combinations of measures and methods. Since only a very small percentage of the total number of pests on this continent has been thoroughly studied from the standpoint of biological control, pesticidal and other approaches must be enlisted. No general would rely completely on a single weapon; no industry should be allowed to dictate a single answer to control problems.

13. INTEGRATED CONTROL

PESTICIDE PROMOTERS ARE wont to scoff at biological control as mere humbug dreamed up by ivory-tower theorists at a safe distance from the realities of ledgers and fields. "They can afford to gamble," is the argument. "It is not their money they're betting with."

Although less dogmatic and usually willing to acknowledge the value of some agricultural chemicals as emergency measures, biological control enthusiasts say that *they* are the realists: their way is the safe, effective way. And the less costly way.

To test those contrary opinions, I acted on a suggestion made by Dr. DeBach. "If you want to see how biological control works for farmers, why don't you go up to Ventura County and talk with Howard Lorbeer?" So on an August day in 1969 I found myself hearing about and looking at the "realities" presented by the manager of the Fillmore Citrus Protective District. This is a unique farmers' cooperative that relies mainly on beneficial insects to curb the pests that plague the citrus industry in California.

A chunky, balding man with a snub nose on which his glasses ride uneasily and a chin deeply creased, Mr. Lorbeer looks like a jolly Bavarian wood carving. His normally placid manner, however, changes abruptly when he is confronted with the challenge. "We're no gamblers up here," he was decisive. "We know we have some pretty wonderful country here; we are going to keep it that way."[1]

The "we" refers to the 350 growers who own the 8,800 acres included in the protective district—part of a beautiful and fertile valley that narrows as it stretches east from the Pacific between the San Rafael Range and the Sierra San Fernando. The district's center is the little town of Fillmore, near the "Moreno Ranch" of the novel *Ramona* and the mouth of thickly wooded Sespe Canyon, where deer and quail hunters sometimes see the almost extinct California condor.

For miles around, the countryside is patterned with bushy orange trees, their dark foliage dotted with orange globes and topped with a "frosting" of pale green new growth. The trees are naturally encouraged by the thick morning fogs that sweep in from the ocean. And the earth in which they are rooted is some of the finest in the world —light alluvial soil 6,000 feet deep. But the groves are also familiar with the harsher aspects of nature: killing frosts; floods, like a serious one in 1969; virus diseases; and the insect pests that growers dread—aphids, citrus thrips, spider mites, mealybugs, and an assortment of scales.

Keenly aware of its darker aspects, nonetheless, "we regard nature as an ally," Mr. Lorbeer says. That was not the case when the cooperative was organized in 1922 to erect a common defense against the mealybug brought into California from Australia a decade earlier. It spread so rapidly in a few months that growers were forced to acknowledge that one man's pest problem was their problem, too. To solve it required group action.

The district was first committed to a program of chemical eradication. But after that became so costly, so hazardous, and so spotty, growers began to listen to the urgings of the imaginative county agricultural commissioner and researchers at the University of California-Riverside to try living pesticides.

"It was a good decision—for the orchards and for me,"

Mr. Lorbeer said. "It always did and still does make my blood boil to hear people say that the only good bug is a dead bug."

Lorbeer's training and experience, as well as his inclination, prompted him to take the manager's job when it was offered to him in 1926. He had received an excellent education in entomology and botany at Pomona College, from which he was graduated in 1923, and at the Los Angeles County Insectary, which had been established as a result of Koebele's finds. Lorbeer's experience had made him wary of chemicals. As a high school student, he had worked nights fumigating orchards with liquid cyanide gas. "I soon found out why I could make five dollars a night for that work as opposed to only two dollars a day as a laborer." The dangers were impressed upon him when a young doctor summoned to treat the foreman, who had been overcome by cyanide, did not know what to do. Howard Lorbeer later took a course in first aid, which enabled him to save the life of another man overcome by the poisonous stuff when no medical help was available.

Over the years he had developed an admiration for the biological control programs that had followed the first importation. He responded to the opportunity to make further tests in Fillmore, where leaders of the district had voted to build an insectary in 1926 to rear one of Koebele's Australian discoveries, the ladybeetle *Cryptolaemus montrouzieri* Mulsant. "Cryps" were colonized and millions liberated in citrus orchards. Control was only partial, however, and regular mass releases were required. After University of California-Riverside researchers discovered parasites of the mealybug in Australia in 1928, Fillmore leaders decided to put them to work. They were colonized, released, and within a year the pest was controlled. For good.

Some years later when another insect, the black scale,

was creating havoc in citrus orchards, the Fillmore Citrus Protective District extended production to include a tiny parasitic wasp found in South Africa in 1937 by Harold Compere, an entomologist at the University of California-Riverside. Since that time, the insectary has colonized and distributed twenty other species of parasites and predators from far places—China, Japan, India, Pakistan, Israel, and European and South American countries. "They have fought a good fight for us." According to Mr. Lorbeer, they have reduced the four major citrus pests—mealybugs, cottony cushion scale, black scale, and red scale—to minor nuisances in the area. He and his assistants are confident they can also completely control three other minor but troublesome pests.

It is a reassuring experience to watch them map strategy, marshal allies, and direct field operations from their GHQ—two frame and one concrete block insectaries, surrounded by thousands of oleander bushes blossoming red and pink and white. According to the "grand design" worked out by Lorbeer, chief assistant Franklin Hummel, and other staff members, with the approval of the nine-man board of directors, major emphasis is given to control of the red and black scales.

One of the motel-like structures—Mr. Lorbeer prefers the description *hospital-like*—is given over to breeding the red scale parasite, *Aphytis melinus* DeBach. Ten production rooms are used to raise the black scale parasite, *Metaphycus helvolus* Compere—the tiny wasp brought back to California from South Africa by Compere in 1937. The Fillmore insectary is presently the only one in the country rearing that parasite. It has not raised lady beetles since 1950; when any are needed—and more than a million were in 1968—they are obtained from an insectary in nearby Santa Paula in exchange for red and black scale parasites. A laboratory in one of the buildings is used for research on citrus red mite predators. Two other branch insectaries are located on citrus ranches in the district. They are used chiefly to raise black scale eggs for "culture" at the main production unit and to innoculate 500 trees in 31 different orchards. The trees are lightly infested each year with young black scale crawlers so that a constant food supply is guaranteed for the parasites.

The collection units and cabinets, as well as the method of operating, have been tailored to minutely detailed specifications provided by Dr. DeBach and his colleagues. And Lorbeer, Hummel, and other members of the small staff approach the care and feeding of the parasites with the delicacy and thoroughness of medical scientists performing life-and-death operations. They supervise the planting and rearing of the 200 oleander bushes used in each of the parasite producing rooms, where they host the black scale on which *helvolus* is reared. In the summer and fall they go into nearby fields to gather "the best specimens we can find" of mature banana squash that hosts the red scale culture, which will in turn host *melinus*.

Producing the biological control agents is a procedure both simple and complex. In the case of *melinus*, squashes —about a dozen a day—are taken from the storage room, sprinkled with crawlers, and placed on shelves in the holding rooms. The squashes with their destructive burden are held there for about 45 days; at the end of that time, they are taken to the parasite production rooms. Three or four of them are placed in "sting" drawers each day. Parasites are then released, 200,000 to each drawer. They are given one day to lay their eggs, which they insert beneath the shell of the scale. They are then anesthetized with a mixture of carbon dioxide and ether. Thus stupefied,

they fall onto the piece of heavy white paper at the
bottom of the drawer. The paper is removed, and the tiny
anesthetized wasps, which en masse look like a dusting of
orange-gold powder, are placed in a glass jar. In a few
moments they recover. The powder begins to seethe.
"There," Franklin Hummel held out the jar to me almost
reverently. "The force of life."

He then measured out a small quantity of the wasps
into cardboard containers. The quantity *appeared* small,
that is, since a teaspoon will hold about 20,000 of them.
A lid smeared with honey (to provide nourishment) was
placed on each container, and they were lined up like
ice cream cartons—ready to be taken to orchards to continue their pest-destructive productivity. In 1968 nearly
72 million *melinus* wasps were released in infested orchards. Technically, each grower is entitled to a specified
number of each variety, but the board has ruled that "the
best policy is to put them where they'll do the most good
for the district."

Back at the insectary, the curious game of guest-eat-host
continues. The scale-infested squash, which are now also
bearing parasite eggs, are placed on shelves in the production room. During the next ten days, the eggs that were
laid under the armor of the insects hatch into larvae. They
nourish themselves on the body fluid of the scale. When
the larvae are full grown, they pupate. The squash are
returned to collection drawers and second-generation
parasites are then collected. They, too, are put into sting
drawers to lay eggs on new batches of scale before being
taken to citrus orchards.

When they are liberating the wasps, the insectary staff
checks carefully for pest outbreaks of any kind. The goal
is not an absolutely pest-free orchard. "Total eradication
would be stupid," Lorbeer explains. "Without some pests,

the beneficial insects would have nothing to live on. Then there would be real trouble." Rather, the goal is to make sure that any pest population is kept down to an economically feasible level.

District growers generally go along with that system, although someone occasionally panics at the sight of a pest and insists on a spray program. In such cases, Mr. Lorbeer adopts an easy-does-it approach: "If you're going to lose any sleep, go ahead and treat this year. We'll wait to put in the parasites next year."

Like all rational persons, he favors using chemicals as emergency measures. What he objects to is their misuse, regarding "preventive" control and "calendar" spraying with despairing amusement. So far as his own practices are concerned, he uses chemicals to control snails and keep down outbreaks of ants. Ants are major enemies since, like dust and various chemicals, they upset the natural balance by killing off helpful parasites. "The worst thing that can happen to an orchard," he says, "is for it to get *dirty*—loaded with pests. Before we let that happen, we recommend the use of chemicals to knock down the pest quickly. But we go back to biological control the next month."

He and others in the citrus district are totally opposed to DDT and other "hard" pesticides for widespread use. About ten years ago the county agricultural commissioner prohibited tomato farmers from dusting DDT and sulphur on their fields after serious pest infestations occurred in neighboring orchards. The drifting poisons had killed off the beneficial insects that had protected them.

Organic phosphates are also frowned on. In his 1969 annual report, Lorbeer warned against the use of parathion and some of the other highly toxic substances which have been killing off bees so wantonly in many places that growers are now forced to buy new supplies every year for pollination purposes.

His ability to communicate his ideas is partly the result of his rational argument: "Nature will help us if we approach it properly"; partly, it is because Lorbeer is a doer as well as a theorizer. Since 1941 he has been a member of the Fillmore Citrus Protective District as well as its manager. The Lorbeers' ten-acre orchard is tangible proof that he has a stake in the experiment. He and his wife call it their "Ph.D. Orchard" since profits from it helped to pay their son's way through school. Jim, who received the doctorate from the University of California-Berkeley a few years ago, is professor of plant pathology at Cornell. When he brought some of his colleagues to Fillmore a few summers ago, they found it "almost impossible" to believe that the orchard had not been touched by an insecticide for almost a decade. The beautifully tended trees were yielding an average of 600 boxes an acre. Average yield in the state is about 400; in some places, it is only 200.

Some of the FCPD members have always favored biological control. Among them is Harry Felsenthal, son of the second president of the district and a member of the board. One of his orchards has not had chemical treatment for insects other than ants since it was planted in 1949. Felsenthal achieved that record simply by "not panicking." When one of his orchards became heavily infested with black scale, he felt that *helvolus* could do a better job than a chemical spray. Half a million of the tiny wasps were needed to clear the trees, but without them, the owner believes, he would have suffered serious economic losses.

Other growers were converted to biological control by experience. One is Glen Mosbarger, whose crop was ruined for the first time in 1955, when a cold night combined with the effects of cyanide fumigation caused most of the fruit to drop. Two years later, an oil spray followed by a heat wave rendered most of the crop unmarketable. In 1959, acting on the urging of an "expert," he sprayed his orchard three times with chemicals to get rid of an infestation of red scale. The results were so disastrous that he switched entirely to biological controls. The handsomely carpentered cabinets in the insectary are Mosbarger's hand-made "thanks."

For most of the growers, comparative statistics are persuasion enough to keep the emphasis on biological controls. California citrus growers generally pay between $100 and $200 an acre to keep their groves in productive shape. Growers in the Fillmore district in 1968 paid an average of less than $40 an acre. That included whatever chemicals were needed and an $8-an-acre fee to FCPD for parasites—including the million lady beetles that had to be bought elsewhere. It also covered the cost of minimum amounts of micronutrients and an herbicide.

The $8-an-acre assessment has remained constant since 1962, the year growers voted to try to control red scale biologically. That figure contrasts sharply with the $24-an-acre assessment in 1960, when a highly toxic pesticide was applied liberally. And unsuccessfully.

The "good" bugs have dramatically cut costs and reduced the need of chemical treatment. In 1968 only about 5 percent of the acreage was considered to need chemical treatment, in contrast to a previous high of 70 percent. Actually, the 1968 figure would have been lower if it had not been for the readiness of managers of one of the larger ranches to "listen to too many salesmen." Eager to make a showing, they went along with the pitch: "If a little is good, more is better." Production costs so soared

and pest problems so increased that the president and
vice-president of the company owning the ranch called
in Lorbeer in 1968 to "help us out of the mess." As proof
of their earnestness, they offered to build a new insectary
for the district. Lorbeer declined that offer, but promised
to help, warning, "You were three years getting into this
shape, you'll probably be three years getting out."

As a first step, he advised that "soft" pesticides like
oil sprays and rotenone be substituted for "hard" chemicals. As the environment has improved, beneficial insects
have been introduced.

The experiment of the land company was an object
lesson for the whole district, in the event than any faiths
were weakening.

It is not easy to estimate the savings that have resulted
from extensive use of biological controls. The members
of FCPD are in pocket at least $500,000 a year because
of minimal use of chemicals. More than that, soil fertility
continues high so that production and quality are favor-
ably affected.

For that reason, one of the most enthusiastic supporters
of the biological control emphasis is Lloyd Blackwell,
manager of one of the marketing cooperatives and a director of FCPD. "When I first came here and heard about
this business of using natural enemies to fight citrus pests,
I just laughed," Blackwell told me ruefully. "I thought
that no rancher in his right mind could take chances
like that." But now he is convinced that it works. Biological control is profitable, effective, and safer for growers, workers, consumers. "We have a great situation here,"
he added. The rest of the district agrees.

Advocates of integrated control note wryly that such
programs "have invariably been products of crises . . .
(when) growers and researchers, driven to desperation

by a variety of problems associated with largely unilateral use of chemical insecticides were forced to the ecological approach to solve these problems."[2]

Agricultural scientists have generally ignored the promising leads suggested by integrated control programs, although the "landmark" was developed in Nova Scotia twenty years ago. While most other entomologists were so overwhelmed by the new "miracles" that they excluded all controls other than the new synthetic organic insecticides, A. D. Pickett and a few colleagues set about rescuing the declining apple and pear industry by substituting for recklessly applied broad-spectrum pesticides highly selective ones in minimal dosages carefully timed and by allowing the natural enemies of the pests to do their work.[3]

Another brilliant and significant integrated control program was developed in the Cañete Valley in Peru, one of the most advanced agricultural operations in that country. In 1956, growers appealed to their experiment station to save them from disaster. The broad-spectrum insecticides with which they had blanketed the area were bringing them to financial ruin; cotton yield was at its lowest in a decade. The principal pests had developed astonishing resistance to even the most toxic chemicals; their natural enemies had gone down to defeat.

A 7-point program to rescue them was drawn up and approved by the Peruvian Ministry of Agriculture. Among other things, it included prohibition of synthetic organic insecticides and a return to such materials as lead arsenate and nicotine sulfate; repopulation of the valley with beneficial insects from other parts of Peru and from abroad; sanitary practices like plowing under crop residues.

The result? A "rapid and striking reduction" in the pest

problem, an overall reduction in pest control costs, and "most impressive," a sharp increase in cotton yield—up from 603.8 kilos per *hectare* for the "organic insecticide era" to 789.1 for the integrated control period.[4]

Another significant integrated control program was developed in California to control the spotted alfalfa aphid, which was threatening the existence of the industry in 1956. First detected in California only two years earlier, it developed resistance to the broad-spectrum pesticides that were destroying its predatory and parasitic enemies. When organic phosphates were introduced, the aphid developed resistance to them: "Control costs spiraled and aphid damage approached disastrous proportions."[5]

Within a year, an integrated approach—featuring low dosage of a selective chemical and the introduction of biological controls—saw the crisis past. Between 1957 and 1958, costs and losses attributable to the aphid dropped from about $9,700,000 to $1,694,000. Subsequent development of aphid-resistant alfalfa varieties has virtually eliminated the threat of the responsible pest.[6]

Other very dramatic successes indicate the feasibility of integrated control, not only the combination of chemicals with biological controls, but of various other control methods and naturally occurring "mortality factors." One very promising one involves sanitary and cultural practices in combination with sex pheromones and with the blue- and blacklight traps, important breakthroughs in pest control.

14. SOUND AND LIGHT

AFTER THE ADVENT of chemical pesticides, interest in physical means to control insects was generally relegated to the attic, along with the fly swatter, the mousetrap, clothes for the scarecrow, and the horn Jack blew when the cow and sheep were in meadow and corn.

Fortunately, a few persons continued to believe that success in coping with pest problems, as well as other problems, does depend on building a better . . . well, trap of some kind. They have used the resources of modern technology to enhance old methods of luring, snaring, and vanquishing pests with the subtlety and skill exercised by European governments in setting out *son et lumière* "gins" for the tourist dollars.

Noise has been known since earliest times to have a profound effect on living things, including man—to madden and soothe, to attract and repel. Primitive people have always used sounds, drumming and chanting, to ward off evil spirits as well as more substantial pests. Recently, however, sound and ultrasound have become sophisticated weapons in the war against pests.[1]

The effects of some sounds are simple and obvious. Consider the reaction of birds, for instance, to rockets, firecrackers, or shotgun shells.[2] Loud noises protect crops from other creatures—driving them to less desirable sites, and by minimizing their food supply, minimizing their number.

Modern "sound effects" are far more complex, thanks to the knowledge scientists have gained of pest "language"—noises they make for calling, congregating, courting, signaling distress.

For years, Dutch and French airport officials, just before takeoffs, have been broadcasting recordings of the distress calls of gulls.[3] The calls have been successful in reducing bird-plane strikes, the cause of some of the worst modern plane disasters. Scientists have been attempting to extend the principle to other species. They have lured some insects to death by recordings of their own calling sounds and by artificially produced sounds. For example, male mosquitoes were attracted to an electric grid by female flight sounds—invitation to electrocution. Bees are so affected by sounds of a particular intensity that they remain almost motionless while it persists. Beekeepers are thus enabled to care for the hives and gather honey without using smokers.[4]

The sonar principle, which scientists learned from the bat, is also a promising acoustical repellant. In their blind nocturnal flights, bats locate obstacles and the insects they gorge on by echoes which bounce back from the sequences of ultrasonic impulses they emit. Some types of moths can detect the impulses and thus flee from danger—wheeling, looping, climbing, and diving in a wild effort to evade peril.[5] An experiment in Canada using batlike sounds was successful. When they were broadcast over cornfields, moths took off rapidly; infestation was reduced by more than 50 percent.[6] Some sounds affect fertility. A few years ago researchers exposed adult Indian-meal moths to certain sounds during their egg-laying period. The fertility rate dropped by about 75 percent. Curiously, the larvae that emerged from the eggs took longer to mature than normal. As adult moths, they died sooner. Flour beetles were similarly afflicted.[7]

Questions challenge investigators. What wave lengths should be used? What characteristics of sound are important? What is the psychological effect on insects.[8] Clearly, as has been asserted, this research could lead to a new kind of non-chemical control.[9]

Light is already playing an important role in pest control by trapping.

Snaring vertebrates is ancient history; insect trapping is a much more recent activity for man, although it is old stuff in nature. The venus flytrap, the cobra lily, and some 450 known species of plants obtain all or part of their nourishment by their uncanny ways of luring, entrapping, and digesting the small crawling and flying things that pass over their lovely and lethal blooms.[10]

Early traps were simple, based on the premise obvious to anyone who has ever turned over a stone and found creatures clinging to their underside hiding place. Boards, stones, weeds, rags, and paper scattered about orchards and gardens have served as useful traps. Reflective aluminum strips are now being used on a large scale in vegetable fields to reduce attacks by disease-carrying aphids —hard to combat with even very toxic pesticides. Indoors, flypaper and jars containing honey and even intoxicating brews have been effective.[11]

Lighted traps, however, are the biggest news.

The desire of the moth for the star, or the nearest lighted lamp or candle, is proverbial. Farmers exploited that response, lighting bonfires and lanterns to lure insects from crop to crematorium. After the invention of the tungsten filament lamp, they began to build around them simple traps so that insects drawn to the light would drown or poison themselves. Some farmers ingeniously have been stringing lights immediately above duck pens so that the fowl serve as animated traps. They are thus assured of a balanced diet of mosquitoes, beetles, moths, and whatever else is lured into the illuminated area.[12]

Effective as visible light was, it has been "invisible" light that has brought about great gains. Discovery of ultraviolet or "blacklight" dates back to the early part of the last century, but it became apparent only in the 1930's that it might be useful to control insects. Entomologists found that photosensitive insects responded not only to light visible to humans, but to that part of the electromagnetic spectrum in the ultraviolet region. (Human response peaks at about 5,500 Angstrom units, insect response at about 3,650—enabling them to see things in the dark humans cannot.[13]) Scientists first used blacklight to make bug surveys. They were then stimulated to try it for insect control.

One of the early significant studies was made at Purdue University in 1958. Two researchers and two USDA specialists launched experiments to find out if blacklight traps could protect home gardens from insects. They staked out, at some distance from each other, four 50-by-60-foot plots. Each was planted with the perennial favorites (and perennial despair) of summer gardeners: beans, cabbage, cucumbers, potatoes, sweet corn, and tomatoes. Three plots contained blacklight traps of various kinds; the fourth was unlighted, to serve as a check. No insecticides or fungicides were used on any of the plots. The three criteria for protection were (1) the abundance and kinds of insects on the vegetables; (2) the degree of crop damage; (3) the yield.

Bean and cabbage crops were not significantly different. Nor were tomato—although the reason given for that was that the corn had been planted late enough to serve as an efficient trap for tomato pests. However, the contrast in other crops was striking—particularly between Field D (unlighted) and Field C (which contained three 15-watt BL lamps).

Corn borers infested 31.8 percent of the stalks in Field D, only 7.1 percent in Field C. Potato damage was 39 percent in Field D, zero in Field C. Mortality rate of cucumber plants was 45.8 percent in Field D, 6.3 percent in Field C. The cucumber yield from Field D was 212.7 pounds; from Field C, 985.2 pounds.[14]

Besides higher yields and lower damage rates in all lighted fields, blacklight traps had other desirable features. They worked automatically once installed, eliminating strict time schedules that must be observed with other control measures. Chemicals are applied according to weather conditions, the time infestations occur, the development stage of the crop—often incompatible factors. Light traps worked when the soil was wet, temperatures were low and high, winds were gusty. *"Probably most important,"* one Purdue expert noted, is that the *"traps leave no poisonous residues on the plant, they are not injurious to wildlife, and strains of insects resistant to chemicals will not develop."*[15]

In another experiment, Purdue researchers worked for three years on a program to control tobacco hornworms, a major economic pest. Their finding? That under Indiana conditions, one electric trap equipped with a single 15-watt blacklight fluorescent lamp could protect an acre.[16] More significant was a three-year test made by the USDA Entomology Research Division to control tobacco hornworms. Those creatures, like the other principal pest, tobacco budworms, had developed such resistance to chemicals that by 1962 farmers were pouring on at least 28 different kinds of pesticides to curb them.[17]

USDA officials knew that a dangerous peak had been reached. Studies showed that residues far higher than those allowed in food were present in cigarettes, pipe tobacco, and cigars—residues that smokers were absorbing in appreciable quantities.[18] Some were known carcinogens

—yet the information was withheld from consumers and from the Surgeon General's Advisory Committee, then preparing its report on *Smoking and Health*.[19]

The USDA apparently decided that the wisest course of action would be to keep mum about residues and get a study going—just in case the lid blew off.[20] A large-scale experiment with light traps was launched in 1962 in the Oxford area of North Carolina. Within a circle 12 miles in diameter, three light traps of simple design were set up in each of the 113 square miles covered. The goal was to attract insects with radiant energy, luring the moths to their death before they had a chance to lay the eggs that developed into the destructive worms. In addition to the light traps in the circle, four lines of check traps were set up 6 miles beyond the perimeter to determine moth populations in unlighted areas. In 1964 the check traps were extended an additional 8 miles.

Results were impressive as early as the first year. By the end of the 1964 season, the term "impressive" seemed an understatement. In 1962 there were 55 percent fewer female moths at the center of the trapped area than at the other check point; in 1964, 75 percent fewer. The number of hornworm eggs on the plants fell 58 percent in 1962, 71 percent in 1964. The number of damaged plants at the center in 1964 was 77 percent below those at the 6-mile check point; 89 percent below those at the 14-mile check point. Budworms also succumbed to the trap; in 1963 the number of damaged plants in the center of the trapped area was 90 percent below the number at the 6-mile point. (That high was due partly to increased stalk cutting—a sanitary measure used to supplement the light traps.)[21]

Farmers in the trapped area used 90 percent fewer applications of pesticides to control hornworm than those outside the trapped area. On the basis of previously established standards, only one of 24 untreated fields examined in the light-trap area needed an insecticide application for the control of hornworms during the 1964 season.

This major breakthrough was treated coolly by the press. In part, that may have been due to the failure of the USDA to play up the news adequately: the 1965 report began with masterly understatement—"Tobacco growers in some regions have shown interest in the use of light traps to help control tobacco hornworms." In part, it was the result of advertising pressures.

Subsequent reports have also been muted. Yet the accomplishments and implications are major. Light trapping is inexpensive, as the Oxford experiment suggested. Another test on 16,000 acres in Texas in 1967 showed that the lighted areas were as well protected as they would have been by *ten* applications of chemicals.[22] According to one light trap manufacturer, if the 16,000 acres had been sprayed ten times a year at a cost of $3.00 an acre (the lowest possible figure), application expenses would be at least $48,000. Cost of trapping? $28,000.[23]

Nor would the savings stop there. Pest control expenses increase from one year to another when chemicals are used; costs of light-trap control diminish. A USDA report in the spring of 1969 revealed that insect populations had dropped to such an extent in the Oxford area that the blacklight traps would not be activated that season, except for a few used for survey and small-scale tests. Weekly counts in 1968 had shown that fields up to ten miles from the trapped area had been protected:

Although only 15 percent of the farmers in the center of the area and 58 percent outside used insecticides during 1968 after transplanting, field observations indicated that even most of those treatments were unnecessary.[24]

Economic infestations of both hornworms and budworms have occurred "only rarely" in the Oxford area since 1964, either in fields treated with insecticides or those without treatment.[25] In other parts of the country —Texas, for example—budworm populations were higher in some cotton fields treated with insecticides than in untreated fields.

An important distinction between the two methods is that light traps allow the natural enemies to carry on their work in protected areas. As the USDA report noted: "A specific control [such as light traps], even if only 50 percent effective, but which does not destroy the natural enemies, may be as effective as an insecticide which kills 90 percent of both the insect pests and their natural enemies."[26] The ecology is maintained; the problem of residue is eliminated.

Light traps are not the single answer to pest problems. There is no single answer. Moreover, existing traps need to be perfected to insure greater success against all destructive night-flying insects.[27] Chemists, entomologists, and experts from other disciplines will have to work together. One promising experiment on the island of St. Croix showed that when blacklight traps were baited with virgin female hornworms, the pest population fell off sharply. Unbaited traps cut the number of hornworms 63 percent in a two-year period; baited traps achieved an additional 19 percent reduction. Efforts are now being made to develop a long-lasting synthetic sex lure to replace the short-lived virgin females.[28]

Why has so little been done by scientists, legislators,

and public officials to encourage research and development in this promising field? One manufacturer answers that question bluntly: "The truth of the matter is that a lot of them—maybe most of them—are victims of inertia. Furthermore, it seems that some purveyors of pesticides don't give a damn about the public interest."

It may seem curious for an entrepreneur to talk that way, but Grant M. Hegranes, founder of the Insect Management Systems Corporation, is not an average businessman. To be sure, he has a wholesome enthusiasm for dollars and cents. A youthful fiftyish, well-tailored man with a round bespectacled face and a manner that is at once aggressive and decent, he is firmly grounded in the puritanical belief that hard work and intelligence will unlock the door to the chamber of the Elect. He also believes that business involves "doing the right thing."

Money is one concern of Grant Hegranes. So are people and places. He regards the blacklight traps IMS turns out as a mission as well as a product to be marketed. In the course of converting the "heathen," he has made himself an authority on pest control. He has also turned up and had thrust upon him interesting evidence of the willingness of some government officials and educators to "cooperate" with the chemical industry to the exclusion of other control methods.

Money, not mission, was primarily responsible for his getting into the business of manufacturing light traps. A college dropout—he was learning more from extracurricular business ventures than the classes in business administration he was enrolled in at the University of Michigan—he dropped out of business during World War II to serve with the Office of Strategic Services. In a nostalgic mood, after the war he headed back to North Dakota to open a men's clothing store.

It took almost a decade to convince him that a Main Street haberdashery was not for him, even though it was a highly prosperous store, thanks to the TV show he worked up and starred in to promote it. "People thought they were buying clothes from some kind of a star or something."

When he heard of a curb-and-gutter machine invented in Germany, he decided that opportunity had called. He sold the store and bought patent rights. "It was great," he remembers ruefully. "That machine just walked along and laid the curb in the gutter in one fell swoop." But no one was buying. Not one of the 300 guests he invited to see the machine showed up for the steak dinner party he planned. With nothing left but an unsalable machine and a bundle of hotel and catering bills marked "Paid," he accepted an invitation from his brother James to help out with a new business—manufacturing radiant energy devices to lure and trap pests.

He believed in the product, but the first triumph over sales resistance did not come until results of the North Carolina experiment had been revealed. By that time, James was more interested in a company being formed to make a pesticide-free cigarette. So Grant decided to go it alone.

He headed for the Southwest, where he had opened up territory for the company and made friends he felt would support his new organization. He was right. The company was officially made fact in the spring of 1965, thanks largely to Kenneth Suggs, a Texas dairyman and grower. A tall, rangy young man with an easy drawl, Mr. Suggs would be answer to the hope of any casting director of a Lone Star epic. His experiences with pesticides, however, were what prompted him to fulfill the hopes of Grant Hegranes. "No one ever really gets the message until they have lost a crop or have had to dump their milk down the drain," Mr. Suggs told me.

Although he, himself, has not used DDT on his holdings since 1960 and is sparing of any insecticide, he has been penalized heavily because of them. In a three-month period several years ago he was forced to dump more than 72,500 gallons of milk. DDT drifting from neighboring farms had contaminated it. He is equally indignant about the harm done by DDT to the environment. In 1967 he hired the Reeves County Cotton Association to inspect his light-trapped fields to check on beneficial insects and harmful bollworms. Tests on August 29 indicated 7.2 percent beneficials, he said, and 2.3 percent bollworms. By contrast, the record of the nearest farm using the same checker was 1 percent beneficials and 5 percent bollworms. At the time the test was made, the neighbor had sprayed his fields five times; Suggs, not once.[29]

Grant needed loyal friends like Kenneth Suggs and some of the other key people who have stood by him— a small and varied group. Among them have been R. E. Davis of Scranton, Pennsylvania, vice-president of a Boston coal and oil company; William J. Cox, an Albuquerque insurance man and tomato grower; G. S. "Sealie" Mc-Creless, a Texas land developer and builder who is chairman of the board of IMS. Charles Weinacht, a Pecos rancher, drew heavily on his personal credit to pay off some irate stockholders who felt the company wasn't moving fast enough; and Benjamin Rascob, an investor and rose fancier, bought a large number of shares with the knowledge that his money was going to pay other dissatisfied stockholders.

Some of the investors also provided services. E. W. Krauss, a Chicago printer, went to Albuquerque and worked for almost two years without salary: "He knew

we couldn't afford to pay him." A. H. Goldman, another
Chicago stockholder, instituted the early sales program
that kept IMS afloat. Oldest employee (in terms of
service) and an investor is "Mother" Eve DeBruille, the
secretary who has kept the whole office functioning,
Grant says.

Like a proper missionary, Grant Hegranes regarded his
shortage of capital as a temporary inconvenience. He was
convinced that once he was able to get the word around
about his "Night Watch" traps, people who were concerned about pesticides would beat a path to the door
of the nearest distributor. A good many householders did,
snapping up the small models on sale at Sears and other
chain stores and independents. The tiny indoor model, a
plastic gadget to hang on walls, works on the same principal as the larger ones. Night-flying insects are attracted
to the blue-black radiance emitted from the 4-watt lamp.
Attempting to fly into it, they fall into a removable trap,
a tray containing water and detergent which serves as
execution chamber. The somewhat larger patio model
contains an 8-watt lamp.

Owners were impressed. Harry Wicks, who with other
staff writers on *Popular Science* tried out various models
in 1968, reported: "In each case the blacklight attracted
and killed an amazing mass of insects in a very short
time."[30]

Commercial bakers and other food producers have
found the larger models useful. Curiously, one of the most
satisfied customers has been the Atlantic City Racing
Association, which installed blacklight equipment five
years ago to protect the barn and sewerage disposal areas.
According to Harold B. Johnson, chief of maintenance,
"everyone" liked the results. The association has been able
to plan spray programs more efficiently and economically;

owners are pleased to have their horses protected; and the stable help enjoy sitting around the barn area "without being eaten up with mosquitoes and other bugs." Even the horses have responded. "Trainers and their help say horses have never been as quiet and free from insects," Mr. Johnson noted cheerfully.[31]

After trials in 20 countries, overseas business boomed. The president of A. Torres Export, Inc., recently expressed surprise at the reaction: "Normally it takes between two and three years to develop a satisfactory volume of export business. In your case, it will be accomplished in less than one."[32]

Farmers at home were another matter. Conservative, convinced that they are "at the mercy" of nature, they cling to the notion that lethal chemicals are their only line of defense against ruin. Nevertheless, Grant believed that he could sell them (hadn't he sold sartorial splendor to North Dakota?) if . . . *if* they would listen and look. They would listen and look, he knew, *if* the government and university researchers on whose advice they depended and who had been vigorously pushing pesticides would give light traps a "fair shake."

That, apparently, was asking too much.

Warned by the USDA against using the results of the highly significant Purdue and Oxford experiments, he went to Washington in 1965 to get sponsorship of some large-scale tests. A light here and a light there would not demonstrate the real potential. Senator Clinton P. Anderson, former secretary of agriculture, liked the evidence presented to him and arranged for interviews with the Corps of Army Engineers, the Pan American Health Organization, the State Department, and other agencies.

"Each time I started a demonstration," Grant remembers, "I was encouraged by the way viewers called in others to see it." Results were less encouraging: "They had already made up their minds that chemicals were the only answer." The Communicable Disease Center in Georgia finally agreed to make a 12-week test. That inexplicably stretched on and on . . . with tests continuing for 52 weeks; then, 72.

Grant headed back to the Southwest. Texas was the ideal place to work up independently a large-scale experimental installation. Pesticides have been used so widely there that some farmers are under doctors' orders not to set foot on their own farms. In some areas, face masks are standard items of apparel.

Cost of protecting cotton from budworm and bollworm has skyrocketed. By 1968, insects were resistant to all but about two organic phosphate compounds: highly toxic methyl parathion and Azodrin. The head of the Department of Entomology at Texas A&M recently warned farmers: "Should the budworm-bollworm population develop phosphate resistance, we have nothing to turn to."[33]

"This situation could have been avoided," Grant Hegranes says, "if farmers and government advisers had been willing to listen."

One illustration of the "silent treatment" occurred shortly after IMS was incorporated. Grant installed light traps around a 40-acre lettuce field with impressive results. The owner saved nearly $55 an acre on pest control costs and had prime produce. Instead of publicity, a news blackout was imposed. Growers' associations have considerable power. And it is understandable that if the public knew that some lettuce was being grown without pesticides, other lettuce might be less attractive.

After that, he decided that cotton was the most promising test crop—since no embarrassing questions would be raised. Opportunity came by way of a telephone call from

Frank Crews of Pecos, president of the National Pima Cotton Growers Association. His approach was blunt: "Is this a con game, a gimmick? Or is it worth something?" Reassured by Grant's answer, he arranged a meeting with 25 of the top cotton producers in Pecos.

It was a hard audience to face, Grant remembers. The area was "tender," with about 25 percent of the farmers bankrupt. "Here I am trying to talk them into laying a bunch of cable around their fields and putting up lights to catch moths, and many of them had no idea that moths had anything to do with their problem."

He made one sale that night, to the toughest man in the group. "Just what will I have if I spend $7,000 and the traps don't work?" the man asked.

"Looks like you'd have $7,000 in worthless equipment," Grant answered. "I've told you what I think it will do."

The grower hesitated a moment. "You don't know it, but that was the right answer. I'll buy."

Other ranchers were harder to convince. The wall of resistance did not crumble until one morning when he stopped at their favorite coffee shop on his way to install some traps. He was wearing khakis and old boots instead of his customary tailored suit. For the first time, he was warmly greeted: "Hey, Bugman, have you decided to join the human race? Come on over and have a cup of coffee. Meet some friends."

From that moment, it was a salesman's dream. He received orders to put lights on 3,000 acres the first year. Grant worked out plans for installation evenings in his motel room; he spent mornings digging holes and working with his shirt off to position and set up the light traps. Business boomed so that during the second year about 20,000 acres were covered. One farmer persuaded another. One man who had installed lights on 1,300 acres at a cost

of about $35,000 reminded a group of farmers that that
figure should be divided by five at least in order to indicate
the annual cost. By contrast, he said, "the year before I
put the lights in, I spent $1,000 a day for 102 consecutive
days spraying my land. And after the spraying was
finished, I had to sue the chemical company for non-
performance because my crop was so damaged."

The pesticide people were furious. Grotesque caricatures
of him over a caption—"You think Grant took Richmond?"—were pasted up in restaurants and other buildings in town. He worried constantly that installations
would be sabotaged on a major scale. Threats made him
nervous about driving alone at night.

Nevertheless, he took off for California, where Stanford
Research Institute was testing traps for IMS. One Sunday
evening a long-distance call came from Frank Crews: "All
hell has broken loose. Everyone has canceled their contract."

A scientist from the Moth Control Center in Brownsville had come to Pecos to give a speech. When asked
about blacklight traps, he told farmers: "Forget them.
They are no good."

Grant made tracks for Brownsville, and after several
days of vainly seeking an appointment, he managed to
confront the scientist at a private meeting. "He admitted
that he knew nothing about my equipment," Grant said
bitterly. He promised not to speak against it further, but
he did. Farmers who had been skeptical eventually
abandoned the project.[34]

The USDA has rarely acted in a positive way, Grant
Hegranes feels. Nor has the Food and Drug Administration. "Just try to get records of actions taken against
violators. Just ask insiders in the food industry how carefully raw and prepared foodstuffs are checked." Nor have

the schools fulfilled their educational obligation. Although the Oxford experiment was so important that lately even the USDA has been urging farmers to consider it, North Carolina State, Grant says, has been almost deafeningly silent about blacklight traps.

Lately, the situation has been changing, he thinks. "All of a sudden the American people are saying: 'What's going on here? Let's do something about this.'"

Recently, Senator Anderson introduced a proposal for a huge test to be conducted at a cost of $14 million. Academicians and government agencies are showing new interest.[35] Dr. L. D. Newsom, chairman of the Louisiana State University Department of Entomology, is now testing light traps on soybeans. A few years ago he dismissed the devices; now he is concerned that more than 40 million acres are planted in soybeans, for which no satisfactory permanent chemical control is available. Rutgers, Cornell, and Clemson have lately indicated interest in conducting blacklight trap experiments; and the University of California is trying them out in combination with a sex attractant.

At a meeting with Dr. Edward F. Knipling of the Department of Agriculture not long ago, Grant said he "got the feeling that the USDA was now more willing to listen." Dr. Knipling's response is of interest. But whether others in the department share his vision and concern is open to question. He is, after all, the man primarily responsible for one of the most effective nonchemical pest control programs of our time: sterilizing insects.

15. STERILE SEX

SEX IS A powerful weapon, but scarcely a deadly one—as any population explosion expert can vouch. And the idea that the mating game of insects can be manipulated to wipe out their species seemed more fiction than science when it was first proposed.

What led to one of the most significant biological achievements of our time was the brilliant hunch of an entomologist with the U.S. Department of Agriculture back in 1937. Edward F. Knipling, then just a young field researcher, and a colleague were assigned to find a way of treating animals attacked by the larvae of the screwworm flies.

Four years earlier the pest had been introduced from the tropics and subtropics of Central America into the United States, probably on a shipment of infected cattle. Although some of the imports died out in fly-like fashion during cold weather, enough of the mobile ones winging south and west to the winter warmth of Florida and Texas survived to establish huge colonies. In short order, farmers and ranchers throughout the South were listing it first among The Unwanteds. The larva, a maggot which breeds on living tissues of animals, found wounds of cattle, deer, raccoons, foxes, and rabbits perfect nurseries. During the process of feeding themselves, they damaged and even killed their unwilling hosts.

Dr. Knipling and his colleague, Raymond C. Bushland,

decided that the problem could best be solved by prevention. Finding ways to treat wounded animals was less important than keeping the parasites from finding nesting
places.

With the thoroughness of a couple of detectives setting
to work on the "perfect" crime, Knipling and Bushland
settled down to find out "all" about the fly—focusing their
attention on those habits that would enable them to discover its Achilles' heel. One promising clue was the behavior of females. Although the males are sexually active
creatures, females mate only once. Dr. Knipling reasoned
that if large numbers of males could somehow be sterilized and released, the females—or a large portion of them
—might perform the single copulative act without becoming a producer. If the ratio of sterile to normal males
could be built up, it should be possible to eradicate the
species in four generations.[1]

Entomologists scoffed. The idea of performing surgical
operations, the only technique then known for sterilizing,
on thousands, millions of flies was ludicrous. But Knipling,
Bushland, and a few other imaginative scientists in Texas
were persuaded that the flies could be sterilized. At the
end of the war Knipling was appointed chief of the Insects Affecting Man and Animals Branch of the USDA. He
assigned Bushland to work on the idea. Another Texas-
based expert contributed encouragement and skill.[2] Dr.
H. J. Muller, professor of zoology, had discovered that by
exposing an organism to X-radiation he could produce
mutations in succeeding generations. He received the Nobel Prize in medicine for that discovery. In one experiment, he had sterilized fruit flies completely with over-
doses of X-ray.[3]

Stimulated by Muller's finding, Bushland worked after
hours at a hospital near the USDA laboratory at Kerrville.

He established that exposing 7-day-old pupae to 7,500 roentgens of ionizing radiation from an X-ray or gamma ray source would impart sterility to both sexes of emerging adults. Dosages of up to four times that did not seem to affect the vigor of the males or lessen their enthusiasm for copulation. That was important since a high degree of sexual activity is critical to the method. (Florida researchers have been working to develop supersexed flies; one strain evolved from natives there mates seventeen times in contrast to the average fly, which mates only five times.) When normal females were mated with sterile males, they laid only infertile eggs throughout their life.

In Washington, meantime, Dr. Knipling was working overtime to get support for the experiment. His appeals to the Atomic Energy Commission and to large universities were turned down as "fantastic and impractical." Congress was only somewhat less scornful. According to one chronicler, his request for an appropriation was answered with a pittance—the equivalent of the financial losses incurred from screwworm damage to livestock during two hours on a hot summer afternoon.[4]

Nevertheless, it was enough to finish some of the necessary laboratory work and to launch the first field test. Flies were released on Sanibel Island off the coast of Florida at a calculated overflooding rate of four sterile flies to one wild fly. Within three months the population was sharply reduced—a 70 percent drop. The hoped-for eradication did not occur, however. Reason was that only a two-mile stretch of water separated the island from the mainland; isolation was not complete.[5]

The next experiment fared better. Officials of the Dutch-owned island of Curaçao off the coast of Venezuela, hearing of the pilot project, appealed to the USDA for aid. Screwworms had become a severe economic problem because of their attack on the island's goats.

Here was a perfect proving ground. The go-ahead signal flashed, and once a week for a month sterilized flies were released over the island—400 of them to each of the 170 square miles. Within nine weeks, all infestations in goats and other animals had been eliminated. At the end of thirteen weeks, the last egg mass—sterile—was found. According to L. D. Christenson of the USDA Agricultural Research Service, it was the first time man had ever destroyed entirely an insect pest population by introducing into its natural environment sterile insects of the same species in numbers sufficient to cancel out the reproductive potential of the natural population. "The Curaçao demonstration will long remain a classic in scientific achievement."[6]

The success aroused interest. And new production and packaging techniques that had been developed enhanced the possibilities. A research team working with a cobalt-60 gamma ray device was able to sterilize at least 14 million screwworms a week. The sterile flies were boxed like food. Equipment was invented for opening the boxes and releasing the contents in air.

Another major test was made in Florida in 1958, two years after a chemical assault on 2,000 acres of Indian River country resulted in "a substantially complete fish kill."[7] In this trial, millions of sterilized screwworm flies were released into the air over thousands of miles. By the end of the year, most of Florida was freed from infestations. Cost of the program was about $7 million—not including quarantine operations along the Mississippi. Savings to cattle growers in Florida and other southeastern states during the first seven years following the program were estimated at $140 million—200 times the investment cost.[8] What is more, there were none of the costly side effects that inevitably accompany pesticide spray programs.

At that point, Texans decided that what Florida could

do, Texas could do bigger and better. Screwworm flies winging north across the border were seriously damaging wildlife as well as domestic animals. Growers and sportsmen provided funds. Relying on the expertise of the USDA's Entomology Research Division, they built a factory capable of producing 100 million sterile screwworm flies a week—150 million if the need arose. The area to be covered was vast—a barrier zone between 50 to 300 miles wide and about 1,000 miles long. Yet within two years after the program was launched, it was a dazzling success. By 1964, control of the pest was estimated to be 99.5 percent; by 1966, it was 99.9 per cent.[9] During those years, $12 million was spent for control. Savings amounted to "at least $275 million.[10]

Meantime, experiments were being made to control other pests considered likely candidates for the sterile sex treatment. The first field test against the Mediterranean fruit fly was conducted in Hawaii in 1959–1960 with striking results. Another field trial in Costa Rica in mid-1969 was so effective in reducing fruit damage that a United Nations Special Fund project was begun to eradicate the pest from most of Central America.[11]

Two experiments to control the oriental fruit fly revealed important implications of the sterile-male principle as a practical means of getting rid of pests. During 1960–1962, releases of nearly half a billion sterile oriental fruit flies on the island Rota failed to control the pest. Yet the release of only 17 million a year later on Guam *eradicated* it. The reason was that the fly population on Rota was so large that 16 million flies a week would have been needed for overflooding; whereas on Guam, the typhoon of 1963 had wiped out many of the host plants favored by the pest. With the food supply curtailed, the fly population dropped sharply. USDA researchers moved quickly to take advantage of the situation. As a result, the pests were quickly vanquished.[12]

Subsequent experiments in other places have borne out the point that the sterile release method is most effective when the target pest is under "severe stress" because of natural or artificial conditions in its environment. An integrated approach, using a nonpersistent pesticide to knock out a large number of pests combined with sterile male releases has worked effectively in a number of cases.[13]

Those experiments have also constituted a very strong argument in favor of the sterile sex programs. They succeed best where the density of the wild population is low. Chemical pesticides, on the other hand, are most efficient and most economical when employed against dense populations as an emergency one-shot measure. When they are used to eliminate or curb small numbers, the cost is high and the chance of widespread damage is very great.

Case in point was the program to keep Mexican fruit flies from migrating into California. For years residents on both sides of the border had been protesting the spray programs carried on by the United States and Mexican governments and the California Department of Agriculture. South of the border, across a broad band of Mexico, USDA and Defensa Agricola workers were inundating the country with protein hydrolysate-malathion bait. North of the border, California agents were blanketing a three-mile "protection zone" with the stuff. According to a USDA official, the enemy against which this bombardment was unleashed was very small—only a few thousand flies a year. The cost of the program was enormous. Its nuisance value was also high. In Tijuana, for instance, government agents often had to march through houses to spray the host plants flourishing in patios. To calm the understandable furor that the spray program created, weekly releases of sterile insects were begun and the spray program was abandoned entirely. It required only 4,750,000 sterile flies to do the eradication job, according to L. D. Christenson of the Entomology Research Division of the USDA.[14]

The campaign against the Mexican fruit fly was significant for more reasons than the gains it made in economy and good will. It was the first large-scale use of flies sterilized by chemical rather than physical means. Working together in the Mexican capital, a United States and national scientist found that pupae of the flies dipped in a 5 percent solution of TEPA received doses sufficient to sterilize them as they emerged from their cases.[15]

That program stimulated interest in chemosterilants to such an extent that within a few years more than 5,000 potential agents had been evaluated by the Entomology Research Division of the USDA, including a number which have been used on humans as anti-tumor agents.[16]

In one early experiment, a group of chemicals, including TEPA, caused sterility in both sexes when fed to adult houseflies at very low concentrations. In another, both male and female mosquitoes were rendered sterile by exposing them for a few hours to deposits of a chemosterilant on glass surfaces.[17]

Those scientists who see great possibilities in chemosterilants hold it highly advantageous that they may be used against insects in their natural environment. The sterilizing substances may be incorporated in the diet, as they have been for roaches, houseflies, and other pests in various experiments. They may be applied to surfaces so that pests coming in contact with them can pick up enough to inhibit reproduction; chemosterilants have been used as dips, dusts, and sprays. They could be used to sterilize insects in the laboratory, as irradiation is used. Their potential is high, promising a 99 percent control of an insect species compared with the 90 percent that is expected of a conventional insecticide.[18]

Unfortunately, chemosterilants have one decided drawback. They are dangerous.

USDA officials, optimistic about finding chemical agents that may be used to curb the reproductive activities of pests, nevertheless stress that "many precautions" must be taken with the ones available for experimentation. Many of the chemosterilants that have been developed have alkylating properties, which are known to have adverse effects on mammals—damaging to certain cells of the bone marrow, germ cells, embryos, and other tissues.

Britain's Dr. Kenneth Mellanby is frankly opposed to the use of chemicals to induce sterility for purposes of pest control. "Such chemicals are really just chemical insecticides. They have to be applied to the habitat like poisons, and I think that they are more likely to have unpleasant side effects, including poisoning and reproductive upsets in man, than are the majority of ordinary insecticides."[19]

That charge cannot be made against the irradiation technique. Nor can it be made against the use of genetic manipulation to curb pest productivity. An interesting experiment to employ the sexual instinct as a pest control was made in the spring of 1967 in Burma, under the auspices of the World Health Organization. The goal was to eliminate the mosquitoes that transmit filariasis, a debilitating tropical disease that afflicts persons of all ages in that country. Male mosquitoes from California were introduced into an area near Rangoon. When they mated with native females, the eggs did not hatch because of a genetic incompatibility between the Burma and U.S. mosquitoes.[20]

The possibility of using defective rats to eliminate their own kind in rat-infested urban centers was advanced at a

meeting of the American Cancer Society in 1969. Dr. Allan
J. Stanley of the University of Oklahoma discovered a rat
in 1963 in his animal research laboratory whose genetic
code is out of kilter. Half of each litter of the male rats
of this line are defective in producing sperm. The animals
are highly sexual and can induce false pregnancy in female rats—a condition so convincing to the she rats that
they lose their urging for further mating. Dr. Stanley has
proposed that after as many normal rats as possible have
been killed off by conventional means, the genetically defective rats be turned loose in cities. There they could
occupy all the reproductive time of females without any
visible consequences. All the adults, he estimates, would
thus die off without progeny in six to eight months.[21]

Whether or not people would exhibit the same tolerance
for rat releases that they do for releases of flies and moths
is another matter.

At this stage, sterilized male pests are far from being
an answer to the problem. The man most intimately
associated with development of that weapon, Dr. Knipling,
stresses that fact—urging that this method be combined
with others and explored more fully.[22]

Many areas are open to investigation. According to Dr.
Knipling, Dr. Bushland and other researchers, further
work needs to be done in order to develop the most
practical method of inducing sterility and the most effective type of sterility. More needs to be known about the
biology of insects, and the size of the natural population
must be estimated carefully, along with reproductive
potential, since increase rates under some conditions can
be so "fantastic" as to ruin release experiments.[23]

Unfortunately, the insecticide mentality has kept research and development from advancing more rapidly,
despite the highly successful demonstrations on at least

five serious pest species in recent years. Recently, however, the growing resistance of more and more "bad bugs" to even the most lethal chemicals has been forcing farmers and government officials in the direction that scientists should have led them years ago. For example, in 1970 about 800,000 sterile pink bollworms of both sexes were dropped daily over the principal cotton-raising areas in California to mingle and mate with normal pests—and thus eradicate the creatures whose ravenous appetites have been held responsible for cutting cotton production from 1,700 pounds an acre to 1,000 pounds an acre in the four years since it first appeared.[24]

In any case, the use of sterile males—particularly those rendered infertile by radiation—is a major breakthrough in pest control and an indication of what can be done when scientists tackle the problem in a scientific manner. Although not *the* single answer, it does offer a solution to some of the most perplexing difficulties—how to obtain total eradication in the rare cases in which it is held necessary and how to protect broad areas without subjecting every bit of life in them to poisonous contamination.[25] And that can be done at a reasonable cost.[26]

Unfortunately, not all scientists are capable of working in a scientific way. For that reason, we must also look outside the laboratory for help in curbing the merchandisers.

16. "SUE THE BASTARDS"

AT A MEETING of the staid American Littoral Society in the winter of 1968, the guest speaker paused dramatically after his recital of the devastating ecological effects wrought by the polluters along the Long Island shore. Then, poking a hole in the air with his fingers, he challenged: "What can you do about it?" Before they had a chance to respond, the stocky young man on the platform seized a portable blackboard and whirled it around so that the answer he had printed earlier in large block letters was visible:

SUE THE BASTARDS!

Victor J. Yannacone, Jr., then 32 years old, specializes in drama as well as medicine, mathematics, biology, history, physics, chemistry, philosophy, and a long list of other subjects he finds useful in practicing law. It is a combination calculated to impress judges, awe jurors, delight his family, and turn into eco-activist any listener who agrees with his doctrine that the citizens of this country have a constitutional right to "the cleanest environment technology can provide."

During the past few years, those citizens have come to include a good many persons this side of the agricultural chemicals industry, where he is almost universally regarded as "that wiseacre," "that fanatic," and "Trouble-maker Number One."

Vic Yannacone is not at all disturbed about the name-calling. "After threats and bribes," he dismisses the opposition lightly, "a few insults don't mean a thing."[1]

A good-humored dynamo who seems to be without a care in the world except keeping his waistline from reflecting his appreciation of his wife's gourmet cooking, Vic finds some of those knowledges handy for his general practice, which emphasizes personal injury and workmen's compensation litigation. He regards all of them as essential to his nonprofit legal activities as attorney for nonprofit environmental defenders, scientists, and conservationists who operate largely out of universities and research centers. Their concern is Yannacone's concern—to halt the poisoning of the biosphere by such pesticides as DDT before it is too late.

To that end, he has appeared in federal and local courts in half a dozen states, given talks in dozens of cities and towns, and created an uproar on Long Island, where three generations of Yannacones lead an otherwise placid existence, pursuing the goals and carrying out the obligations of what they consider to be "constructive citizenship." Their most ambitious attempt in that direction came in the fall of 1969, when Vic's pretty wife, Carol, filed a federal court suit against five major manufacturers of DDT "on behalf of all the people of the United States." Charging them with having violated both antitrust laws and the Constitutional rights of the people, Carol sought an injunction against further advertising of the pesticide without warning notices and a cash payment of $30 billion in reparations to local, state, and federal governments.[2]

When the Yannacones feel that the people are being pushed around, they go into court and push back—hard.

"That's what the law is all about," says Vic, practically applying the theory now becoming popular in law schools: "In a society where law is a primary force, the lawyer must be a primary, not a secondary being."[3]

"That's it," agrees his father. The senior member of Yannacone and Yannacone adopted that policy long before it was formulated by Professor Charles A. Reich of Yale Law School. (And he is keen on exercising moral suasion out of court as well as in. One of Victor, Sr.'s, "outside" citizenship achievements was to persuade Mayor Fiorello LaGuardia to remove from Herald Square the statue of William E. Dodge on the grounds that "a memorial to a robber baron is a pretty poor example to young people.")

Also in agreement are Carol, a biologist school teacher; "Mother" Yannacone, a nurse; and V. J. III, alias "Happy" —a winning child with a prodigious vocabulary and a determination to be where things are happening.

Vic himself once had other notions about "primary being." Through his junior year at Kalamazoo College, he alternately considered becoming a football coach and a neurosurgeon. After his transfer to Brooklyn Law College, he almost abandoned the law, too. He found training "so unbelievably dull" that he cut classes to audit electronics courses at Brooklyn Polytech. He flunked contracts and got a "D" in torts, but he had no trouble in passing the bar examination. Once in, he began to appreciate the law as a lever for moving the world. "If there is something good that must be done," he is convinced, "there is a legal way to do it. Nine hundred years ago we eliminated trial by combat and substituted the courtroom for the arena. That is where you challenge the predators, the descendants of the robber barons. That is the only place you can force them to answer you."

He is impatient with the "stupidity" of the exploiters; he is equally impatient with the "stupidity" of those who resort to violence to settle accounts. Recently, he told a campus audience about their alternatives:

> You can lie on your back in a pool of blood in the gutter holding a picket sign up for thirty seconds of late-night TV news, or you can sit on a witness chair in a courtroom and tell it like it is. . . . Industry and government can ignore your protests, ignore your picket signs, and certainly they can repress your demonstrations. But no one in industry or government ignores that scrap of legal cap that begins: YOU ARE HEREBY SUMMONED TO ANSWER THE ALLEGATIONS OF THE COMPLAINT ANNEXED HERETO WITHIN TWENTY DAYS OR JUDGMENT WILL BE TAKEN AGAINST YOU FOR THE RELIEF DEMANDED.

No one in industry or government ignores a summons and complaint, he pointed out—corporation presidents, chairmen of the boards, their lawyers, and their lawyers' lawyers. What is more, they *must* answer it: "Not in the press, where all their flackmen can distort the issues. Not in the marketplace, where all their financial might can overrule the facts . . . but in a courtroom where, as far as the facts are concerned, you the individual are the equal of any man or any corporation."[4]

Vic Yannacone's knowledge of where the power in our society does lie is what brought into existence the Environmental Defense Fund, one of the most important forces in the anti-pollution war. Now a nationwide coalition of scientists, lawyers, and citizens dedicated to the protection of environmental quality through legal action and public education, it got its start in 1966. After workmen had dumped DDT into a Long Island pond killing the fish, Carol "badgered" Vic into doing something about it. He drew up a suit to halt the use of the pesticide.

Four days after he had filed against the Suffolk County Mosquito Control Commission, a letter attacking the use of DDT appeared in a local paper. The author was Dr. Charles F. Wurster, assistant professor of biological sciences at the State University of New York at Stony Brook, only a few miles away from the Yannacone quarters at Patchogue. Although also very young, Dr. Wurster is considered one of the outstanding authorities on the subject. Dr. George M. Woodwell, chief ecologist at Brookhaven National Laboratory, has described him as "knowing more about persistent pesticides than anybody in the world."

Vic called Charlie, who agreed to testify. The first pooling of minds and talents resulted in a "temporary" injunction, which appears to be permanently in effect. It also resulted in EDF's getting off to a running start.

"At first we were taken for a bunch of bird watchers," Dr. Wurster said recently, "but the industry is worried now. They've got the money, we've got the science."[5]

Actually some members of the industry were worried early. Just ten weeks after EDF was incorporated on October 18, 1967, the editor of *Farm Chemicals* warned: "Storm clouds are gathering over the pesticide industry and the group seeding them is Environmental Defense Fund, Inc."[6] Dr. Wurster is quite accurate, however, about industry's having the money, but EDF's having the science. Thanks largely to his efforts, a committee has been built up, making more than 100 top scientists from all over the world available to furnish opinions and testimony in the court actions it has brought against polluters. And not for profit. None of the witnesses has been paid for appearing in New York, Michigan, Wisconsin, and other places where Yannacone and the EDF have acted. Some of them have even paid their own travel expenses, in contrast to industry witnesses and consultants who may receive hundreds or thousands of dollars a day.

Yannacone, also unpaid, devised the legal approach and for several years provided the legal muscle. Traditionally, conservation groups have timidly shunned litigation or filed lawsuits only to protect the limited interests of members—fishermen, for example, or bird lovers. The Yannacones and EDF were after larger game. Instead of seeking limited remedial measures, Vic felt that they should establish legal precedents—that they should do for "environmental law" what the American Civil Liberties Union and the Legal Defense Fund of the NAACP had done for civil rights legislation.

Scientists were also aware that the strength of the enemy made courtroom confrontations imperative:

> The offenders are not just a handful of fly-by-night operators. To the contrary, they are usually highly respected and include some of the largest private and public enterprises. They wield enormous economic and political power. The pressures they exert explain why it is so very difficult to take effective action through legislative or administrative channels. . . .[7]

By seeking judicial rather than other types of relief, Yannacone and the EDF could move swiftly—a critical point. It may take years to get a legislative ban or an administrative order to halt the use of a substance; obtaining a court injunction may be a matter of hours. Yet the results are no less effective. Moreover, they felt that the condition of the biosphere was proof that legislative and administrative bodies were dominated by the pesticide Goliaths. To gain public support and force action, David would have to issue public challenges and demand public dueling grounds.

The public approach alienated many potential allies in the conservationist movement. As Harmon Henkin pointed out recently, what organizations like the Sierra Club, the Wilderness Society, the National Wildlife Federation, the Audubon Society, and Izaak Walton League had in common was "a basic social and political conservatism."[8] The educational tactics they favored were "genteel and proper —and usually unsuccessful." Names were not named, publicly at least.

By contrast, Yannacone's tactics were direct, blunt, and successful. No polluter could any longer be sure that his respectable anonymity would be maintained lest it cause hard feelings in the clubs and board rooms where polluters and conservationist leaders have traditionally sat down together. Thus, the Aububon Society uttered a polite "no thank you" in 1967, when Yannacone offered to help it take the Army Corps of Engineers into court for denying water to the Florida Everglades. A year later, a San Francisco group representing a number of leading conservation organizations called Yannacone's assertion that citizens have a Constitutional right to a pollution-free environment "just too far-fetched."[9]

Undaunted, EDF built its scientific strength and perfected its maneuverability. "We can put together a full-blown law suit in 24 hours," Vic Yannacone boasted. It did just that in the fall of 1967, after Dr. H. Lewis Batts, an EDF founder from Michigan, called to report that the state department of agriculture planned to drop 5,600 pounds of dieldrin from planes to wipe out an infestation of Japanese beetles in Berrien County. Yannacone, Batts, and Wurster spent the weekend drawing up a suit and filing it, and the following Monday applied successfully to the Michigan Court of Appeals for a restraining order. Testimony was revealing about the pesticide mentality. "That much dieldrin would have killed 10 to 80 times as many animals as beetles."[10]

Though only partial, the victory was a major one. The original grandiose killing scheme was replaced by a modest one: to handspray 160 acres with 320 pounds of dieldrin the next season.

A few months later EDF was in court again, this time in Manhattan, to prevent the U.S. Department of Agriculture from going ahead with the original Michigan plan. It lost that round. As Dr. Wurster pointed out later, during the fall of 1968 the state and federal departments of agriculture had attempted to dump dieldrin aerially at the rate of two pounds an acre over 3,000 acres in Berrien County. According to the state agency's own data, infestation amounted to one beetle an acre on land that was primarily non-agricultural. Dr. Wurster charged that the "extensive propaganda campaign" carried on by the state agriculture officials made the infestation seem of such magnitude that farmers feared a multi-million dollar loss. Moreover, the officials had failed to mention that far less dangerous insecticides could be used, as well as milky spore disease and other biological techniques *recommended by the USDA* for the pest.[11] He also noted that the Michigan Department of Agriculture had given assurance—falsely—that dieldrin would not enter Lake Michigan or contaminate other areas; and it ignored the pesticide's ability to cause "heavy mortality" of non-target organisms, including fish, birds, and mammals. "How long must we tolerate such dangerous naivete; and how much of this kind of treatment can our environment withstand?"[12]

Those questions were raised again in 1968, when EDF

joined with a group of Montana Environmental Defenders to halt alleged air pollution by the Hoerner Waldorf Corporation, which operates a kraft pulp mill west of Missoula.[13] In that instance, too, Vic Yannacone pushed the suit "on behalf of all those entitled to the full benefit, use, and enjoyment of the natural resource of the Missoula environment." He based his arguments on the unenumerated rights guaranteed by the Ninth Amendment and protected by the "due process" and "equal protection" clauses of the Fifth and Fourteenth Amendments to the Constitution. Recent photos show that Montana skies are still darkened at noon from the wastes spewed out by pulp mills; nevertheless, the suit encouraged conservationists to join forces, pool resources, and start to "push back" together. Businessmen were reluctant to join the eco-activists publicly, but according to a local report: "There is no doubt that the major strength comes from the business community and the community as a whole."[14]

In January of 1969 Yannacone and the scientists Dr. Wurster had assembled made a show of strength in Wisconsin. The occasion was an administrative hearing inaugurated by the Citizens Natural Resources Association of Wisconsin before the State Department of Natural Resources. It was viewed in a larger way by a good many persons. Columnist James J. Kilpatrick, a conservationist and a conservative, called it "a trial of godlike dimensions" having to do with "man's pollution of the universe around him."[15]

The basis for the hearing was Wisconsin's novel statute that allows private citizens to petition a state agency for a ruling on how the laws it administers apply to a particular situation. A group of conservationists in the association, headed by the activist wife of Dr. Owen Otto, noted psychiatrist, decided to use the statute to get a ruling declaring DDT a pollutant that violates the water quality standards. The Izaak Walton League joined the Citizens Natural Resources Association. Yannacone and Wurster were asked to prepare the case.

In short order, Madison became an international capital. Scientists flew in from Sweden, Washington, and other points to support the attack against DDT. More than 200 scientific articles and exhibits were introduced to show the damage being done. Biologists and other life science experts offered evidence to show how DDT was annihilating birds by upsetting their calcium metabolism and causing them to lay thin-shelled eggs; pharmacologists and biochemists testified that the entire population of the planet had become involuntary subject-victims in the worldwide experiment.[16]

The agricultural chemicals industry struck back with heavy artillery—a battery of lawyers, headed by Louis A. McLean, and a small army of public relations workers, who picked up their cues from him to demonstrate that nature was the prime polluter of the universe (dusts, bacteria, pollens) and that DDT critics were food faddists, publicity seekers, and persons insecure about their sexual performance.

The hearings went on for months; deliberations for even longer. The hearing commissioner's job was monumental. "A legal case is like a wall, and you have to put it in brick by brick," he told *Science* reporter Luther J. Carter. "Usually the scientist has been interested only in his own brick. Now ecologists are trying to put all the bricks together."[17]

Even before he had an opportunity to render a decision things began to happen. Wisconsin's Senator Gaylord A. Nelson introduced a package of eight bills in the Senate to prohibit the interstate sale and shipment of eight pesticides in the chlorinated hydrocarbon family—aldrin, chlordane, DDT/TDE, dieldrin, endrin, heptachlor, lindane, and toxaphene—a total ban effective by mid-1972. More significantly, he also proposed a Constitutional amendment that would make Yannacone's "far out" legal concept far in: *"Every person has the inalienable right to a decent environment. The United States and every state shall guarantee this right."* Senator Nelson said that he proposed the amendment because:

> I believe the environmental crisis is the greatest single threat to our pursuit of the inalienable rights of life, liberty, and the pursuit of happiness. The tragedy is that the citizen has few clear legal or constitutional avenues to protect the sensitivities and well-being of himself, his family, or his community from environmental hazards.[18]

Meantime, other conservationist organizations had been drastically revising their attitudes, asserting rights and demanding justice. No longer could the charge be leveled that organized conservation is "educating each generation in the position that the natural environment is absolutely subject to ruthless, unscientific, ecologically suicidal degradation in the quest for private gain."[19] As an official of the Audubon Society said, "Vic has gotten us to think in terms of legal action."[20]

By 1970, when it became apparent that the statements by the Secretary of HEW and the Secretary of Agriculture about banning DDT were little more than semantic exercises, the Sierra Club, EDF, and other conservationist groups and individuals—including some California mothers who planned to nurse their babies—filed in the U.S Court of Appeals in Washington to contest the failure of the two officials to grant relief from further spraying.

"The failure of Agriculture to respond positively to the requests to begin cancellation proceedings at once and to suspend registrations is deplorable," said James Moorman, attorney for the Sierra Club in matters involving DDT. Mr. Moorman sharply rejected the refusal of the HEW Secretary to set zero tolerances for DDT because it was so all pervasive.[21]

All over the country, lawyers have been following the example of EDF and the advice of such legal authorities as Dr. N. William Hines of the University of Iowa College of Law. Although Professor Hines feels that protection from such environmental hazards as pesticides requires government regulation as well as recourse to private damage suits, he is well aware of present deficiencies.[22] He is convinced that the standard "soft-sell tactics" of education must be supplemented by realistic enforcement of anti-pollution laws—something that is not now occurring. Meantime, he is encouraged by recent indications that the courts "seem to be moving rather quickly toward a strict liability concept in the area of pesticide injury."[23]

Suits against farmers who "offend" their neighbors by the way they use their land are not new.[24] Suits to collect pesticide injury damages are, however. Farmers themselves who have suffered losses have gone to the government for reparations, obtaining millions through "The Cranberry Fund" and OEO grants. Lately, the government has been called upon to pay up. In January 1970, in a landmark case, a 17-year-old farm worker was awarded $447 for the loss of five months salary in response to his claim that he had been incapacitated by contact with an organic phosphate pesticide. Jerome Cohen, general counsel for the United Farm Workers Organizing Committee, which pressed the suit, said that it was the first time an agricultural laborer had ever been so compensated.[25]

Private damage suits are usually costly and time-consuming affairs, quite beyond the reach of most persons. Now "class actions" are making it possible for a few persons to protest on behalf of all who have been similarly abused. Until recently "unity of interest" suits were limited to groups of stockholders who sued company officers for mismanagement, acting on behalf of themselves and all shareholders in the company. During the last few years leaders of the "consumer revolution" have used class actions as a weapon to permit the unrepresented to strike back. These actions are the only way in which those unable to afford the luxury of going to court can obtain legal relief. One indication of their importance and power came to light recently when a group of New York lawyers brought suit on behalf of all the state's "ultimate consumers" against five drug companies for overcharging for antibiotic drugs. The companies offered to settle claims for $120 million.[26]

Yannacone initiated class actions in environmental litigation in 1962, when he recovered for public use more than five miles of beach along the Long Island shore. In his suit against the Incorporated Village of Oldfield, he claimed successfully that by its being made a private beach, the people of the area had been deprived of their rights guaranteed under seventeenth-century colonial charters to the "benefit, use, and enjoyment of the property."[27] That concept enabled EDF to act against pesticide use in Michigan, Wisconsin, and several other states.

UFWOC's class actions are assuming important significance. Shortly after the union negotiated a contract with A. Perelli-Minetti & Sons Company prohibiting the use of "hard" pesticides on wine grapes—"a first major breakthrough for the protection of both farm workers and consumers"—UFWOC sought to extend that victory broadly. On behalf of Vicente Ponce, a 34-year-old grape picker, "representing all consumers and farm workers,"[28] it asked the Federal District Court in Los Angeles to outlaw the use of DDT and 30 other pesticides "even more dangerous." The complaint asked that the state director of agriculture be enjoined from issuing permits for the customary eight villains in the chlorinated hydrocarbon family and also for some highly toxic organic phosphates. Although the director had announced that some of the poisons could no longer be used on certain crops, UFWOC attorney Charles Farnsworth said that there were so many loopholes in the order it was simply a means of deluding the public: "This is a deceptive move to protect the chemical companies and the growers, and we will not let them get away with it."[29]

The moral purpose and humanistic concern of Cesar Chavez and other UFWOC leaders have been amply demonstrated in the stand on pesticides. Despite pressures within and without, Chavez has consistently rejected contracts specifying that the union agree "it will not embark on any program which will in any way harm the industry to which the employer is a member." That clause, he said, would prevent the union from seeking better laws on the regulation of pesticides. "If they think that once we sign a contract we are going to become docile little lap-dogs, they're crazy."[30]

Even politicians and bureaucrats are abandoning their cautious attitudes and are trying to bring polluters to face accusations before the bar. Oregon authorities recently took the unprecedented action of seeking extradition of a Chicago businessman on criminal charges of violating air pollution laws. Governor Tom McCall made the successful appeal on the grounds that a county grand jury had indicted the board chairman of Frye Roofing Company

on twelve misdemeanor counts. Although the lawyer for
the executive protested that his client was being harassed,
the district attorney of Multnomah County stood ground.
He acknowledged that extradition proceedings were "unusual," but "his company is such an aggravated offender
we feel this is a matter of considerable public importance."
Moreover, he told reporters: "The person responsible for
this pollution should be held accountable."[31]

Accountability was also the issue during a recent hearing in Joplin, Missouri, in the first federal enforcement
action taken under new provisions of the national water
pollution law. Charged with allowing mine wastes to foul
rivers in Kansas and Oklahoma, officials of Eagle-Picher
Industries signed an agreement promising to mend company ways.

That was a major victory for conservation, the beginning of a series of actions against even larger industries
by the Federal Water Pollution Control Administration.
According to Louis S. Clapper, Washington editor of
National Wildlife, it "heralded a new get-tough policy"
on the part of the government agency.[32] Law enforcement,
he noted, is only one weapon in the attack on pollution,
"but long experience has shown that the big stick, vigorously applied, is the only method which gets the attention of some polluters."[33]

The "some" should be amended to "most." Yet government agencies have deftly avoided using the big stick,
rarely carrying a case through the preliminary stages so
that the Department of Justice could take it into court.
For example, of 49 federal water pollution actions dating
back to 1948, only one had ever been sent to the Justice
Department by the Department of Interior for prosecution. The attitude toward the agency was forthrightly
expressed in the fall of 1969 by Iowa officials. Interior

officials had announced that further dumping of sewage into the Missouri River would be prohibited. Kansas and Missouri agreed to install secondary treatment facilities "in about ten years." Iowa, which was given until 1973 to act, made no promise. The chairman of the state water pollution control agency said, "The federal people are miffed because we have stood on a matter of principle, because we refuse to say we're going to do something when we have no intention of doing it."[34]

That polluting should be regarded as a matter of principle may seem novel. But it is understandable, considering the record of regulatory agencies all along the line. On the national level, the performance of the USDA and the Food and Drug Administration has encouraged that sort of thinking. So has that of other federal agencies, including the Interior Department, whose 75,000 employees generally ignored the ban invoked against DDT in 1964 for five years.[35] Locally, the regulatory agencies have so consistently refused to prosecute polluters and have so baldly granted them exceptions that in Houston, for example, the clean air act is contemptuously know as "the dirty air act."[36]

Actually, there is no reason why the U.S. Attorney General, his counterparts in the fifty states, and the district attorneys in thousands of counties could not and cannot initiate action, thus bypassing the regulators who encourage poisoners to flout the law. Some have acted recently. A precedent was set in 1970, when the Justice Department used a 71-year-old federal law to bring charges against eleven companies for polluting Chicago-area rivers and canals. International Harvester, Proctor & Gamble, Olin Mathieson, Penn Central Railroad, and a number of other giants were charged under the 1899 Rivers and Harbors "Refuse Act" with dumping a wide

variety of pollutants into the bodies of water that serve
the "hog butcher to the world."[37]

In some states, public lawyers have gone beyond routine
actions and acknowledged their public obligations. After
it became "increasingly clear" to the California attorney
general's office that regulators and polluters were involved
in a "curious alliance," the staff began to go into court
successfully against both regulators and polluters.[38]

To aid both public and private efforts in that direction,
two California lawmakers proposed a measure in 1970
authorizing the attorney general or any citizen to bring
suit when he believes that any program or product is
causing major abuse or destruction of the environment.
"Political puttering will not stop pollution," Senator
George R. Moscone and Assemblyman James A. Hayes,
Democrat and Republican respectively, said in a joint
statement. On the other hand, they said, a judicial relief
measure such as they urged "would make the courtroom
the battleground for pollution control—far removed from
the influences of special interests or political maneuvers."[39]

17. A LASTING TRUCE

WHILE COURTROOMS ARE fine in their way, legislative chambers are also needed. In place of the dove-ish statutes now on the books, new laws must be enacted to curb pollution—particularly pollution by pesticides and other dangerous chemicals too new to be covered by precedents. The laws must be realistically drafted, uniformly applied, and rigidly enforced.

About the only hawk measure now in existence is the Refuse Act of 1899, which was unearthed by federal prosecutors after almost 70 years to indict industrial polluters in New York and the Middle West. The law could have been of value if it had been enforced. Instead, enforcement was actively discouraged. It could have been of value if it had carried stiff penalties. Instead, the average fine imposed for violation in 1969 was $650— not a fine, as one United States official pointed out, but a "permit to pollute."[1]

So far as bug and weed killers are concerned, the present law to protect people from those dangerous substances is totally inadequate. Even those chemicals considered so hazardous that their use has been banned are readily available. Senator Philip A. Hart, chairman of a subcommittee studying environmental problems, reported in the summer of 1970 that when his investigators checked ten garden supply stores in Baltimore, they found seven of them were offering 2,4,5-T for sale, although the herbicide had been banned months earlier for such use because of its "imminent danger" to public health.[2] Supposedly banned DDT was similarly available.

Now that fear as well as moral outrage has been generated by the growing knowledge of pollution hazards, new measures will be enacted. Whether they will be meaningful safeguards or additional permits to pollute is the issue.

"Clean up the Environment" has become a political battle cry safer than urging love and respect for mothers and dogs. As a consequence, candidates for office are throwing bills into legislative hoppers as if they were tossing outsized confetti. Many of them are confusing, contradictory, and shrewdly calculated to increase the verbal pollution that has provided a shield for the environment polluters.

A good many of the polluters, needless to say, have climbed aboard the bandwagon, contributing to the semantic wastes that veil the problem. A rather amusing illustration occurred early in 1970, when Henry Ford II pledged his giant motor corporation to a fight against environmental pollution. Apparently encouraged by his outburst of citizenship, Michigan state and local authorities promptly charged the Ford Company with violating air pollution regulations and with fouling the Rouge River, which flows past one of its plants.[3]

The goal of many of the newly emerging corporate environmentalists was spelled out clearly a few months later when Herbert D. Doan, president of the Dow Chemical Company, addressed manufacturers of devices to monitor and eliminate pollution at a convention sponsored by the Houston Chamber of Commerce. In what was reported to have been a stirring speech, applauding clean-up agitators and supporting the levying of fines and penalties for polluters, Dr. Doan outlined his blueprint for curbing global contamination. Towns and cities should be in charge of things, he told convention goers: "I would just as soon see the federal government let the municipalities get the job done."[4]

So would most polluters. "Local control" has always been the cry of those who would have things change by remaining the same.

One of the reasons we have reached a crisis stage is that polluters have found it so easy to dominate legislative as well as regulatory bodies on local levels. The cure, consequently, requires the enactment of laws at the highest possible level.

Ideally, the place to launch the offensive is on the global level. So far as pesticides are concerned, national boundaries are meaningless when foods produced in Iowa may be eaten in Austria, or when meat processed and packed in New Zealand may show up on supermarket shelves in New York and Chicago, or when fish caught off the coasts of Japan and Ireland may be contaminated with poisons drifting from United States farms out into the Pacific and Atlantic.[5]

However, until there is more willingness to regard national boundaries in an objective fashion, great pressure should be exerted on national representatives and greater support be given to those among them who have exposed themselves to attacks by polluters.

Federal authorities can act. After all, it is one thing for the Congress of the United States to insist that pulp mill owners stop spewing factory wastes into the air; it is quite another for the mayor and councilmen in the towns where mill owners can make or break political careers with a few judicious telephone calls. It is one thing for Congress to force oil and automotive industries to stop poisoning the atmosphere—although even at that level the fear of reprisal is great; it is quite another to expect city and county officials to do battle with those superpowers. It is one thing for Congress to move against unsafe pesticides; it is unrealistic to imagine that officeholders in California, Texas, Mississippi, and other farm states would risk the wrath of agribusiness and chemical interests.

Because Congress has not acted, all is confusion. That was underscored for me in the summer of 1969, when I read responses to a questionnaire seeking information about the regulation of pesticide use that had been sent out by Senator Gaylord A. Nelson to 150 state agriculture, commerce, and health agencies. Some states regulated pesticide use; others did not—indeed, officials had no information at all about the kinds and amounts used, to say nothing of their effects. Some state officials appeared totally uninterested in the problem; others, seriously concerned, were fighting for tight controls.[6]

Congress would act to halt pollution pesticides and other dangerous substances—if it were insisted upon. It has been "by the consent of a lethargic public," Senator Nelson pointed out recently, that "up to now, the decisions that have destroyed our environment have been made in the boardrooms of giant corporations, in the thousands of government-agency offices protected from public scrutiny by layer on layer of bureaucracy, and even in the frequently closed committee rooms of Congress."[7]

By acting to insure that only those representatives who are concerned with the national interest take seats in those "closed committee rooms in Congress," people can influence the decisions that are made in government-agency offices and ultimately in the boardrooms of giant corporations—and thus hold back the poison tide.

Because most of the laws and regulations governing pollution have been written with the aid of (if not *by*) the polluters themselves, they are woefully inadequate. The new regulations governing pesticides should be worked out by objective scientists and public representatives. The scientists should be drawn from a wide variety of specialties: biology, zoology, ecology, entomology, agriculture, chemistry, physics, medicine, and any other appropriate discipline. All of them should be committed to science rather than corporate interests.

For that reason, excellent recruiting grounds would be organizations like the Society for Social Responsibility in Science, whose members are pledged not only to their own disciplines, but to an organized effort to "foster throughout the world a tradition of personal moral responsibility for the consequences to humanity of professional activity."[8]

Medical specialists on the commission should be similarly drawn from the American Public Health Association, Group Health Association of America, Medical Committee on Human Rights, or some other organization truly concerned with the public interest in the practice of medicine. And public members should reflect public interest rather than polluters' interests. (And who is sitting on the air and water quality control commissions in your state and your city?) Recognized conservationist groups— Audubon Society, Committee for Environmental Information, Environmental Defense Fund, Friends of the Earth, Izaak Walton League, the Sierra Club, and others— should be asked to name the public members.

If the advice of industry is required, getting it is not likely to pose problems. Lobbyists will be knocking at commission doors every morning.

Nor should industry consent be a consideration. When

objective experts in various fields have raised reasonable doubts about the safety of pollutants—particularly highly toxic ones—the burden of proving them otherwise should be placed on the producers. Pending that proof they should be removed from the market. Presently, it is difficult, almost impossible, to do that.

Under current procedures, sale and manufacture of dangerous products may continue until all legal appeals have been settled. Thus, government plans to phase out all but essential uses of DDT have been blocked by legal challenges by the major pesticide companies.[9] Those blocks may continue, as they did in the FTC action against Geritol, for more than a quarter of a century.

The primary issue so far as the sale of pesticides is concerned is not the freedom of a business to engage in profitable activities, but the protection of all of the people and their environment against poisoning.

Stiff penalties must be built into the law and the penalties imposed. Individuals, acting as individuals, are required to pay for damages they incur. For example, Johnny Cash, the singer, was recently fined $82,000 after a defective exhaust system on his camper truck set off a fire that destroyed 508 acres of growth in a national forest in California.[10] Surely, corporations, which are guaranteed all of the Constitutional protections afforded individuals, should be held equally responsible. Yet no one was fined when smog recently destroyed more than 3 million trees in a forest.

Not long ago a Stanford University professor of business administration pointed out that "although we tout the merits of free enterprise, we haven't fairly assigned its cost."[11] He is correct. Any person or corporate entity polluting a river should be made to bear all the costs of purifying the water again; whoever contaminates earth and air should be charged for restoring them to their former condition.

An effort is being made to shift the $300 billion clean-up bill to the taxpayers—a preposterous effort, in the United States. It might be a reasonable solution to pollution in Russia, but such socialistic janitorial service is not compatible with our capitalistic way of doing things. New York Congressman Richard Ottinger, who has led a number of successful anti-pollution fights, feels that industry—therefore, the consumer—should pay for cleaning up. "I think that it is a better solution than trying to have government pick up the entire cost and have people pay for it through taxes and through the bureaucracy that you would have to build up in order to supervise the job."[12]

Here is where the competitive system could exercise control. If some corporate polluters upped the prices of their goods and services ten cents or ten dollars to compensate themselves, tidier manufacturers who had to charge only two cents or two dollars would attract more customers. Polluters would not pollute if it were made unprofitable for them to do so.

Here, too, is an opportunity for American ingenuity to exercise itself. There is money—lots of it—in cleaning up the environment. Wastes have been turned into fertilizer and into mountains for skiing. Lumber scraps have created fortunes for chipboard manufacturers. Chemicals have been trapped for resale in other guises. Even thermal pollution is being exploited by commercial fisheries set up near power plants. By 1970 the American Chemical Society was listing more than 1,000 manufacturers of products, services, and supplies devoted to environmental control, ranging from Aerojet-General to Zurn Industries.[13]

If polluters rather than taxpayers generally were forced to pay, some protection would be afforded against our falling further into what Harvard Professor George Wald has called the "insidious" trap of allowing anti-pollution to become a superbusiness designed to intensify the crisis. "Powerful forces," he said, are promoting the trap "to let pollution go on merrily in all its present forms, and superimpose a new multi-billion dollar business of anti-pollution on top of it." He pointed out that in these days of conglomerates, "it would be the same business. One branch of it would be polluting, and the other branch of it antipolluting."[14]

The agencies appointed to administer the laws will have to revise their attitudes about profits and "progress" coming before people. Until they do, not even the most rigid law would be consequential—as many of those administered by the U.S. Department of Agriculture, the Food and Drug Administration, the Federal Trade Commission, and others have amply demonstrated.

The agencies should possess only the most limited power to grant exceptions—now handed out in carload lots to the chief offenders. Also, if the law obtained nationally, another deterrent to a clean environment would be eliminated. Now counties, states, and whole regions allow assaults to continue because the assailants threaten to pack up and take their business, and their filth, elsewhere. Such threats would be meaningless if exemptions did not make available less finicky pastures.

Importantly, the agencies should have plenty of enforcement officers to apprehend polluters. Senator Hart concluded his hearings on pesticide dangers by introducing a bill making it a federal crime to sell or misuse a government-banned pesticide: it set criminal penalties.[15]

The concern for law and order is meaningful and proper. But one of this country's major problems is its curious attitude toward crime. When an individual violates the law, especially on a petty scale, he is branded a criminal and sentenced harshly. When corporation executives violate the law, they are rarely considered criminals and rarely punished. "That's business." Men have gone to prison for decades without arousing attention for stealing less than $1,000; yet the whole country was shocked not long ago when some electrical company officials were given 30-day jail sentences, with time off for good behavior. They had been convicted of conspiring to defraud the American people of almost $3 billion![16]

The cost of such attitudes is very high. Senator Hart has estimated that between $30 and $40 of every $100 spent by consumers in this country in 1969 went to pay for inefficient and illegal practices.[17]

If business criminals were treated like criminals, some improvement might result. The neighborhood is notified when persons wanted on charges of assault or of destroying and defacing property are being picked up. But what cars carrying law enforcement officers have ever screeched up to the doors of manufacturers who annually poison hundreds of thousands of Americans, deface the landscape, and damage billions of dollars worth of public and private property? What portraits of polluters have ever been displayed on Post Office bulletin boards among the "Wanted"?

Genuinely constructive and corrective measures will require a major overhaul of our views about law and economics and politics as well as ecology.

For that reason, the classrooms are as important as the courtrooms and legislative chambers, if the planet is to be saved. Whatever is of greatness about our country and culture is tied to the belief that the right of Everyman to life, liberty, and the pursuit of happiness supercedes the freedom of the exploiters to line their pockets at any social cost. Whatever is of glory is tied to the belief that

Everyman can and must live harmoniously with his fellows and with nature. "The characteristic of a barbarous society is not devotion to acts of cruelty, but the indifference that permits and undergirds the cruelty and violence of the few, the indifference which does not know what its intentions are"—is the way in which one educator, an activist nun, expressed it recently.[18]

Educators, who have long encouraged indifference among the many and ignored the cruelty and violence of the few, are now beginning to speak out. In many schools eco-activist professors and their students are launching counterattacks on those who contaminate the planet and use men and animals as involuntary guinea pigs. They are developing "the new means of salvation."

That is the phrase of Dr. Barry Commoner, director of the Center for the Biology of Natural Systems at Washington University, who is known more widely as "the Paul Revere of Ecology."

Aware that the crisis involves political and economic approaches in addition to scientific ones, he advocates a master plan to achieve a lasting truce in the war against man and nature. That covers broad areas, from banning further oil drilling until risks are effectively mastered to taking "steps toward the permanent dismantling of the war machine that holds the world in terror."[19] The job cannot be done by scientists alone, he believes. For that reason he has organized a movement among academicians to educate the public about the scientific and technological facts relevant to the major issues of the day, forcing a new alliance between scientist and citizen. "On this alliance," he says, "depends the hope that the morality of man can, at last, turn the enormous new power that science has given us from the path of catastrophe toward the goal which is common both to science and humanity —the welfare of man."[20]

Other educators from a variety of disciplines have taken leading roles in that effort: Paul Ehrlich of Stanford, who has advanced a new Bill of Inalienable Rights, René Dubos of Rockefeller University, Lamont Cole of Cornell, George Wald of Harvard, Garrett Hardin of Berkeley . . . The list is long. And the achievement is impressive. All across the country they are helping to transform the failed and failing educational establishment into the *relevant* and *righteous* institutions of the sort envisioned by John Fischer in his blueprint for "Survival U."[21]

They have given students the encouragement and the means to translate intellectual and moral outrage into a positive philosophy, rejecting nihilistic despair. They have motivated them to build constructively, to seek answers to providing the good life for all, instead of indulging in mindless revolt and futile escape.

Those students who have been "turned on" have already begun to reshape America-the-toxic into a land of promises kept. They made April 22, 1970—D-Day in the struggle for an ecologically balanced planet—one of the most significant dates in recent American history.

Fanning out from 2,000 colleges and universities and nearly 10,000 high schools across the country, they served notice as much by their example as by their words and actions that, in the words of Denis Hayes, national coordinator of Environmental Action:

> We are building a movement, a movement with a broad base, a movement which transcends traditional political boundaries. It is a movement that values people more than technology, people more than political ideologies, people more than profit. It will be a difficult fight. Earth Day is the beginning.[22]

Not surprisingly, this positive aspect of the anti-pollution drive, this affirmation of life, won the eco-activists' support from the whole spectrum of society this side of the lunatic fringe. Not surprisingly, Daughters of the American Revolution worried about "pollution of the mind," and members of the John Birch Society noted that by dark and subversive coincidence Earth Day happened to fall on the birthday of Lenin. Generally, however, the rest of the country "turned on" with the activists. Girl Scouts planted trees; women from Canada and the United States picketed industrial polluters along the Great Lakes, neatly shaved and dressed students called on local and national officials with petitions for action. Militant conservation groups and mild-mannered garden clubs in thousands of towns joined forces. Even churches celebrated Earth Day, Earth Week, and "Earth Sunday."

That, too, was important. The restructuring of values involves religious institutions and homes as well as schools, courts, legislative chambers, and government offices. Many religious leaders acknowledge that the crisis has given them "a great new opportunity and a heavy responsibility."[23]

The old notion that man has the right to plunder and destroy nature to show his God-given "dominion" over it will have to be replaced by a new ethic, a new theology, they say. At a Theology of Survival Convention in California in 1970, a theology professor warned that unlike civil rights and other demands that are in the "mainstream" of Christian concerns, the environmental crisis implies that the ideals of the faith have been at fault. "Churches have the responsibility of arousing public support for needed action," Dr. John B. Cobb, Jr., said. They can help man avoid the "absolutization" of the gulf between himself and nature; they can help him to extend the "otherness" directed toward fellow human beings to sub-human life as well.[24]

Encouragingly, Earth Day was characterized by idealism rather than illusion. No one seemed to be suffering from the belief that the job would be easy or sudden. And cautions against believing otherwise were repeated by almost every speaker to every gathering. Perhaps the most succinct was that given to the students at Kansas Wesleyan by Republican Congressman James B. Pearson, who said:

> I want to warn that anti-pollution is not what we politicians call a "warm puppy" issue, one which if we pass enough laws, spend enough money and have a good heart, happiness is assured and soon America will be beautiful again. Anti-pollution means that someone will be hurt. Profits must be cut, comforts reduced, taxes raised, sacrifices endured. And, as in all human struggles, the powerful will fight the hardest to be hurt the least.[25]

Herculean labors are not all that will be required to cleanse the Augean stables—particularly of pesticide contamination. It will require a change of attitude, a change of heart.

Women will have a special role to play, since they are held chiefly responsible for the extravagant use of poisons on the farms and in the house. It is they, apologists for chemical warfare say, who have made the choice between bugs and people, between good and wormy apples.

The defense is unreasonable. Cleanliness and reverence for life are not incompatible, although paranoid thinking can make them seem so. Admittedly, to be against pollution in general is a lot easier than trying to cope with specific pest problems in a nonpolluting way. But it can be done. Flies, ants, roaches, moths, mice, and other household horrors can be controlled in most cases by other than chemical measures. Garden nuisances can be curbed without subjecting family and neighbors to a lethal shower. It is more human to use imagination and ingenuity, to say nothing of soap and water; it is usually more rewarding.

When emergencies dictate the need for chemical weapons, women should insist that products be realistically labeled and that the most dangerous ones be left for professionals. Amateur gardeners of both sexes should exercise equal caution. For instance, when Consumers Union evaluated 177 brands of pesticides in 1969, it found only 52 of them "safe enough for use by nonprofessional home gardeners and have sufficient and intelligible labeling.[26]

Since women are the principal purchasers of goods containing pesticides used commercially, they should insist on proper identification. Foodstuffs, carpeting, clothing, and other items dosed with toxic and persistent pesticides should carry cautionary notes. Perhaps if the choice were between a *wormy* apple and a *poisoned* one, more realistic decisions could be made.

Men and women are equally responsible for the political choices that will ultimately determine the safety of the world in which we live. Ecology makes clearer than almost any other issue the difference between those candidates who are on the side of people and those who opt for poisoners and profiteers.

Beyond remedial measures, we must all seek the knowledge that is the ultimate defense against the pesticide mentality. Instead of emphasizing the "miracle" of killers, education should emphasize the miracle of life. One of the more interesting assignments my daughter had during her first year in high school was to make a study of a ten-foot square of backyard over a period of two weeks, checking it at all hours of the day and night to learn how marvelously the web of life was patterned—how even the tiniest thing played an important part in the whole.

It was a memorable experience for her and a reminder for the rest of us—a reminder that we must learn to live with the earth instead of against it; that we, as guardians of our small part of the globe, are infinitely related and infinitely responsible.

NOTES

FOREWORD

[1] *Science Year: The World Book Science Annual, 1967* (Chicago: Field Enterprises Educational Corp., 1967), p. 119.

Fertile as people are, their record is quite different from that of flies. In 1969—despite all fanciful claims—there were only about 750,000 Americans who could trace their ancestry to the shipload of saints and strangers who landed at Plymouth 349 years earlier.

[2] Ironically, those questions are being raised by pesticide manufacturers themselves. In a brochure announcing the 1970 line of Gulf household products, the attention-stopper was a ferocious looking creature above a bold-face demand: "Who will stop the Superbugs?"

My informant told me again on September 14, 1970, that their resistance continued high. In a conversation that day with Dr. Herbert L. Schoof, he had learned that the flies and mosquitoes had thrived on the treatment of DDT and the organic phosphate insecticides—22 years for the flies, about 13 for the mosquitoes. Although the resistant strains were not bigger or healthier, as they had seemed to him at the time, he said, the official described them as "exceedingly strong." In at least one case, resistant insects have been reported unusually fecund.

CHAPTER 1 AMONG THE SURVIVORS?

[1] An excellent historical account of the achievements of the legendary king is given by Will Durant in *Caesar and Christ* (New York: Simon & Schuster, Inc., 1944), pp. 516–19.

[2] Glenn C. Klingman, *Weed Control: As a Science* (New York: John Wiley & Sons, Inc., 1961), p. 203

[3] (New York: The Viking Press, Inc., 1966), p. 28.

[4] Quoted, Los Angeles *Times*, October 9, 1969. Many scientists regard that as overly optimistic, including Dr. Paul Ehrlich, Stanford University biology professor and author of a number of books, including *The Population Bomb*. He has set 1979 as the date for "Eco-Catastrophe!" *The Environmental Handbook*, ed. Garrett De Bell (New York: Ballantine Books, Inc., 1970), p. 161.

[5] Many variations are current of the parody sung by a group called Ecology Action in Berkeley, California. This is one popular among students I know.

[6] A rather futile debate rages over the question of whether refineries or automobiles produce smog. The point is that smog first made its appearance in 1943 in Los Angeles, during the days of gasoline rationing, when relatively few cars were on the streets. That coincided with the establishment of the first of the catalytic cracking plants, which refine petroleum far more cheaply than can be effected with the distillation process, but which produce "dirtier" gasoline. In cities all over the world where catalytic cracking plants are located and where gasoline produced by "cat cracking" is used in large quantities, the smog problem exists.

[7] Dr. Charles C. Johnson, Jr., administrator of the Consumer Protection and Environmental Health Service of the Department of Health, Education, and Welfare, July 25, 1969. (Mimeo copy of speech)

[8] The ten leading areas in air pollution are New York, Chicago, Philadelphia, Los Angeles-Long Beach, Cleveland, Pittsburgh, Boston, Newark, Detroit, and St. Louis, according to a 1968 report by the U.S. Public Health Service. Less populous areas are also affected, a 1970 study indicated— citing Steubenville, Ohio; Charleston, West Virginia; Scranton, Pennsylvania; and Niagara Frontier, New York as holding records for "dirtiest air." However, the particular poisons in Los Angeles smog, which contains extreme amounts of hydrocarbons, led Dr. Willard Libby, Nobel Prize scientist, to suggest the possibility of a major ecological disaster for

that place in 1970, with perhaps "several hundred deaths."
UPI dispatch, "Dr. Libby Predicts L.A. Smog Disaster,"
Los Angeles *Herald-Examiner*, August 17, 1970.

[9] The annual bill, according to U.S. Public Health Service
estimates, was reported by Congressman Richard T. Hanna,
Congressional Record, March 17, 1969, p. E2059.

[10] Others set the agricultural damage higher than the USPHS.
Frederick Smith, a Harvard University ecologist, has set the
annual cost of environmental deterioration in this country
at about $30 billion a year. Lamont Cole, "In Unison,"
Earth Day—The Beginning, ed. the national staff of Environmental Action (New York: Bantam Books, 1970), p.
29.

[11] First serious warning that air pollution might exceed
cigarette smoking as a cause of lung cancer was made at
the annual meeting of the American Cancer Society in
1953. Although newspapers and radio reports gave top bill-
ing to Dr. Ernest L. Wynder's paper linking cancer with
cigarette smoking, many scientists were more disturbed by
the reports of Dr. Paul Kotin of the University of Southern
California and Dr. William E. Smith of New York University's Institute of Industrial Medicine. Both, as I reported
("Danger in the Air," *Frontier*, November 1955, p. 5), maintained that air pollution is a primary cause of lung cancer,
which has become "practically epidemic." Since then, it has
been linked with heart disease as well as other respiratory
illnesses. Dr. Boyle reported on his findings at a meeting on
October 28, 1970 in Los Angeles.

[12] Kenneth Mellanby, *Pesticides and Pollution* (London: William Collins Sons and Co., Inc., 1967), pp. 47–48.

[13] Ambassador College Research Staff, *Our Polluted Planet*
(Pasadena: Ambassador College Press, 1969), p. 38.

[14] Robert and Leona Train Rienow, "Last Chance for Our
Nation's Waterways," *Saturday Review*, May 22, 1965, p. 36.

See also, Senator Gaylord A. Nelson, "Our Polluted Planet," *The Progressive*, November 1969, p. 13. For a more extended account of the despoilation of the nation's waterways read Donald E. Carr, *Death of the Sweet Waters* (New York: W. W. Norton Company, Inc., 1966).

[15] According to Dr. N. William Hines, law professor at the University of Ohio, the front runners in the "industrial pollution derby" are the pulp and paper processing plants, the food packers and dairy products manufacturers (who think nothing of dumping into waters blood, hooves, paunch manure), the chemicals industry, metals manufacturing and mining, textiles, petroleum, power production, and nuclear industries—not, obviously, in the order of hazards. "Controlling Industrial Water Pollution: Color the Problem Green," *Boston College Industrial and Commercial Law Review*, Spring 1968, p. 555.

[16] *U.S. Consumer Newsletter*, July 23, 1969, citing a report to Senator George McGovern's committee by Dr. John Olney of Washington University.

[17] A detailed account of those and other substances in foods is given in Booth Mooney, *The Hidden Assassins* (Chicago: Follett Publishing Company, 1966). Dr. Herbert S. Goldberg, professor of microbiology at the University of Missouri School of Medicine, reported several years ago that more than half of the $114.6 million worth of antibiotics sold each year in the U.S. were used in animal feeds or added to food crops. Cited, *Prevention*, October 1969, p. 117. The most recent and carefully documented study of the subject is the 336-page report prepared by Ralph Nader's "Raiders," *The Chemical Feast* (New York: Grossman Publishers, 1970)—"a story of the truly massive deception" by the food industry and of "camouflage against the consumer" by the Food and Drug Administration. Margaret E. Duffy pointed out, "Penicillin by the Pound," *Environment*, Oct. 1969, p. 14) that farmers can buy antibiotics by the pound from feed stores, although they need a doctor's prescription to buy a tablet for themselves.

[18] The dramatic contrast in views is reported by Dr. Barry Commoner in *Science and Survival*, pp. 14–15. How correct the latter appraisal was was underscored in an article in the August 1, 1969, *Bulletin of Atomic Scientists*, which indicated that the amount of radiation released in a nuclear exchange would eventually destroy all our own fetal and infant life and that of the rest of mankind. In November 1969, at hearings by the Senate Public Works Subcommittee on Air and Water Pollution, considering Alaska Senator Mike Gravel's bill to set up a commission to investigate AEC, two of the agency's scientists recommended "an immediate and drastic reduction in the permissible radiation dose for the public." Senator Gravel said that their data indicated plans to promote energy under present radiation guidelines "would reverse every single advance made in public health during the last generation." Mike Gravel, "The AEC: The Ultimate Pollution," *Earth Day—The Beginning*, pp. 119–20.

[19] *U.S. News & World Report*, July 7, 1969, p. 6. According to subsequent reports, precisely what had happened was perplexing scientists. Although endosulfan (Thiodan, as it is also called) was known to be a primary contaminant, other elements—the hundreds of poisons held to be in the Rhine at any given time and place—were also involved, as were climatic conditions. Joe Alex Morris, Jr., "Rhine Still Holds Secret to Great Fish Massacre," Los Angeles *Times*, June 24, 1970.

[20] The 1951 estimate was made by Leonard Wickenden, *Our Daily Poison* (New York: The Devin-Adair Company, 1956), p. 3. He based figures for production on the U.S. Department of Agriculture's *Agricultural Statistics*, and those for toxicity of average toxic doses. *Official Publication* of the Association of Economic Poisons Control Officials, 1954. The production has since skyrocketed; new and sophisticated means to detect toxic effects would make that figure also rise greatly.

[21] An interesting account of the trial, which suggests that James Richardson's conviction was a miscarriage of justice,

is given in Mark Lane *Arcadia* (New York: Holt, Rinehart & Winston, Inc., 1970).

[22] The accident in Colombia is considered the second most serious episode of pesticide poisoning in recent years. A tabulation was made by the Human Relations Agency of the California Department of Public Health in *A Report to the 1970 Legislature on the Effects of the Use of DDT and Similar Pesticides on Human Health and the Environment*, December 10, 1969, Table 1, Section VI. (Xerox copy)

[23] Los Angeles *Times*, December 25, 1969. When I spoke with Assistant Deputy Attorney General Paul Richmond on January 7, 1970, he said that the American Potash and Chemical Company, which had been cited for the offense, had dumped materials against regulations. The California Department of Public Health had been authorized to re-bury the deadly stuff properly, with costs paid by the company.

[24] Interview with James Sorenson of Venture Cigarettes, Continental Tobacco Company, Inc., November 18, 1969. He gave me a copy of a report of an analysis made by Southern Testing and Research Laboratories showing the following residues on one randomly selected batch of tobacco: parathion, 7.99 parts per million; DDT, 570 p.p.m.; endrin, .48 p.p.m.; dieldrin, .57 p.p.m.; DDE, 10.65 p.p.m. He also provided me with correspondence about advertising from the National Association of Broadcasters to his company. The 1969 recommendations of the state agency were given in *Tobacco Information for 1969*, The North Carolina Agricultural Extension Service, December 1968. How the refusal of both government and private agencies may aggravate problems was made clear by Senator Gaylord A. Nelson's report in the summer of 1969, in which he said that pesticide residues on tobacco had risen sharply since 1965—the year in which Mr. Sorenson's company was vainly appealing to make public that pesticide-free cigarettes were available.

[25] The British government was almost totally frustrated in its efforts to collect for damages incurred when the *Torrey*

Canyon crashed on Pollard Rock off the coast of Cornwall in 1967. Its bill for $7.5 million was supplemented by bills from individuals for about half that amount to cover costs of cleaning and repairs after 119,000 tons of crude oil gushing from the tanker left deposits up to 18 inches deep along English and French beaches—destroying marine life, killing some 75,000 birds, ruining fishing and tourist businesses, and making life almost intolerable for thousands of persons. Union Oil Company of California had taken maximum precautions to avoid paying, according to Richard Petrow, *In the Wake of Torrey Canyon* (New York: David McKay Company, Inc., 1968). Technical owner of the ship was the Barracuda Tanker Corporation, a Union subsidiary chartered by Liberia and registered in Bermuda. If it had not been for the alertness of a government employee, whose careful perusal of shipping news made possible the seizure of the *Torrey Canyon's* sister ship in Singapore, British property owners and taxpayers would have had to foot the entire bill.

[26] Kenneth Reich, "Harbor Pollution Case Goes to Court Thursday," Los Angeles *Times,* June 23, 1969.

[27] Although the harmful effects of smog have been known to medical experts and to many lay persons for more than a decade, it was not until the spring of 1969 that "smog alerts" were issued, banning youngsters in Los Angeles County schools from indulging in vigorous physical activities when levels were high—about one day out of three in some parts of the basin during some months.

[28] Bill Ballantine, *Nobody Loves a Cockroach* (Boston: Little, Brown and Company, 1967), p. 172.

[29] *The Farm Quarterly,* Summer 1968, pp. 44, 97.

[30] Amarillo *Daily News,* April 10, 1970. The Community Pesticide Laboratory in San Benito, a facility of the Texas Health Department, reported that tests indicated the presence of dieldrin in specimens of dead robins which had died in a western section of Amarillo.

[31] Quoted, *The Progressive*, November 1969, p. 4. A full-fledged indictment of the agency is given by Edward F. Cox, Robert C. Fellmeth, and John E. Schulz, *Nader's Raiders Report on the Federal Trade Commission* (New York: Grove Press, Inc., 1969).

[32] *The Progressive*, November 1969, p. 4.

[33] James E. Reynolds, chief of current information division, Agricultural Research Service, U.S. Department of Agriculture, *USDA Yearbook of Agriculture, 1966* (Washington, D.C.: Government Printing Office, 1966), p. 247.

[34] Quoted, *Conservation Foundation Letter*, May 5, 1969, p. 6.

[35] Aldrin-grape episode reported in detail in *El Malcriado*, September 15–October 1, 1969, p. 2; also by Thomas J. Foley, "Murphy Retracts Accusations Against Union on Pesticides," Los Angeles *Times*, October 1, 1969.

[36] Quoted, Los Angeles *Times*, October 28, 1968.

[37] Consumers Union acted over the objection of a good many government regulatory officials. For a complete account, see *Consumer Reports*, June 1960, pp. 289–92.

[38] AP dispatch, "Kennedy's Chief Science Adviser Warns on Danger of Pesticides," *The New York Times*, May 17, 1963.

[39] Dr. Edward D. Goldberg, chemistry professor at Scripps Institution of Oceanography, quoted by Bryant Evans, "Birdlife Deaths Appear Warning of DDT Dangers," San Diego *Union*, March 2, 1969.

CHAPTER 2 WITHOUT KNOWLEDGE, WHAT CONSENT?

[1] The significance of the achievement was pointed out by Dr. Irma West of the California Department of Public Health's Bureau of Occupational Health in "Detection and Control

of Pesticide Poisoning: A Public Health Problem," *Chemical Fallout: Current Research on Persistent Pesticides,* ed. Morton W. Miller and George G. Berg (Springfield, Ill.: Charles C. Thomas, Publisher, 1969). Pointing out that "there are probably more unsound diagnoses and more missed diagnoses in chemical poisoning than in most other areas of medicine" since tests do not exist for many chemicals or are not available locally and since circumstantial and clinical evidence alone are frequently inadequate for diagnostic purposes, Dr. West complimented the "remarkable acumen" of California physicians in recognizing pesticide poisoning. "Of all of the incidents of pesticide poisoning occurring throughout the world because foodstuffs or other cargo became contaminated in a spill of a pesticide during transportation or storage, *the only two instances in which the pesticide poisoning was immediately suspected because of the appearance of patients on admission to the hospital occurred in California.*" (italics added) (p. 454)

2 "The Dead Mosquitoes," *Annals of Medicine series, The New Yorker,* October 11, 1969, pp. 123–42. (Earlier study, M.C. Warren, *et al.,* "Clothing-Borne Epidemic," *Journal of the American Medical Association,* CLXXXIV:266, 1963.)

3 "The Dead Mosquitoes," p. 132.

4 Harry Bernstein, "Court Upholds Jobless Man's Right to Refuse Farm Work," Los Angeles *Times,* July 4, 1969.

5 Norman Cavender, "Tragedy and Hope: Pesticide Accidents," *The Farm Quarterly,* Summer 1968, pp. 102–4.

6 Affidavit submitted by Dr. Irma West, January 24, 1969, to court considering petition by United Farm Workers Organizing Committee to force Kern County Agricultural Commissioner Seldon Morley to release spraying records. She noted in the article in *Chemical Fallout* other instances of carelessness. During a 15-month period in California, six Spanish-American farm workers died because they mistook

a pesticide for drinking water or other beverage. In one instance, two identical unlabeled bottles were on a spray rig, she said; one contained drinking water, the other paraquat (a potent pesticide). (p. 453)

[7] Charles Bell and Joe Dan Boyd, "Today in the Southwestern States," *Farm Journal*, August 1968, p. 18, quoting the director of the Community Pesticides Study Laboratory in San Benito, Texas. There is usually little question when it comes to a choice between worker safety and profits. For example, health officials in California warned in 1963 that it was dangerous to permit farm workers to go into orchards since the leaves on the peach trees were so contaminated with parathion that poisoning could not be avoided. Agriculture officials—noting that 60 percent of the crop was still not harvested—called such a precaution "unwarranted." "Help Stymied for Poison Victims," Los Angeles *Times*, August 25, 1963.

[8] In September 1969 the California Rural Legal Assistance organization filed suit against several grape growers on behalf of Mrs. Carmen Velasquez and Mr. and Mrs. Carmen Uranday for damages of more than $35,000. The suits charged that when they and about 40 other workers were picking grapes at the Mamanuzzi and Pantaleo farms they were sprayed by a crop-dusting airplane. According to Jim Smith, CRLA attorney, applicator records indicated that Dibrom and Sevin, an organic phosphate and a carbamate, had been used to spray the fields. *El Malcriado*, September 15 October 1, 1969, p. 7.

[9] *A Report to the 1970 Legislature on the Effects of the Use of DDT and Similar Pesticides on Human Health and the Environment*, December 10, 1969, Section VI. (Xerox copy)

[10] Congressman McCarthy said that he began his campaign against chemical warfare weapons as a result of the "horror" he experienced after seeing a television documentary about the killing of 6,500 sheep in Utah's Skull Valley during military "nerve gas" operations. The account of that ex-

perience is described in his book, *The Ultimate Folly* (New York: Alfred A. Knopf, Inc., 1969). The Atlantic shipment was halted; so were shipments of nerve gas to Okinawa. In that case, suits to halt shipments were filed in Federal court by the governors of Washington and Oregon and by the American Civil Liberties Union.

11 *A Report to the 1970 Legislature*, Section VI.

12 *Ibid.*

13 *Ibid.* In 1970 Senator Vance Hartke proposed that a permanent joint Congressional committee be set up to oversee the shipment of hazardous materials and "to inform the American people whenever anyone is taking unnecessary risks with their lives." Donald Robinson, "Danger! Hazardous Materials in Transit," *Reader's Digest*, May 1970, p. 184. Senator Hartke noted that some important points in his safety program do not require new laws—merely action by the Secretary of Transportation. He urged him to: (a) set up a super-agency in his department to fix safety standards for transporting all hazardous materials and for their containers; (b) review and update all hazardous-materials standards and regulations; (c) launch research into preventing hazardous-materials accidents.

14 *Interagency Coordination in Environmental Hazards; Hearings Before the Subcommittee on Reorganization and International Organizations of the Committee on Government Operations,* U.S. Senate, 88th Congress (later referred to as *Ribicoff Hearings*), Testimony of Bernard Lorant, Part II, pp. 2484–527. An investigation of the disposal practices of the company that tried to stop the publication of *Silent Spring* in 1962 was undertaken in 1964 by the U.S. Public Health Service at New Orleans. In *Since Silent Spring* (Boston: Houghton Mifflin Company, 1970), Frank Graham, Jr., notes that after the corporation came under new ownership, company officials were "very cooperative" with water pollution control agents. (p. 108)

[15] *A Report to the 1970 Legislature*, Section VI. Eldridge G. Hunt of the Pesticide Investigations Division of the California Department of Fish and Game reported (*Chemical Fallout: Current Research on Persistent Pesticides*) that a number of fish losses in lakes had occurred because drums containing parathion had been used as boat floats instead of being properly dumped. (p. 458)

A couple of experimental programs were launched in 1969 to minimize the disposal problem. One, financed by a $65,000 grant from the U.S. Public Health Service, was started by scientists from the Oregon State University Environment Health Center. Empty pesticide containers were gathered and stacked inside a fenced area, where the cans were flushed and wastes mixed with alkaline and acid solutions being tested; containers were later smashed, baled, and sold to smelters. According to Stan Federman, "Western County Seeks Ways to Dispose Safely of Pesticide Containers" (*The National Observer*, December 1, 1969), one of the experiments said that "*in five years the pesticides should be broken down by soil micro-organisms, solar radiation, and chemicals to the point where the soil could be diverted to other use.*" (Italics added)

[16] A study made for *Consumer Reports* (July, 1969, p. 410) revealed that only 78 of the 177 pesticide products examined were accompanied by any instructions about disposal.

[17] *Ribicoff Hearings*, Part I. Statement of Secretary of Agriculture Orville L. Freeman, May 13, 1963, Part I, p. 86.

[18] *Effects of 2,4,5-T on Man and the Environment, Hearings before the Subcommittee on Energy, Natural Resources, and the Environment of the Committee on Commerce*, U.S. Senate, 91st Congress (Washington, D.C.: U.S. Government Printing Office, 1970), p. 12.

[19] Statistics are difficult to obtain. However, manufacturers' sales of household insecticides, repellents, and rodenticides were set at $150 million in 1968. Retail value is about twice

that. Agricultural Stabilization and Conservation Service, *The Pesticide Review, 1969* (Washington, D.C.: U.S. Department of Agriculture, 1969), p. 6.

[20] Labeling regulations of the USDA require that the four categories of pesticides be identified with signal words that indicate the degree of toxicity. Class I poisons must bear a skull and crossbones, with the words "Danger" and "Poison" clearly printed, plus a description of an antidote and advice to call a physician immediately if persons are accidentally contaminated by them. Most consumer experts consider all of the poisons in this group too dangerous for home use; yet they are so readily available in some places that even children may be sent to buy them. The next two categories, identified by the words "Warning" and "Caution" respectively, are also potent enough to poison people and are also highly questionable items for household use. Even the fourth category, which must be labeled "Keep Out of Reach of Children," is considered suspect; it should be used with great care.

[21] The first realistic account of chemical warfare in Vietnam was given by two zoology professors, Dr. E. W. Pfeiffer and Dr. G. H. Orians of the state universities of Montana and Washington, who went on an ecological fact-finding mission from March 17 to April 1, 1969, under the auspices of the Society for Social Responsibility in Science. Their report was published in the *SSRS Newsletter,* May 1969, and in greater detail in *Scientific Research,* June 9 and June 23, 1969.

[22] *Conservation Foundation Letter,* May 5, 1969, p. 7.

[23] *U.S. Consumer Newsletter,* November 12, 1969, p. 1.

[24] Press release, U. S./R. & D., Palo Alto, Calif., 1969.

[25] Former Secretary of Interior Stewart Udall described the episode in San Joaquin, Bolivia, in "Public Policy and Pest Control," *Scientific Aspects of Pest Control* (Washington,

D.C.: National Academy of Science—National Research Council, 1966), p. 430. In that article he noted: "There is certainly a moral here for the man who can no longer afford the single-minded innocence of his past when using dangerous chemicals."

[26] Even in advanced countries like Japan, pesticide expenditures annually exceed sums spent on machinery and services in agriculture. J. C. Headley and J. N. Lewis, *The Pesticide Problem: An Economic Approach to Public Policy* (Washington, D.C.: Resources for the Future, Inc., 1967) p. 88. Yet as early as 1962 some economists were worrying that the effects of toxic residues on foodstuffs would affect their freedom of movement in international trade. See S. Dormal and H. Hurtig, "Principles for Establishment of Pesticide Residue Tolerances," *Residue Reviews,* I, 140–51.

CHAPTER 3   CHEMICAL WAR IS NOT HEALTHY FOR
             PEOPLE . . .

[1] Dr. Hoskins, under further questioning, said that he did not think it "especially" important that human beings used as guinea pigs give their consent to experiments. "The really significant test," he said, is to feed a considerable amount of "naturally" contaminated food to a numerous group of people—as is "already being done in an unplanned way with every new agricultural chemical." *Chemicals in Foods and Cosmetics, Hearings Before the House Select Committee to Investigate the Use of Chemicals in Foods and Cosmetics,* House of Representatives, 82nd Congress (Washington, D.C.: U.S. Government Printing Office, 1952), Part 2, pp. 790–92. (Later references will be to *Delaney Hearings.* B)

[2] J. L. Radomski and William B. Deichmann, "Pesticide Levels in Humans in a Variety of Natural and Experimental Conditions," *Chemical Fallout: Current Research on Persistent Pesticides,* ed. Morton W. Miller and George G. Berg (Springfield, Ill.: Charles C. Thomas, Publisher, 1969). The Florida researchers pointed out the "disquieting" nature of

the concentrations found in fetuses since: "Teratogenicity can occur with minute concentrations of compounds and their obvious existence during the first trimester of pregnancy should be a matter of considerable concern." (p. 302)

3 Dr. Goran Lofroth, quoted in *Society for Social Responsibility in Science Newsletter,* June 1969.

4 The practice of using persistent pesticides to mothproof woolen items is widespread. By 1965, 95 percent of all wool carpets were being treated with insecticides to ward off moths and carpet beetles. Blankets and sweaters are also mothproofed routinely. *Prevention,* March 1965, p. 87. The most commonly used pesticide has been dieldrin, a highly toxic chlorinated hydrocarbon. Most dry-cleaning establishments, including the coin-operated ones, provide mothproofing as part of the process, whether or not customers wish it or can tolerate it.

5 *Ribicoff Hearings* (See Chapter 2, Note 14), Part I, p. 53. Although a zero tolerance was set, in some cases residues were allowed at detectable levels lower than those believed to be "pharmacologically significant." During 1969 and 1970, very strong efforts were made to abandon the zero tolerance concept on the grounds that no foods were free of residues.

6 *Congressional Quarterly Almanac,* 1964, p. 139. Despite protests, the inspection staff and enforcement staff have continued to be so small that the same figure was given to me by an FDA official in 1970. He pointed out that in many areas less than one percent of food shipments were inspected.

7 *Ribicoff Hearings,* Part I, p. 53.

8 It is difficult to give a more detailed comparative study since in the U.S. the tolerances vary widely from crop to crop. The setting of tolerances item by item makes the problems of inspection vastly more difficult than they

should be. Common Market countries, on the other hand, have simplified matters enormously by setting residues for fruits and vegetables generally. There were sharp differences in every category checked. The official FDA tolerances were published in *N.A.C. News and Pesticide Review,* January–February 1969. Common Market country tolerances were taken from D. R. Thompson's "Report to the California-Arizona Citrus Industry," December 20, 1968: *An Unofficial Translation of Proposed Pesticide Regulation of the Common Market.* (Mimeo copy)

[9] "The Effect of Known Repeated Oral Doses of Chlorophenothane (DDT) in Man," *Journal of the American Medical Association,* October 27, 1956, p. 897. (Actually, the paper had three authors: Dr. William F. Durham and Cipriano Cueto, Jr., also signed it.) Although it has been rendered obsolete, the article is still used as a principal defense for the continued wide-scale and unrestricted use of DDT. I received three copies during a single visit to the offices of the National Agricultural Chemicals Association in Washington, D.C., in June 1969.

[10] *Ibid.,* p. 893.

[11] After a federal investigation was launched into drug testing in Kilby Prison in Alabama, where drug company experimentation had resulted in the death of four inmates and the hospitalization of 10 percent of the prison population, FDA Commissioner Dr. Herbert L. Ley, Jr., made some interesting revelations about the use of prisoners as guinea pigs. He said that the generous fees paid to inmate volunteers "offered a high stimulus not to report adverse side effects." (In cases where fees are not high, inmates are often given credits that count toward early parole.) *Newsweek,* August 25, 1969, p. 71.

[12] Press release issued by the National Agricultural Chemicals Association, April 29, 1969.

[13] R. A. M. Case, "Toxic Effects of DDT in Man," *British Medical Journal,* December 15, 1945, pp. 842–45.

[14] V. D. Wigglesworth, "A Case of DDT Poisoning in Man," *British Medical Journal,* April 14, 1945, p. 517.

[15] *Insects in Your Life* (New York: Sheridan House, 1951), p. 288.

[16] Tremors in insects are followed by loss of motion and apparent paralysis; in mammals by convulsions, both tonic (rigid) and clonic (frenzied uncoordinated movements). Finally, weakness and prostration occur. R. D. O'Brien, *Insecticides: Action and Metabolism* (New York: Academic Press, 1967), p. 111.

[17] *Delaney Hearings* B (Part 2), pp. 948–63. Dr. Bernard Krohn submitted as part of his testimony an article written by him and Dr. Francis M. Pottenger, Jr. The two doctors told that they had recorded in their own clinic in California during a single year more than 100 cases of a syndrome resulting from the widespread use of chlorinated hydrocarbons—a syndrome of hepatic and neurologic damage and sometimes death. Women as well as men were affected. Many of the cases involved ranchers, agricultural inspectors, farm wives, and workers who had frequently handled pesticides. Also included was a 44-year-old California dentist. A commander in the U.S. Navy during World War II, he had experienced "heavy exposure" to DDT on Midway, where he was stationed in 1943 and 1944. He was also exposed to DDT in 1945 and 1947. Shortly before the illness that led him to seek medical aid from Dr. Krohn and Dr. Pottenger, he had been using an aerosol bomb around the house.

[18] *Our Daily Poison* (New York: The Devin-Adair Company, 1956), pp. 2–21.

[19] Quotations of statements by Dr. Welch and Dr. Robert Risebrough from transcript of hearings conducted by the Wisconsin Department of Natural Resources were given to me in June 1969 by Victor J. Yannacone, Jr., legal counsel

for the Environmental Defense Fund, which was petition-
ing for a ban on DDT in that state.

[20] Dr. Risebrough has spoken up sharply about the failure of
government and industry to fulfill their responsibility to
ascertain effects of persistent pesticides accumulating in the
ecosystem of the globe. The "major efforts" of manufacturers, he has said, "have consisted of writing letters to *Science*
which comment upon the relative abundance of robins."
And because of the "inherent limitations" of government
and international organizations, which prevent them from
taking the initiative, "the answer must come from the cooperative efforts of individual ecologists, naturalists, and
molecular biologists." (That is what happened at the Wisconsin hearings.) Risebrough's comments were made during a discussion reported in *Chemical Fallout*, p. 21.

[21] Quoted, *The Connecticut Conservation Reporter*, May-June
1969, p. 3.

[22] "Pesticide Levels in Humans in a Variety of Natural and
Experimental Conditions," *Chemical Fallout*, pp. 297 and
307–9.

More recently, a study associating lung cancer with organ-
ochlorine pesticides was presented at the March 1970
meeting of the Society of Toxicology by Ralph Jennings of
the U.S. Food and Drug Administration and Jack Dacre of
New Zealand. The two researchers made detailed studies
of 27 corpses, 11 of whom were lung cancer victims. They
found more than twice the mean level of dieldrin and DDT
and its derivatives in the lungs of the cancer victims and
almost twice as much lindane. *Medical World News*, March
27, 1970, p. 5.

[23] An interesting discussion of the Hueper-Hayes conflict
appears in Laura Tallian's *The Pesticide Jungle* (privately
printed, 1966), p. 25. (The brief book, carefully written and
researched, may be obtained from Mrs. Tallian, Box 34,
Phillipsville, Calif. 95559.) The substance of Dr. Hueper's

testimony before the Wisconsin hearing examiner is contained in a report in *Medical World News*, March 14, 1969.

24 Karl Lutz, "FDA Discovers DDT Dangers—20 Years Late," *Prevention*, November 1969, pp. 74–77.

25 *Delaney Hearings* (see Note 1), 81st Congress, 1951, p. 389. (Referred to later as Delaney Hearings A)

26 *Ribicoff Hearings*, Part 10, pp. 2164–72.

27 Dr. Hargraves' statement about the dangers of lindane were made to the Ribicoff Subcommittee. (Since that time he has repeated and amplified them.) *Ribicoff Hearings*, Part 2, pp. 484–97.

28 Dr. Jerome B. Wiesner, *Ribicoff Hearings*, Part 1, p. 48.

29 *Delaney Hearings* A, 1951. He stressed in his protest that chlordane, "very toxic to liver and kidneys," should never be sold as a household spray—as it has been.

30 Although the high levels of acetylcholine have persuaded investigators that cholinesterase inhibition is the biochemical lesion responsible for death, the consequences of the lesion have not been traced in insects. In them, the cause of death is "completely unknown." R. D. O'Brien, *op. cit,* p. 58.

31 Affidavit of Dr. Irma West, January 29, 1969. (See Chapter 2.)

32 Statement of Jerome B. Gordon before the U.S. Senate Subcommittee on Migratory Labor, August 1, 1969. A typescript of Mr. Gordon's statement was given to me by Senator Walter Mondale.

33 Testimony of Dr. Lee Mizrahi before the House Subcommittee on Labor in San Francisco, November 24, 1969; reprinted in *El Malcriado*, November 15–30, 1969, pp. 3, 7.

[34] *Ibid.*

[35] California health report summarized in *El Malcriado,* September 15–October 1, 1969, p. 3.

[36] S. Gershon and F. H. Shaw of the University of Melbourne, *The Lancet,* June 1961, pp. 1371–74.

[37] Dr. Paul Smith, *Ribicoff Hearings,* Part 10, p. 2165.

[38] A warning that could have averted the disaster was issued some months before by *Environment* magazine, May 1969. A detailed history of mercury poisoning is presented by Dr. Neville Grant, "Legacy of the Mad Hatter," pp. 18–24.

[39] *Ibid.*

[40] Goran Lofroth with Margaret E. Duffy, "Birds Give Warning," *Environment,* May, 1969, p. 12.

[41] *Ibid.* p. 13.

[42] Robert Sherrill, "The Real Villains," *The Nation,* September 14, 1970, p. 210. The official who so testified was Dr. Harry W. Hays, whose activities are reported in Chapter Six.

[43] "Chemical Hazards in the Human Environment," paper delivered at the 11th Science Writers Seminar of the American Cancer Society, New Orleans, La., March 28–April 2, 1969, pp. 3–4.

[44] *Quarterly Bulletin of the Association of Food and Drug Officials of the U.S.,* XIV (Fall 1950), 90.

[45] J. Frawley, H. Pugot, E. Hagan, J. Black, and O. Fitzhugh reported their experiment in the *Journal of Pharmacology,* CXXI, 96.

[46] Kenneth P. DuBois, "Potentiation of the Toxicity of Organophosphorus Compounds," *Advance in Pest Control Research,*

IV, 134. The synergistic effect obtained by combining malathion with TOTP seems to have been the highest observed. In commenting on the phenomenon, J. C. Headley and J. N. Lewis, *The Pesticide Problem: An Economic Approach to Public Policy* (Washington, D.C.: Resources for the Future, Inc., 1967), say: "By its very nature, synergism or potentiation constitutes an uncertainty and not a measurable risk. Even if observations over time would eventually yield meaningful estimates of risks, it is unlikely that this way to their measurement would be left open. This is especially true if the risk to be assessed is not the chance of a few thousand deaths or obvious cases of genetic mutation . . . but whether in the long run we shall all be dead of synergistic poisoning." (p. 99)

[47] Harry Nelson, "Cancer Tied to Mix of 'Safe' Food Additives," Los Angeles *Times*, November 9, 1969.

[48] *The Hidden Assassins* (Chicago: Follett Publishing Company, 1966), p. 106.

[49] Report from the Mississippi Agricultural Experimental Station, quoted in *Prevention*, January 1969, p. 72.

[50] After the California Department of Agriculture limited the use of DDT, a group of farm workers, represented by the California Rural Legal Assistance organization, asked state and federal officials to declare a "pesticide emergency," since organic phosphates are more dangerous than DDT. Philip Hager, "DDT Substitute Called Far More Dangerous," Los Angeles *Times*, March 12, 1970.

[51] *Washington Highlights Newsletter*, July 14, 1969.

CHAPTER 4 . . . AND OTHER LIVING THINGS

[1] UPI dispatch, "Technology-Ecology Conflict Perils Mankind, Scientist Says," Los Angeles *Times*, November 27,

1969. The Borneo episode told at the UNESCO commission's 13th national meeting in San Francisco had been told earlier in *Science Digest,* September 1968.

2 Report quoted in *Conservation Foundation Letter,* April 25, 1969, p. 5. In that, it was noted that "even the lightly paralyzed birds . . . unable to feed . . . unable to adopt the proper posture in case it rains . . . become soaked, are unable to keep up thermo-regulation, and die of exposure."

3 AP dispatch, "Russian Raps Pesticides for Animal Deaths," Los Angeles *Times,* April 27, 1970.

4 Andrew Duncan, *A Year With the Queen. Look,* May 5, 1970, p. 40. Prince Philip's comment was made in response to his having been chided for taking part in a pheasant hunt in the spring of 1969.

5 Quoted, Leonard Wickenden, *Our Daily Poison* (New York: The Devin-Adaer Company, 1958), p. 16. The point was made as early as 1951 by A. W. A. Brown, *Insect Control by Chemicals* (New York: John Wiley & Sons, Inc., 1951), that the "favored few" with a margin of resistance had been allowed by chemicals to survive and breed. "Normally they would be eliminated by parasites and predators, to whom this kind of resistance means nothing. But if the chemical treatment has removed the biological control species, the more resistant individuals of the pest species can then survive to breed." (p. 723)

6 An excellent discussion of resistance appears in Robert L. Rudd's *Pesticides and the Living Landscape* (Madison, Wisc.: The University of Wisconsin Press, 1964), pp. 141–48.

7 *International Harvester FARM,* Spring 1969, p. 5.

8 Because of the presence of U.S. servicemen, resistance of flies in Italy caused an international furor in 1947. How-

ever, the first example of DDT-tolerance in houseflies was observed in 1946 in Sweden, in a dairy farming region about 400 miles north of Stockholm. A. W. A. Brown, *Insecticide Resistance in Arthropods* (Geneva: World Health Organization, 1958), p. 104.

9 According to Dr. E. Gorton Linsley, dean of the College of Agricultural Sciences at the University of California, Berkeley, a growing genetic resistance by mosquitoes to insecticides has helped to make control in California "increasingly difficult." In particular, a species of *Aedes* demonstrates strong resistance to all larvicides normally used. *Science News,* June 21, 1969, p. 599.

10 "Indestructible Roach Faces New KO Punch, Insecticide Firm Says," *The Wall Street Journal,* Feburary 14, 1968. The demonstration arranged for newsmen was less than successful, however. At the press conference the chief entomologist of Chemagro Corporation placed several dozen small cockroaches in each of two glass trays. Both had been treated 24 hours earlier—one with Black Flag, which contained the new chemical hope, Baygon; the other with a popular insecticide without Baygon. According to the WHJ reporter: "In 30 minutes the roaches in the Black Flag beaker were to be lifeless while those in the second jar were supposed to show no ill effects. The demonstration was foiled, however, because the cockroaches were too cold from their trip to Cranford, N.J., and didn't walk around in the trays enough to collect Baygon on their feet."

11 "Farm Pest Resisting, UC Says," San Jose *News,* March 11, 1969. It was pointed out that only a few applications were needed to do the job in 1948.

12 *Our Plundered Planet* (Boston: Little, Brown and Company, 1948), p. 61.

13 C. H. Curran, *Insects in Your Life* (New York: Sheridan House, 1951), p. 288.

[14] "Slave-Labourers in the Vineyard," *Sunday (London) Times Magazine*, February 1, 1970, p. 32. Mr. Lewis noted that the insects against which the pesticides had been developed had survived, however. He reported that when David Montgomery, the photographer, took his pictures of the grape pickers "he was astonished to find himself working in a blizzard of flying insects—survivors of all the dusts and sprays. So many of them were there that his problem was to keep his lenses clear, and when he unscrewed a lens to change it, insects got into the body of the camera." (p. 35)

[15] Alexander Sprunt, IV, president of the Audubon Society, quoted in *Conservation Foundation Letter*, April 25, 1969. The shell-less egg was found in 1969 along the shore of Lake Superior in Michigan by two ornithologists doing research for the society.

[16] *Petitioner's Brief* prepared by Yannacone and Yannacone for the Citizens Natural Resources Association, Inc. and Wisconsin Division, Izaak Walton League of America, Inc. pp. 34–35. (See also, *Transcript* of Hearings before Department of Natural Resources, State of Wisconsin, pp. 1216–21.)

[17] "Chlorinated Hydrocarbon Insecticides and the World Ecosystem," *Biological Conservation*, I (1969), 48. (Taken in part from Wurster's affidavit to the U.S. Federal Court in Michigan: Environmental Defense Fund *vs.* Michigan Department of Agriculture.)

[18] *Ibid.*, p. 50. Dr. Wurster singled out the widespread DDT spray campaign to control Dutch elm disease, which occasioned massive bird kills. "The best record," he noted, "has been achieved by destroying dead and dying branches."

[19] *Ribicoff Hearings* (see Chap. 2, Note 14), Part 1, p. 46. Described in detail was an early indication of the acute toxicity of DDT. When British Columbia forests were sprayed at the rate of only one pound an acre, the morbid-

ity rate of Coho salmon in four major streams in the area reached almost 100 percent. More recent appraisal of the effect of DDT on aquatic life was given by Senator Gaylord A. Nelson: "The Effects of Pesticides on Sport and Commercial Fishing," statement before the Senate Subcommittee on Energy, Natural Resources, and the Environment, May 19, 1969. (Mimeo copy, p. 3)

[20] The Clear Lake story is perhaps the most frequently cited episode in recent ecological history. An excellent account was presented in an article, "UCD Scientist's Transplanted Fish Are Eating Clear Lake Back to Health," written for the Sacramento *Bee* and reprinted in the *University of California Clip Sheet*, November 25, 1969.

[21] *Ibid.* For a fuller description, see S. G. Herman, R. L. Garrett, and R. L. Rudd, "Pesticides and the Western Grebe," *Chemical Fallout: Current Research on Persistent Pesticides*, ed. Morton W. Miller and George G. Berg (Springfield, Ill.: Charles C. Thomas, Publisher, 1969), pp. 24–51.

[22] Richard Poole, marine biologist with Marine Resources Laboratory of the California Fish and Game Department, quoted in the Los Angeles *Herald-Examiner*, May 13, 1969. Researchers from that agency have also suggested that DDT was a major cause of the death of California's sardine industry based at Monterey, which provided the setting for John Steinbeck's *Cannery Row*.

Newest concern was revealed by Dr. Bruce Halstead, biotoxicologist and consultant to the United Nations Committee on Health, Food, and Agriculture. He said that more than 50 percent of "a large number of fish" pulled out of the Pacific near one river in southern California showed signs of cancer and other abnormalities caused by pollution. "Cancer in Fish an Issue," Los Angeles *Herald-Examiner*, May 2, 1970.

[23] Statement cited, p. 1.

[24] *Ibid.*

[25] Jerry Ruhlow ("Mackerel Withdrawn After Pesticide Tests," Los Angeles *Times,* December 3, 1969) reported a similar episode later in the year in which more than 4,000 cases of mackerel were held off the market because of residues of up to 10 ppm.

[26] Charles F. Wurster, Jr., and David B. Wingate, "DDT Reduced Photosynthesis by Marine Phytoplankton," *Science,* March 29, 1968, pp. 1474–75.

[27] William A. Albrecht, "Physical, Chemical, and Biological Changes in the Soil Community," *Man's Role in Changing the Face of the Earth,* ed. William L. Thomas, Jr., International Symposium, Wenner-Gren Foundation for Anthropological Research (Chicago: University of Chicago Press, 1956), p. 670.

[28] An excellent popular book on the subject is John H. Storer, *The Web of Life* (New York: New American Library, 1953).

[29] The fertility of the soil is closely related to the activity of earthworms. Studies have shown that in some areas of England's rich farmland, earthworms pass more than 40 tons of castings annually on an acre of ground; in the extraordinarily fertile Nile Valley, as many as 200 tons. Beatrice Trum Hunter, *Gardening without Poisons* (Boston: Houghton Mifflin Company, 1964), p. 57.

[30] Storer, *op. cit.,* p. 34.

[31] The debate about the effect of agricultural chemicals on the soil is presented succinctly by J. C. Headley and J. N. Lewis. *The Pesticide Problem: An Economic Approach to Public Policy* (Washington, D.C.: Resources for the Future, Inc., 1967), pp. 77–78.

[32] *Ibid.,* p. 77.

33 Agricultural Stabilization and Conservation Service, *The Pesticide Review, 1969* (Washington, D.C.: U.S. Department of Agriculture, 1969), p. 33.

34 Report of a Statewide Weed Control Committee in California in 1956, quoted by Wheeler McMillan, *Bugs or People?* (New York: Appleton-Century-Crofts, 1965), p. 125.

35 Agricultural Research Service, "Losses in Agriculture," *Agricultural Handbook* (Washington, D.C.: U.S. Department of Agriculture, 1965), p. 291.

36 Alden S. Crafts and Wilfred W. Robbins, *Weed Control* (New York: McGraw-Hill Book Company, Inc., 1962), pp. 19–24.

37 Glenn C. Klingman, *Weed Control: As a Science* (New York: John Wiley & Sons, Inc., 1961), p. 203.

38 *Pesticides and Pollution,* p. 79.

39 *USDA Yearbook of Agriculture, 1966,* p. 77.

40 There is a good comprehensive account of the various types in Klingman, *Weed Control: As a Science.*

41 *The Pesticide Review, 1969,* p. 8.

42 McMillan, *op. cit.,* p. 123.

43 *El Malcriado,* February 15, 1969.

44 Excellent studies of the U.S. chemical war in Vietnam have been written by Robin Clarke, editor of *Science Journal,* (*The Silent Weapons,* New York: David McKay Company, Inc., 1968) and Thomas Whiteside (*Defoliation,* New York: Ballantine Books, Inc., 1970). Also of interest is the United Nations Report, *Chemical and Bacteriological (Biological)*

Weapons and the Effects of Their Possible Use (New York: Ballantine Books, Inc., 1970), with a special foreword by George Wald.

[45] Clarke, *op. cit.*, p. 146.

[46] *Ibid.*, p. 147.

[47] Dixon Donnelley, assistant secretary of the Department of Defense, said in his reply that the destruction of crops had been undertaken "only in remote and thinly populated areas under Viet Cong control" and that the defoliants used were "not harmful to people, animals, soil, or water." *The Silent Weapons*, p. 218.

[48] "Mission to Vietnam," *Science Report*, Part I, June 9, 1969.

[49] Typewritten statement by Professor Pfeiffer.

[50] In April 1969, 273 weed killers were suspended from interstate sale because they contained 2,4,5-T. However, less than a month later they were returned to the market by the Department of Agriculture with "revised labels," omitting suspended uses, but including directions for the uses still approved. UPI dispatch, "Relabeled Weed Killers Okayed," Los Angeles *Herald-Examiner*, May 11, 1970.

[51] Professor Pfeiffer's statement.

[52] George C. Wilson, "Defoliation Damages Cost U.S. Millions," Los Angeles *Times*, February 5, 1970.

[53] An uproar occurred in Arizona after the Forest Service admitted that drift from its spraying operations had fallen on inhabited areas of Arizona, 90 miles east of Phoenix. Residents complained of ruined gardens, dying trees, deformed animals, and poor health. Philip Fradkin, "More Curbs on Use of Herbicides Sought," Los Angeles *Times*, May 10, 1970.

The latest and most complete information is contained in
*Effects of 2, 4, 5-T on Man and the Environment, Hearings
Before the Subcommittee on Energy, Natural Resources,
and the Environment of the Committee on Commerce,*
91st Congress (Washington, D.C.: U.S. Government Printing Office, 1970).

CHAPTER 5 WHAT PROTECTION? (I)

[1] The account of the 1837 Supreme Court decision and Chief
Justice Roger B. Taney's comment are from an excellent
study of the weaknesses and failures of some of the protective agencies, Louis M. Kohlmeier, Jr., *The Regulators* (New
York: Harper & Row Publishers, Inc., 1969), pp. 3–10.

[2] "The Role of the Attorney General as a Public Lawyer,"
Los Angeles Bar Bulletin, September 1969, p. 495.

[3] Lewis Herber, *Our Synthetic Environment* (New York:
Alfred A. Knopf, Inc., 1962), p. 229.

[4] Brinkley quoted, *The Conservation Foundation Letter,* May
5, 1969, pp. 3–4.

[5] Loevinger quoted, James Bishop, Jr., and Henry W. Hubbard, *Let the Seller Beware!* (Washington, D.C.: The
National Press, Inc., 1969), p. 88.

[6] *Deficiencies in Administration of Federal Insecticide, Fungicide, and Rodenticide Act: Hearings before a Subcommittee of the Committee on Government Operations,* 91st
Congress, First Session (Washington, D.C.: U.S. Government Printing Office, 1969), p. 142. (Subsequent references
will be to *Fountain Subcommittee Hearings.*)

[7] By 1969 there were 45,000 registered products and 900 registered compounds.

[8] *Fountain Subcommittee Hearings,* p. 151.

[9] *Ibid.,* pp. 159–62.

[10] *Ibid.,* p. 155.

[11] *Ibid.,* pp. 156–57.

[12] The first major indictment of lindane vaporizers was made in an article in the *Journal of the American Medical Association* in October 1951, when the Committee on Pesticides reported that pharmacological findings "were not consistent." Less than two years later (July 1953) the AMA Committee on Pesticides reported that at least 14 states and 35 municipalities had banned lindane's use near food. In that year the Secretary of HEW was also questioning use of the vaporizers. A detailed account of the background is given in *Fountain Subcommittee Hearings,* pp. 192–97.

[13] *Deficiencies in Administration of Federal Insecticide, Fungicide, and Rodenticide Act, Eleventh Report by the Committee on Government Operations,* 91st Congress, First Session (Washington, D.C.: U.S. Government Printing Office, 1969), p. 71. The quotation is from an article by Kenneth D. Quarterman, then head of the Communicable Disease Center in Savannah, published in *Public Health Reports.* It further states: "It was decided also that the Government should not seek to obtain a domestic patent on the invention because prior publications on the invention by the Government scientists who developed it are deemed sufficient protection against the prosecution of a successful patent application by a later inventor. These publications will within 1 year from the first date of publication, constitute a dedication of the invention to the public. Such a dedication adequately protects the interests of the Government. On the basis of this determination and decision, any manufacturer who wishes to do so may proceed with the domestic production of DDVP in the United States without seeking a license from the government."

Despite the Quarterman statement, the report noted, Shell claims exclusive U.S. patent rights.

(Further references will identify this document as *Eleventh Report*.)

14 *Ibid.*, pp. 59–61.

15 *Ibid.*, pp. 61–62.

16 *Ibid.*, p. 65. Some years earlier Dr. Zavon had bewildered the Ribicoff Senate Subcommittee by his ambivalent attitudes about keeping records of pesticide poisonings. In an article in *Modern Medicine* (August 20, 1962), he and two other scientists had been listed as the three persons in the country to whom doctors should send reports—a matter of importance since that was "the only way in which human experience can be accumulated and added to our body of knowledge." (p. 305) Yet when he testified before the subcommittee as an industry witness (on that occasion he was identified as chairman of the Toxicology Committee of the NACA), Dr. Zavon told the legislators that he objected to making it necessary for manufacturers or their representatives to send their findings to the U.S. Public Health Service. That would, he said, "only clutter up our files." (*Ribicoff Hearings*, Part 1, p. 294.)

17 *Eleventh Report*, p. 65.

18 *Ibid.*, p. 66.

19 *Ibid.*, p. 57. Dr. George W. Irving, ARS Administrator, told the subcommittee that he had been unable to determine who was responsible for the clearance statement.

20 *Ibid.*, pp. 69–70.

21 *Ibid.*, p. 53.

22 Dr. Thomas H. Harris, director of the pesticide registration division at HEW, told the subcommittee that he had attempted to obtain answers to a number of questions about the use of certain powerful pesticides around food and in

homes. When no reply was made to his letter, he called Dr. Hays, who told him, Dr. Harris said, that as a result of the GAO reports "he was suspicious of everybody . . . that if he gave the information requested in our letter he was of the opinion it would be used against him." *Fountain Subcommittee Hearings,* pp. 131–32.

Dr. Hays was "removed quietly from his post in May 1970 and reassigned to a staff job in the "broad area" of "how we process and handle foods." (AP dispatch, "U.S. Pesticide Chief Shifted to Staff Post," Los Angeles *Times,* May 27, 1970.)

23 *Fountain Subcommittee Hearings,* pp. 55–56.

24 *Ibid.,* p. 63.

25 *Ibid.,* p. 23. Later in the proceedings, Dr. Hays revised that estimate upward, saying that he meant only six main chemicals or groups of chemicals that might involve 252 products. (p. 64)

26 *Ibid.,* p. 64.

27 *Eleventh Report,* p. 14.

28 *Ibid.,* pp. 13–17.

29 *Ibid.,* p. 58.

30 Press release, USDA, November 13, 1969.

31 "U.S. Says Shelf-Paper Pesticides Seep into Food, Orders Use Ended," *The National Observer,* December 22, 1969. Registration of the thirteen anti-bug shelfpapers was canceled after "recent tests" showed that "the pesticides soak through cardboard of paper wrapping into food inside in as few as five days on the shelf." Pesticide-impregnated paper used to pack fruit and other produce continued to be observed.

[32] *Ribicoff Hearings,* Part 1, p. 232.

[33] One illustration of Congressman Whitten's power involved Dr. George Irving, Jr., ARS administrator who back-stopped Dr. Hays during the Fountain Subcommittee Hearings. Dr. Irving called the congressman to alert him that Mississippi was included in a proposed National Nutrition Survey. Mr. Whitten, who is sensitive about his state's image, was able to stop that. Thus, the agency executive's "fear of one congressman stopped cold" the significant attempt to learn the fact about hunger in Mississippi, reported Nick Kotz in *Let Them Eat Promises: The Politics of Hunger* (Englewood Cliffs, N.J.: Prentice-Hall, Inc., 1969), pp. 84–85.

[34] Booth Mooney, *The Hidden Assassins* (Chicago: Follett Publishing Company, 1966), p. 112.

[35] *Ibid.,* p. 135. Mr. Whitten's own glowing tribute to pesticides, *That We May Live* (New York: D. Van Nostrand Company, Inc., 1966), draws heavily on the opinions of Dr. Wayland Hayes, Jr., Dr. Zavon, and the long list of other experts whose opinions have been widely publicized by NACA in attacking "the fantasy" of Rachel Carson's *Silent Spring.*

CHAPTER 6   WHAT PROTECTION? (II)

[1] The USDA is responsible for fat content; yet, according to Senator Abraham Ribicoff, its record in that regard is "outrageous." His charge was made in reaction to a USDA memo telling regional marketing directors that the department "will not take hasty action in enforcement of the regulations." Quoted in "Fat Hot Dogs," *Prevention,* May 1970, p. 164.

[2] R. E. Duggan and Keith Dawson, "Pesticides: A Report on Residues in Food," reprinted from *FDA Papers,* June 5, 1967, by National Agricultural Chemicals Association, p. 2. An important reference in preparing this chapter was *The*

Regulation of Pesticides in the United States, prepared by the USDA and the Department of Health, Education, and Welfare, Food and Drug Administration (Washington, D.C.: Government Printing Office, 1968).

[3] Some chemically minded advisers went further, insisting, for example, that some types of turnips might be 100 times more potent in regard to anti-thyroid activity than cranberries "badly contaminated" with aminotriazole. William F. Durham, "Pesticide Residues in Foods in Relation to Human Health," *Residue Reviews*, IV (1963), 31–81.

[4] Congressman Delaney's address to the National Health Federation, quoted, Lewis Herber, *Our Synthetic Environment* (New York: Alfred A. Knopf, 1962), p. 233.

[5] Booth Mooney, *The Hidden Assassins* (Chicago: Follett Publishing Company, 1966), p. 111. Dr. Paul Ehrlich noted in *The Population Bomb* (New York: Ballantine Books, Inc., 1968): "The setting of tolerances by the FDA is much too open to error (as can be seen by repeated readjustments), and the power available to enforce tolerances is completely inadequate." (pp. 122–23)

[6] Mooney, *op. cit.* The FDA had refused to grant tolerances because experimental animals were grossly affected by the stuff. Even the cranberry growers' marketing association had warned members against using the weed killer. When the HEW Secretary halted the sale, a USDA official pleaded for time to straighten things out: "His position was that if the year's cranberry crop did in fact present a hazard, the whole matter should be handled quietly." (p. 120)

[7] Justus C. Ward, director of the Pesticides Regulation Division from 1957 to 1966, *USDA Yearbook of Agriculture, 1966* (Washington, D.C.: Government Printing Office, 1966), p. 277.

[8] "Unofficial Translation of Proposed Pesticide Regulation of the Common Market," *Report to the California-Arizona*

Citrus Industry by D. R. Thompson, European representative, December 24, 1968. In 1968 the FDA lowered DDT residue tolerance on 36 fruits and vegetables from 7 p.p.m. to 3.6 p.p.m.

⁹ Charles C. Johnson, Jr., administrator of Consumer Protection and Environmental Health Service, HEW, statement before Subcommittee on Migratory Labor of the Senate Committee on Labor and Public Welfare, August 1, 1969. (Typed copy. See especially p. 3.)

¹⁰ The extraordinary story of the 2,4,5-T episode, beginning with the suppression of the Bionetics Laboratory report, to final reluctant action by U.S. government agencies, is spelled out in full detail in hearings conducted by Senator Philip A. Hart's subcommittee in the spring of 1970: *Effects of 2,4,5-T on Man and the Environment, Hearings before the Subcommittee on Energy, Natural Resources, and the Environment of the Committee on Commerce*, United States Senate, 91st Congress (Washington, D.C.: U.S. Government Printing Office, 1970). (*Hart Hearings*)

¹¹ Scientists associated with Dow Chemical Company made the claim that a contaminant was responsible—a claim contradicted by other tests conducted showing that even "purest" 2,4,5-T produced birth defects in test animals at significant levels. *Ibid.*

¹² Duggan and Dawson, *op. cit.*, p. 5.

¹³ *Ibid.*, p. 4.

¹⁴ J. C. Headley and J. N. Lewis, *The Pesticide Problem: An Economic Approach to Public Policy* (Washington, D.C.: Resources for the Future, Inc., 1967), p. 55.

¹⁵ Quoted, *Prevention*, November 1969, p. 62.

¹⁶ Dr. Verrett, who was also an important witness in the investigation of 2,4,5-T, reported the results of her tests with

chicks in similar terms: "I would say that . . . this material is not for the birds." *Hart Hearings*, p. 201.

[17] AP dispatch, Los Angeles *Times,* May 15, 1970. It reported also that, "In apparent anticipation of the congressional investigation [of the FDA], Commissioner Charles C. Edwards last week decried what he called harassment of the agency."

[18] Dr. Ley quoted, Los Angeles *Times,* January 1, 1970. In an interview, he said of industry pressures, "Some days I spent as many as six hours fending off representatives of the drug industry."

[19] Bryce Nelson, "Welfare Department Will Eliminate Blacklist of Science Advisers," Los Angeles *Times,* January 3, 1970.

[20] AP dispatch, "Critic of Bureaucrats in FDA Gets Demotion," Los Angeles *Times,* May 27, 1970.

[21] AP dispatch, "FDA Officials Changed Data, Inquiry Finds," Los Angeles *Times,* May 1, 1970.

[22] AP dispatch, May 27, 1970. Failure to appoint a pathologist was significant since that is the highly specialized branch of medicine that deals with the causes of tissue injury and death.

[23] "You Aren't Ingesting Sufficient Pesticides to Poison Yourself," *Wall Street Journal,* September 1, 1967.

[24] Dr. O. G. Fitzhugh, quoted, Los Angeles *Times,* September 8, 1969.

[25] Dr. William F. Durham of the FDA's Primate Research Branch in Florida, quoted, San Diego *Evening Tribune,* August 22, 1969.

[26] *U.S. Consumer Newsletter,* April 2, 1969.

[27] Statement by Dr. Endicott, no date, sent to me by Congressman George E. Brown, Jr., on May 2, 1969.

[28] Letter from Secretary Finch stamped May 6, 1969.

[29] *Recommendations and Summaries of the Secretary's Commission on Pesticides and Their Relationship to Environmental Health* (Washington, D.C.: Department of Health, Education, and Welfare, November, 1969), p. 6.

[30] *Ibid.*, p. 18.

[31] *Interim Report on Studies of Pesticides and Other Agricultural and Industrial Chemicals* (National Cancer Institute, 1969), pp. 2–3. Washington, D.C.

[32] *Safe Use of Pesticides in Public Health; Sixteenth Report of the WHO Expert Committee on Insecticides,* World Health Organization Technical Report Series, No. 356 (Geneva, 1967), p. 5.

[33] UPI dispatch," UNICEF Shipments of DDT Come Under Cloud," Los Angeles *Times,* November 20, 1969.

[34] Interview with L. Thapalyal at U.N headquarters, New York, June 13, 1969.

[35] During the GAO investigation described in the preceding chapter, an investigator said that he had received two ads in the mail at his home for such products while he was working on the case. See *Eleventh Report,* pp. 1–2. Yet earlier that year the Federal Trade Commission had announced that new regulations had been drafted prohibiting pesticide advertising that "claims that the product is safer, less toxic, or less hazardous than indicated in the labeling." *El Malcriado,* March 1, 1969, p. 5.

[36] Material about the UFWOC effort to have the restraining order set aside was obtained during court hearings in Bakersfield, Calif., in January and February 1969.

[37] Dr. Irma West of the California Department of Public Health, and Edward Lester, president and director of Central California Medical Laboratories.

[38] Dr. Thomas Milby of the California Department of Public Health repeated much of the testimony he gave in Bakersfield at a hearing some months later conducted by the House Subcommittee on Labor in San Francisco on November 24, 1969. Reports of that from *El Malcriado*, November 15–30, 1969, pp. 3, 7.

[39] Many instances in which California government agencies have disregarded their obligations to protect farm workers are cited in Steve Allen's *The Ground Is Our Table* (Garden City, N.Y.: Doubleday & Company, Inc., 1966).

[40] Copy of UFWOC-Perelli-Minetti contract. (Additionally, the company agreed to every point turned down by the courts in Bakersfield and Riverside, insuring that workers would be guaranteed their right to know about poisons: the kinds, amounts used, dates and times applied, location of crops and plants treated, type of formulation, and method of application.)

[41] *Southern California Business*, September 23, 1969, p. 1.

[42] "State Bans Usage of 91 Pesticides," Los Angeles *Times*, December 24, 1969.

CHAPTER 7   HIGH EDUCATION

[1] Robert Engler, "Social Science and Social Consciousness," *The Dissenting Academy*, ed. Theodore Roszak (New York: Pantheon Books, 1967). Engler says:"As for the professors, they too have become operators. . . . The more successful have learned to deal with other institutions—universities, institutes, foundations, business, government." (pp. 190–91)

[2] James Ridgeway, *The Closed Corporation* (New York: Random House, Inc., 1968). Institutional prestige is an

important factor in determining pay. MIT experts received far more than colleagues at "less prestigious institutions." (p. 98)

Daniel S. Greenberg, in an article in *Science* in 1964, also noted that some companies were paying academic consultants high annual retainers. One drug firm was handing out sums ranging from $6,000 to $12,000 a year; duties involved attending week-long meetings three times a year with the company's staff. Cited by Spencer Klaw, *The New Brahmins, Scientific Life in America* (New York: William Morrow & Company, Inc., 1968), p. 77.

[3] "In Academic Jet Set, Schedule Is Hectic, Reward High," *The New York Times,* June 18, 1969.

[4] "Professors Fill New Roles on Outside Jobs," Los Angeles *Times,* March 6, 1969.

[5] Professor Kampf quoted by Reinhold.

[6] "First Obligation of Professors," Los Angeles *Times,* August 2, 1965.

[7] Charles Powers, "University Oil Experts Refuse to Aid State Suit, Official Says," Los Angeles *Times,* April 7, 1969.

[8] Address by Mr. O'Brien to Channel City Club, Santa Barbara, April 8, 1969. (Mimeo copy, p. 10) The facts were verified for me by Mr. O'Brien, along with other quotes indicated in a personal interview on August 14, 1969.

[9] Charles Hillinger and Dial Torgerson, "Hickel Shuts Down Drilling Operations," Los Angeles *Times,* February 4, 1969.

[10] Robert L. Jackson, "Continued Channel Oil Pumping Urged," Los Angeles *Times,* June 2, 1969.

[11] Robert L. Jackson, "5 of 11 on Drilling Panel Had Oil Firms' Support," Los Angeles *Times,* January 18, 1970. It

was pointed out that two were with companies doing business with Union Oil, three at universities that got grants.

12 Press release, June 5, 1969, issued after joint press conference by Senator Edmund S. Muskie and Senator Alan Cranston. In an article on that date, Los Angeles *Times* reporter Robert L. Jackson said that Dr. John S. Steinhart, executive secretary of the panel, acknowledged: "It's true that at our meeting the only people we got data from were Union Oil, its partners in the lease, and the Geological Survey. They were the only people who had scientific information on that lease." The panel later seemed to experience a conversion about the value of public hearings. According to a Los Angeles *Times* report by Rudy Abramson (October 19, 1970), it decided that although public hearings were "costly and time-consuming . . . we feel there is no satisfactory substitute for hearing a variety of views in a public forum."

13 *Uses of the University* (New York: Harper & Row Publishers, Inc., 1966), p. 16. Dr. Kerr also points out that in the "idea" of a Multiversity, "students identify less with the total community and more with its subgroups." (p. 41)

14 *The Dirt on California: Agribusiness and the University* (Berkeley: ISC Press, 1968), p. 6.

15 Quoted, "Profiting from Poverty with Hire Education," *El Malcriado*, January 1, 1969, p. 11.

16 Dr. Alex C. Sherriffs, quoted by John Dreyfuss, "Chico Teacher Hit for 'Social Problems' Exam," Los Angeles *Times*, July 2, 1969. Jack H. Zeilenga, the physics instructor, told Mr. Dreyfuss he would continue to give "exams relevant to social problems. Students must realize the social problems they may confront as physicists."

17 "DDT: Sifting and Winnowing on the Ag Campus," *The Daily Cardinal*, University of Wisconsin, April 29, 1969, p. 12.

[18] *Ibid.*

[19] *The Closed Corporation*, pp. 97–98.

[20] *Ibid.*, pp. 98–99.

[21] Press release, National Agricultural Chemicals Association, pp. 1–3.

[22] Press release, NACA, May 13, 1969, p. 1.

[23] Luke West, "Expert: No Proof DDT Cancer Cause," Columbia, South Carolina *Post Dispatch*, November 19, 1969. The expert quoted was Dr. Robert White-Stevens, chairman of the bureau of Conservation and Environmental Science at Rutgers. To support his claims, he cited WHO reports and "a recently published summary of the situation prepared by Dr. Wayland J. Hayes of Vanderbilt," in which Dr. Hayes "reasserts that there is no valid evidence that DDT is a carcinogen."

[24] Press release, NACA, May 2, 1969, p. 4.

[25] Quoted, Bill Ballantine, *Nobody Loves a Cockroach* (Boston: Little, Brown and Company, 1967), p. 318. According to Mr. Ballantine, "the obvious effect" of Miss Carson's book on the reader "will be to aggravate unjustifiably his own neurotic anxiety."

[26] "Expert Scoffs at Food Additive Uproar," Los Angeles *Times*, February 26, 1970. In his speech, Dr. Darby was reported to have defended monosodium glutamate, which has been widely attacked as a possible cause of mental deficiency in infants. He took pot shots at the scientific community and "flayed the mass media for blowing up tidbits of scientific information relating to foods out of all proportion to their significance."

[27] "Grocery Industry on Shopper's Side," Los Angeles *Times*, April 8, 1965.

[28] "Guest Privilege," *Life* Magazine, March 6, 1970, p. 38.

[29] Dr. Stare quoted by Wheeler McMillen, *Bugs or People?* (New York: Appleton-Century-Crofts, 1965), p. 215.

[30] Quoted, *Nobody Loves a Cockroach,* p. 315.

[31] Russell S. Adams, Jr., "Misconceptions about Pesticide Residues in Soil," *Minnesota Science,* Fall 1969, p. 13.

[32] Some of the "scientific" articles indulge in some curious comments about the lack of patriotism among opponents of pollution. In an article of highest praise for DDT, Max Sobelman, superintendent of a DDT plant in California and industry representative on the Pesticides Specifications Committee of WHO, quoted an article by Dr. Thomas H. Jukes, University of California biochemist. After alluding to the "big setback" in Soviet agriculture that resulted from "the anti-scientific measures introduced by Lysenko and fostered by Stalin," Dr. Jukes warned, "Progress in American agriculture must not become similarly hamstrung by legislation resulting from inaccurate statements regarding the dangers of pesticides." "DDT: Millions of People Owe Their Lives to It," Los Angeles *Times,* July 6, 1969.

[33] *Gardening with Nature* (New York: The Devin-Adair Company, 1958), p. 386.

[34] *The Closed Corporation,* pp. 163–64.

[35] *The Daily Cardinal,* April 29, 1969. According to Mr. Knee, Professor Lichtenstein, head of a high-powered research team, had received during the previous year: $4,000 from a DDT manufacturer (Stauffer Chemical Company); $7,000 from a heptachlor manufacturer (Velsicol); and $10,000 from the principal maker of aldrin (Shell).

[36] Dr. William E. Smith quoted, Booth Mooney, *The Hidden Assassins* (Chicago: Follett Publishing Company, 1966), pp. 91–92.

[37] *Since Silent Spring* (Boston: Houghton Mifflin Company, 1970), p. 167.

[38] *Ibid.*, p. 168. The book, which was published by the University of Wisconsin only after eighteen reviewers "hashed over its premises," has since been published in four countries and was translated into Swedish not long ago.

[39] "Courts of Equity to Protect Our Environment," reprint of an address given at the 63rd annual convention of the National Audubon Society, September 29–October 3, 1967.

[40] "UIC's Chancellor Aldrich: 'University and Industry,' " *University of California Clip Sheet*, May 27, 1969, p. 2. Not all associated with the university got Chancellor Aldrich's message, however. At any rate, during the summer of 1970 Chief Deputy Attorney General O'Brien accused the university of "conflict of interest" for refusing to reveal the results of a study it made for the Federal government on damage to animal and plant life from the Santa Barbara oil spill. Richard West, "Oil Spill Study Conflict of Interest Charged," Los Angeles *Times*, July 3, 1970.

CHAPTER 8   MERCHANDISING DEATH

[1] Testimony offered at court hearings in Bakersfield, Calif., on the United Farm Workers Organizing Committee's petition to force Kern County Agricultural Commissioner Seldon G. Morley to release pesticide application records, January 30, 1969.

[2] Grant G. Cannon, *Great Men of Agriculture* (New York: The Macmillan Company, 1963), pp. 22–145. Some of the early pioneers created works of enduring importance. Jean Baptiste Boussingault, who spent ten years in Latin America with Simon Bolivar and the revolutionists, returned to France, where he had laws to protect soil fertility enacted and wrote *Rural Economy in Its Relations with Chemistry,*

Physics, and Meteorology. That was translated into all major languages, and it remained a standard text until the 1930's.

3 *Ibid.,* pp. 137–45.

4 *Pesticides and Pollution* (London: William Collins Sons and Co., Ltd., 1967), p. 19.

5 E. B. Weiss, "A Prediction: When Farming Outgrows Family Plots . . . ," *Marketing Insights,* March 24, 1969, p. 12.

6 Leonard Wickenden, *Our Daily Poison* (New York: The Devin-Adair Company, 1956), p. 23.

7 *Agricultural Newsletter,* published by Extension Division, Public Relations Department, E. I. du Pont de Nemours Co., Inc., September-October 1948, p. 83. That article makes an interesting contrast with those on DDT published in the January-February 1946 *Newsletter,* pp. 2–13.

8 Dr. Francisco Bravo, quoted in *El Malcriado* ("Grower Blasts Pesticides 'Fraud' "), February 15, 1969, p. 15. Dr. Bravo, a member of the State Board of Agriculture, accused the chemical industry of sponsoring "chemical warfare not only on the bad bugs, but also on the good bugs and human beings." He called for an investigation of labeling and pricing practices. He said that preliminary investigations showed "considerable price gouging" and "possible collusion" among chemical companies to fix profits.

9 In 1969 William V. White, executive director of the National Council on Product Safety, said, "We think there might be quite a gap between what magazines say seals mean and what consumers believe they mean." The commission was investigating testing procedures after President Nixon named a *Good Housekeeping* executive Consumer Adviser. Peter Weaver, "Semantics and Product Safety," Los Angeles *Times,* October 9, 1969.

¹⁰ *National Agricultural Chemicals Association Annual Report* for the year ending August 31, 1968, p. 10.

The attitude of many advertisers was advanced by Robert E. Launey to the American Business Press recently: "I do believe that . . . every editor owes his advertisers the courtesy of *primary editorial consideration*. . . . Rather than hardnosed objectivity, an editor owes the advertiser at least a modicum of interest and favorable prejudice. . . ." *Consumer Reports* ("Quote without Comment"), March 1968, p. 120.

¹¹ *NACA Annual Report,* p. 12.

¹² A. R. Wilcox, "Has Not Caused Harm to Man," Letter to the Editor, Los Angeles *Times,* May 24, 1969.

¹³ Letters to the Editors, *Life,* March 27, 1970, p. 18A.

¹⁴ Reprinted as a special appendix in Wheeler McMillen's *Bugs or People?* (New York: Appleton-Century-Crofts, 1965).

¹⁵ The briefing papers stress the safety of DDT; its protection of soldiers in World War II; its use by WHO and the U.S. Public Health Service; its importance to the world food supply. Principal sources for the NACA briefing paper, "Pesticides and the Farmer" and "The DDT Story," are books by Congressman Whitten, *That We May Live* (New York: D. Van Nostrand Company, Inc., 1966); and by Wheeler McMillen, *op. cit.*

¹⁶ "Cotton Research Reports," *Cotton* (reprint, dated only 1968).

¹⁷ "Agriculture Not Pesticide Culprit," press release, Michigan State University's Department of Information Services, January 1969. Professor Matthew Zabik said that between 60 and 80 percent of pesticide contamination entering the Red Cedar River comes from waste water treatment plants, with only 20 to 40 percent from agricultural pesticide use.

[18] "Up with People," *Barron's*, May 5, 1969.

[19] *That We May Live*, pp. 217–30.

[20] *Bugs or People?*, p. 161.

[21] *Ibid.*, p. 162.

[22] Mr. Still's book (New York: Hawthorn Books, Inc., 1967) includes *Bugs or People?* in its "Select Bibliography," but does not include *Silent Spring* or any other major criticism.

[23] (Boston: Little, Brown and Company, 1967).

[24] A good many of the comments call attention to themselves because of their heavy-handedness—quite at odds with the deft writing characteristic of most of the book. For example, one pesticide dealer's critique of Rachel Carson's book—chronicled in full—concludes with the assertion: "The whole book was like that—full of half truths and scare statements that maybe you could prove and maybe you couldn't." *Nobody Loves a Cockroach*, p. 172.

[25] *Ibid.*, p. 327.

[26] Cynthia Westcott, *The Gardener's Bug Book* (Garden City, N.Y.: Doubleday & Company, Inc., 1956), p. 30.

[27] George Abraham, *The Green Thumb Garden Handbook* (Englewood Cliffs, N.J.: Prentice-Hall, Inc., 1961), p. 255. Mr. Abraham, who operates a greenhouse and florist business, writes the widely circulated "Green Thumb" newspaper column.

[28] *Nobody Loves a Cockroach*, p. 170.

[29] Los Angeles *Times*, June 29, 1969.

[30] "Geigy Plans to Stay 'No. 1,'" *Farm Chemicals*, July 1968, p. 18.

[31] *Ibid.*, p. 16.

[32] *Ibid.*

[33] " 'Living with Pesticides' SEPFA's Convention Theme," *Farm Chemicals,* November 1968, p. 62. Dr. Francis J. Mulhern, deputy administrator of the Agricultural Research Service, USDA, had high praise for the industry. "We believe the industry has reacted nobly to the challenges made upon it by the experiences of the last decade. We feel sure that it will continue to meet those challenges and produce products that are both effective and safe."

[34] "Wanted—Pesticide Advocates," *Agricultural Chemicals,* September 1968, p. 110.

[35] "Pesticides and the Environment," *BioScience,* September 1970, p. 616.

[36] "Legislation and Regulation of Insecticide's Impact Upon Economic Entomology Industrial Viewpoint," *Bulletin of Entomological Society of America,* March 1970, pp. 18–20. (Reprinted from a talk given at a symposium at the Annual Meeting of the Entomological Society of America, December 2, 1969).

[37] John D. Weaver, "It Was a Very Good Year," *West* magazine, Los Angeles *Times,* January 25, 1970, p. 14.

[38] Interview with Grant Hegranes of IMS Corporation, September 10, 1969.

[39] According to Mrs. Tallian, Hugh McDonald, the Imperial Valley farmer opposed to pesticides, saved his ranch and built up extensive market for citrus in Europe and this country. *The Pesticide Jungle* (privately printed, 1966), (See Chapter 3, Note 23.)

[40] Dr. Cottam quoted, "Pesticide Plan Dangers Cited," Albuquerque *Journal,* July 11, 1969.

[41] Jerry Deal, San Antonio *Express*, July 10, 1969. He reported that the USDA, "bombarded with complaints the past few weeks" over the proposed use of dieldrin at Air Force bases, had called a halt to its use in the pest control programs.

CHAPTER 9 A SPECIAL PROBLEM

[1] Karl B. Mickey, *Man and Soil* (Chicago: International Harvester Company, 1948), p. 18.

[2] Barry Commoner, "Nature Unbalanced: How Man Interferes with the Nitrogen Cycle," *Scientist and Citizen* (now *Environment*), January-February, 1968, p. 9.

[3] Mickey, *op. cit.*, p. 49. Perhaps the best general discussion of the problems of soil conservation is given by R. Burnell Held and Marion Clawson, *Soil Conservation in Perspective* (Baltimore: Published for Resources for the Future, Inc., by the Johns Hopkins Press, 1965).

[4] *The Grapes of Wrath* (New York: The Viking Press, 1939), pp. 5–6.

[5] Hugh Bennett, the crusading first chief of the Soil Conservation Service, estimated that "approximately 125 million acres of land had lost all or the greater part of their irreplaceable topsoil and that erosion was getting actively underway on another 100 million acres." Economic Research Service, USDA, *Century of Service* (Washington, D.C.: U.S. Department of Agriculture, 1963), p. 191.

[6] The commercial fertilizer industry was begun in England in the nineteenth century by Sir John B. Lawes. Its growth was slow until the 1940's—2 million tons was the 1905 world consumption; 10 million in 1942. By 1964 the U.S. alone was producing and consuming about 30 million tons.

[7] *Time*, January 3, 1964, p. 73.

8 *Ibid.*

9 *The Use of Chemicals as Fertilizers,* Agricultural Chemicals Technology Publication #1, The Ohio State University, Columbus, 1965, p. 1.

10 *Ibid.,* p. 5. That optimistic opinion of their value may be due in some degree to the instructional materials recommended. Students are urged to "contact local dealers for information," since many of them provide the publications and films put out by major manufacturers. (p. 119)

11 *Ibid.,* p. 13.

12 *Ibid.*

13 Gordon Berg, editor of *Farm Chemicals,* asserted in December 1968: "The great fertilizer robbery has taken on staggering proportions." Although 1968 purchases were up 9 percent over the 1967 purchases, "farmers literally stole the extra tonnage since they paid no more for the goods." Government (the USDA) and state agricultural stations and university extension services were joining with the fertilizer manufacturers trade association to halt that. Weapon was a 300-page bulletin, *Crop Yield Response to Fertilizers in the United States,* which was expected to turn the tide with its "hard sell." (p. 109)

14 Harold Keen, "Nuns Learn Lab Work to Meet Costs," Los Angeles *Times,* August 5, 1939.

15 *The Use of Chemicals as Fertilizers,* p. 14.

16 "Settlement Is Near in the Estes Tangle," *The National Observer,* September 22, 1969.

17 Commoner, article cited, p. 17.

18 John H. Storer, *The Web of Life* (New York: New American Library, 1953), pp. 38–39.

[19] L. B. Nelson and D. B. Ibach, "The Economics of Fertilizers," *Soil: The Yearbook of Agriculture 1957* (Washington, D.C.: U.S. Government Printing Office, 1957), p. 268.

[20] "Duty of Science in the Ecological Crisis," address presented before the Scientists' Institute for Public Information, 1969. (Mimeo copy, p. 17)

[21] Commoner, "Nature Unbalanced," p. 15. Erie is not the only body of water so contaminated. At least 46,000 shoreline miles between Maine and Texas were held to be deteriorating, due in large measure to nitrates and phosphates from sewage and farm runoff. "Diseased Estuaries," *The New Republic*, March 1, 1969, p. 7.

[22] Excellent account of the problem is given in an *Environment* Staff Report, "Poisoning the Wells," *Environment* January-February. That pointed out that nitrates, even in large quantities, do not seem to harm adults who drink nitrate-contaminated water—although breast-fed infants of mothers drinking such water may be poisoned. Nor are all children equally susceptible; there appears to be a relationship between the quantity of nitrite-forming bacteria in the upper intestine and susceptibility to the disease, pp. 17 and 23.

[23] *Ibid.*

[24] *Ibid.* In revising its drinking water standards in 1962, the U.S. Public Health Service noted that although infants were chiefly affected, "Both man and animals can be poisoned by nitrate if the concentration is sufficiently great."

[25] In California particularly, which consumes a large share of the chemical fertilizer output, levels were very high. In December 1966, residents of some farm communities in California were told not to allow small children to drink tap water. "Growers Poison Delano Water," *El Malcriado*, August 15-September 15, 1969. Also, Harry Nelson, "Nitrates in Water Called Cancer Cause," Los Angeles *Times*, March 30, 1969.

[26] Barry Commoner, "Nitrate in Baby Food," *Science and Citizen* (now called *Environment*) January-February, 1968, pp. 13, 28.

[27] *Ibid.*, p. 11, quoting news release by Canadian Department of Health and Welfare, February 13, 1968.

[28] *Ibid.*

[29] The policy set by the U.S. Public Health Service was reversed in California in 1967, when the California Public Health Department issued a new directive saying that public agencies and utility companies did not need to issue warnings to the public when the nitrate level exceeded 45 or even 90 parts per million. "Growers Poison Delano Water," p. 2.

[30] *Ibid.*, pp. 2, 12.

[31] Dr. Epstein is internationally known for his work and publications on cancer and mutation-producing chemicals in air and water pollutants.

[32] Nelson, "Nitrates in Water Called Cancer Cause."

[33] W. M. Beeson of Purdue University Agricultural Experiment Station cited *Prevention*, April 1969, p. 68.

[34] *Prevention*, June 1969, p. 78.

[35] *FDA Fact Sheet*, May 1967: "Nutrition Nonsense—and Sense."

[36] Most complete account of the problem is *Malnutrition, Learning, and Behavior*, ed. Dr. Nevin S. Scrimshaw and Dr. John E. Gordon (Cambridge: MIT Press, 1968). The book contains the proceedings of the international conference on that subject in 1967, attended by about 600 scientists from 38 countries.

[37] Harry Nelson, "Mental Ills of Elderly Tied to Poor Nutrition," Los Angeles *Times*, October 24, 1967. Dr. Maurice E. Lindon, medical director of Philadelphia State Hospital, reported that the response to good food of elderly patients hospitalized for psychiatric care has been so rapid that at first he "suspected that the families were misrepresenting facts when admitting elderly patients or else they were simply rejecting them."

[38] *USDA Yearbook of Agriculture, 1947* (Washington, D.C.: U.S. Government Printing Office, 1947), p. 577.

CHAPTER 10   FOR EMERGENCY ONLY

[1] *Consumers All: USDA Yearbook of Agriculture, 1965* (Washington, D.C.: U.S. Government Printing Office, 1965), pp. 237, 263. Note frequency of such words of advice as "drench," "sprinkle thoroughly," "repeat at 7–14 day intervals."

[2] Dr. Alice Ottoboni, "DDT Is Only One Pesticide," *California's Health*, September 1969, p. 5. That very low figure, the public health official said, applies to the spraying of pesticides by aircraft and ground rigs.

[3] Rachel Carson, *Silent Spring* (Boston: Houghton Mifflin Company, 1962), pp. 87–91.

[4] R. L. Metcalf, "Requirements for Insecticides of the Future," *Pest Control by Chemical, Biological, Genetic, and Physical Means: A Symposium* (Agricultural Research Service, U.S. Department of Agriculture, 1965), p. 10.

[5] Walter W. Dykstra, "The Role of Chemicals for the Control of Vertebrate Pests," *Symposium*, p. 33.

[6] UPI dispatch, "Firm Invents Pigeon Birth Control Pill," Los Angeles *Times*, February 15, 1970. The pill causes temporary loss of fertility in pigeons.

[7] Morton Beroza, "The Future Role of Natural and Synthetic Attractants for Pest Control," *Symposium*, p. 36.

[8] *Ibid.*

[9] *Ibid.*, p. 35. The achievement was impressive considering that the insect was found on a million acres, scattered over much of Florida.

[10] *Ibid.*, p. 36.

[11] M. Jacobson and C. Harding, "Insect Sex Attractants, IX," *Journal of Economic Entomology*, April 1968, p. 394. R. S. Berger and T. D. Canerday, "Specificity of the Cabbage Looper Sex Attractant," *Journal of Economic Entomology*, April 1968, pp. 452–53.

[12] Jerome A. Onsager, L. M. McDonough, and D. A. George, "A Sex Pheromone in the Pacific Coast Wireworm," *Journal of Economic Entomology*, January 1968, pp. 691–93.

[13] Morton Beroza, *op. cit.*, p. 38.

[14] Much interest has recently been centered on the aggregation pheromones produced by the bark and ambrosia beetles. The chemical secretions they release after finding a suitable host tree orient flying populations of the creatures. H. H. Shorey and L. K. Gaston, "Pheromones," *Pest Control: Biological, Physical, and Selected Chemical Methods*, ed. Wendell W. Kilgore and Richard L. Doutt (New York: Academic Press, 1967), pp. 249–52.

[15] R. L. Metcalf, *op. cit.*, p. 10.

[16] Bill Ballantine, *Nobody Loves a Cockroach* (Boston: Little, Brown and Company, 1967), p. 313. Another reason he cited for the less hazardous pesticide's not being sold more widely in the U.S. is that government regulations make distribution of any specific pesticide "difficult because of its usually high toxicity." That is a novel argument. Ray F.

Smith and Robert Van den Bosch emphasize that the reason specific pesticides are few is that they are not considered "commercially feasible" by the developers and exploiters. Kilgore and Doutt, *op. cit.*, p. 326.

[17] R. L. Metcalf, *op. cit.*, p. 21. In spite of its desirable properties as contrasted with those of DDT, *USDA Handbook 120*, "Insecticide Recommendations," listed only 81 uses for it as compared with 334 for DDT.

[18] Dr. Alice Ottoboni, *op. cit.*, p. 4.

[19] The damage done by DDT and other hard pesticides cannot be minimized. Neither can the damage done by those in the other principal categories. Eldridge G. Hunt of the California Department of Fish and Game reported in 1969:

"Although the nonpersistent pesticides are not normally associated with fish losses, some of the newer organic phosphate and carbamate insecticides are highly toxic to fish. Extreme care must be taken in the use of these new materials if fish losses are to be avoided.

"Losses of nontarget wildlife have been associated primarily with the use of highly toxic nonpersistent insecticides or toxic baits used for the control of rodents. During the last two years most of the bird losses investigated by the Department of Fish and Game have been caused by an organic phosphate widely used in control of insect pests in cotton. Special controls were imposed on the use of this chemical during 1969 for the purpose of preventing bird losses. These controls reduced bird losses significantly; however, additional safeguards are needed if birdlife is to be adequately protected. Incidental wildlife losses have also been caused by several other nonpersistent insecticides. . . ."

Human Relations Agency, California Department of Public Health, *A Report to the 1970 Legislature on the Effects of the Use of DDT and Similar Pesticides on Human Health and the Environment*, December 10, 1969, Section V. (Xerox copy)

20 R. L. Metcalf, *op. cit.*, p. 22.

21 *Ibid.*, p. 12.

22 *Ibid.*, p. 17. See also, Donald E. H. Freer, *The Chemistry of Pesticides* (New York: D. Van Nostrand Company, Inc., 1933), pp. 79–82.

23 R. D. O'Brien, *Insecticides: Action and Metabolism* (New York: Academic Press, 1967), noted more recently that in the course of only two days test animals voided more than 90 percent of administered carbamate—a finding that is "reassuring from the point of view of potential hazard from persistence of ingested material." (p. 101)

Evidence of the need for further tailoring was given by Bionetics study. For example, carbaryl has generally been held almost totally non-toxic and approved as a dusting powder for body lice. However, teratogenetic findings for carbaryl were reported. In another study of beagle dogs fed the substance during gestational periods, teratogenetic effects were found at all but the lowest dose level. *Effects of 2,4,5-T on Man and the Environment, Hearings before the Subcommittee on Energy, Natural Resources, and the Environment of the Committee on Commerce. U.S. Senate, 91st Congress* (Washington, D.C.: Government Printing Office, 1970), p. 438.

24 Rollie E. Deering, "Cotton Pests Controlled from the Inside Out," *The Farm Quarterly*, Spring Planning, 1968, p. 100.

25 Testimony at court hearing in Bakersfield, Calif., January 30, 1969. Dr. Van den Bosch also selected Azodrin to show the difficulties of getting an insecticide withdrawn, once it has been registered. The university is the "official research and recommendation agency" in California; the researchers could not recommend it, after four years of work; "yet it was registered and caused disruption of agricultural ecosystems." The flaw in the registration system is this, he pointed out: "All the company has to show is reasonable

pest kill, and that it is reasonably safe to humans. As insect ecologists, we have criteria which are basic to this whole problem, and they are completely ignored." *Chemical Fallout, Current Research on Persistent Pesticides*, ed. Morton W. Miller and George G. Berg (Springfield, Ill.: Charles C. Thomas, Publisher, 1969), p. 111.

[26] J. R. Brazzel, W. W. Watson, J. S. Hursh, and M. H. Adair, "The Relative Efficiency of Aerial Application of Ultra-Low-Volume and Emulsifiable Concentrate Formulations of Insecticides," *Journal of Economic Entomology*, April 1968, p. 408.

[27] "Summary and Conclusions" and "Recommendations," Sections XI and XII, *Report of Senate Committee on Government Operations' Subcommittee on Reorganization, Interagency Environmental Hazards Coordination—Pesticides and Public Policy* (Washington, D.C.: U.S. Government Printing Office, July 21, 1966).

[28] E. F. Knipling, "Introduction," *Pest Control by Chemical, Biological, Genetic, and Physical Means: A Symposium*, p. 2.

[29] UPI dispatch on pest control symposium at Oregon State University, San Diego *Evening Tribune*, August 22, 1969.

[30] Press release, USDA, November 14, 1969.

CHAPTER 11   FIRST BASIC STEPS

[1] *Pesticides and Pollution* (London: William Collins Sons and Co., Ltd., 1967), pp. 47–48.

[2] Agricultural Research Service, USDA, "Research on Controlling Insects without Conventional Insecticides," October 1963, p. 63.

[3] H. Ivan Rainwater and Claude A. Smith, "Quarantine—First Line of Defense," *Protecting Our Food: USDA Year-*

book of Agriculture, 1966 (Washington, D.C.: U.S. Government Printing Office, 1966), p. 220.

4 Johannes Nohl, *The Black Death* (New York: Ballantine Books, Inc., 1960), provides a vivid and carefully documented account of that enduring disaster.

5 I became familiar with the consequences of the campaign in 1947–49, when I was working as a reporter and editor on the Mexico City *Herald;* my husband was the U.S. information director of the Aftosa Commission.

6 *USDA Yearbook of Agriculture, 1966,* p. 222.

7 *Ibid.,* p. 224.

8 *Ibid.,* p. 219. The figure set for 1966 was 186 million; it has increased greatly since then.

9 Kenneth Mellanby, *Pesticides and Pollution,* p. 27.

10 "Fighting the Pink Bollworm," *Cotton Farming,* January 1968, p. 16. The requirements are minimal: shredding the stalks and plowing them under—a measure which enhances soil fertility. Yet, the report notes, "all along the path of the pink bollworm, there has been a tendency on the part of some cotton farmers to object to certain cultural control regulations."

11 David K. Wetherbee, "Vertebrate Pest Control by Biological Means," *Pest Control by Chemical, Biological, Genetic, and Physical Means: A Symposium* (Washington, D.C.: Agricultural Research Service, USDA, 1964), p. 104.

12 *Malabar Farm Newsletter,* August 1962 (Lucas, Ohio: Louis Bromfield Malabar Farm Foundation).

13 For a more complete list of protective plantings, see Beatrice Trum Hunter, *Gardening without Poisons* (Boston: Houghton Mifflin Company, 1964), p. 242. The same principle has been found effective on large-scale farms. Dr.

Vernon M. Stern of the University of California-Riverside has conducted successful experiments in planting narrow strips of alfalfa in cotton fields; the alfalfa strips act as attractant and trap-crop, keeping lygus bugs out of the cotton. (*UC* [University of California] *News,* June 16, 1970.)

[14] Hunter, *op. cit.,* pp. 126–28.

[15] *Ibid.,* pp. 46–47.

[16] *Ibid.,* p. 120.

[17] Agricultural Stabilization and Conservation Service, USDA, *The Pesticide Review, 1969,* pp. 39–41.

[18] R. D. O'Brien, *Insecticides: Action and Metabolism* (New York: Academic Press, 1967), pp. 149–67.

[19] *Gardening with Nature* (New York: The Devin-Adair Company, 1958), pp. v-vi. Sears proposes a "truce" between organic gardeners and scientists in the interests of agriculture as well as ecology.

[20] *Ibid.,* pp. 16–17.

[21] *Farming with Nature* (Norman: University of Oklahoma Press, 1954), p. 28.

[22] *Ibid.,* p. 31.

[23] Rodale Press, Inc., 33 East Minor Street, Emmaus, Pa.

[24] Ehrenfried Pfeiffer, *Bio-Dynamic Farming and Gardening* (New York: Anthroposophic Press, 1943). The association (Route 1, Stroudsburg, Pa.) also issues regular publications. Pfeiffer is highly praised by Cocannouer for having given "closer study to scientific compost starters of several kinds than any other scientist in America." (p. 33)

[25] Material supplied from talks and letters in 1968–69.

[26] Cecil Woodham-Smith, *The Great Hunger* (New York: New American Library, 1964). Although official estimate of the number of deaths was 2.5 million, the author points out that the number was probably much greater. (p. 409)

[27] Ralph M. Caldwell, "Advances and Challenges in the Control of Plant Diseases through Breeding," *Symposium,* p. 118.

[28] *Ibid.,* p. 118.

[29] *Ibid.,* pp. 118–19.

[30] Reginald H. Painter, "Plant Resistance as a Means of Controlling Insects and Reducing Their Damage," *Symposium,* p. 138.

It has been pointed out, however, that as with other pest control techniques, "such varieties should be utilized only after taking into account their role and impact on other elements in the agro-ecosystem." One example cited as error was the introduction into California of strawberry varieties with high resistance to a certain pathogen. The varieties lost much of the advantage because of their high susceptibility to cyclamen mite, a minor pest on the older strawberry varieties. Ray F. Smith and Robert Van den Bosch, "Integrated Control," *Pest Control: Biological, Physical, and Selected Chemical Methods,* ed. Wendell W. Kilgore and Richard L. Doutt (New York: Academic Press, 1967), p. 328.

[31] "Tests Find Stale Beer Lures Pests to Deaths," Los Angeles *Times,* December 4, 1969. In a series of experiments Dr. Floyd F. Smith of Beltsville said that stale beer had attracted more than 300 slugs, while metaldehyde—standard chemical bait—attracted only 28. The beer was placed in shallow pans; insects crawled in to drown.

[32] Hunter, *op. cit.,* p. 60.

[33] John Davenport, "Industry Starts the Big Cleanup," *Fortune,* February 1970, p. 114.

[34] Hunter, *op. cit.*, pp. 1–6.

[35] *The Pesticide Jungle* (privately printed, 1966), p. 5. (See Chapter 3, Note 23.)

CHAPTER 12 LIVING PESTICIDES

[1] Federal Writers' Project, *Utah* (New York: Hastings House, 1939), p. 61.

[2] *Ibid.*, pp. 61–62.

[3] Paul DeBach, ed., *Biological Control of Insect Pests and Weeds* (New York: Reinhold Publishing Corporation, 1964), p. 6.

[4] Richard L. Doutt, "The Historical Development of Biological Control," *Biological Control of Insect Pests and Weeds*, pp. 21–42.

[5] *Ibid.*, p. 34.

[6] *Ibid.*, p. 37. The larva of an ordinary ladybug will consume from 200 to 300 aphids before it begins its transformation. Full grown, it is even more voracious.

[7] Koebele sent back to Hawaii a number of effective fighters —a lace bug, a gall fly, a seed fly, two butterflies, and a plume moth. However, success was not as rapid; it was not until 1953 that control was obtained.

[8] C. B. Huffaker, "Fundamentals of Biological Weed Control," *Biological Control of Insect Pests and Weeds*, p. 633.

[9] The technique has also been used in India, Hawaii, and the Celebes, where prickly pear cactus is also a pest. It was less successful in South Africa, where other forms of cactus were also attacked. For account of the latter, see Robin Clarke, *The Silent Weapons* (New York: David McKay Company,

Inc., 1968); and Sir Vincent B. Wigglesworth, *Science Journal*, April 1965. According to Wigglesworth, *Cactoblastis* was successful up to a point; however, when the cochineal insect was introduced to supplement its effect, the latter attacked a species of spineless cactus used for feeding stock and caused much damage. (p. 155)

[10] J. K. Holloway, "Projects in Biological Control of Weeds," *Biological Control of Insect Pests and Weeds*, pp. 657–59.

[11] C. L. Metcalf, W. P. Flint, and R. L. Metcalf, *Destructive and Useful Insects* (New York: McGraw-Hill Book Company, Inc., 1962). The authors quote H. A. Gossard, American entomologist, who pointed out years ago that the human race could not survive more than five or six years except for "warfare within the insect household."

[12] *University of California Clip Sheet*, January 13, 1970. Under his leadership, the International Organization for Biological Control will work to foster that science worldwide, with experts in all geographical areas cooperating in the effort.

[13] All quotations, unless otherwise indicated, from personal interview with Dr. DeBach, May 26, 1969.

[14] H. L. Maltby, Eleazer Jimenez-Jimenez, and Paul DeBach, "Biological Control of Armored Scale Insects in Mexico," *Journal of Economic Entomology*, August 1968, pp. 1086–88.

[15] P. H. Westgard, L. G. Gener, and D. W. Berry, "Present Status of Biological Control of the Pear Psylla in Southern Oregon," *Journal of Economic Entomology*, June 1968, p. 740.

The campaign to control apple and pear pests in Nova Scotia has been called "the true landmark program." *Pest Control: Biological, Physical, and Selected Chemical Methods*, ed. Wendell N. Kilgore and Richard L. Doutt (New York: Academic Press, 1967), p. 329.

[16] The university does not profit financially by its research programs.

[17] "Bug Business Boom: Farmers Use Insects to Kill Harmful Pests," *Wall Street Journal,* September 6, 1968.

[18] A. M. Heimpel, "Insect Pathology, Present and Future," *Pest Control by Chemical, Biological, Genetic, and Physical Means: A Symposium,* Agricultural Research Service, U.S. Dept. of Agriculture, Washington, D.C., 1964. p. 71

[19] *Ibid.,* p. 72. By 1966 pathologists had recorded about 1,100 microbial agents—fungi, protozoa, rickettsiae—in addition to bacteria that parasitize insects. *USDA Yearbook of Agriculture, 1966* (Washington, D.C.: Government Printing Office, 1966), p. 33.

[20] Comprehensive account, Y. Tanada, "Microbial Pesticides," *Pest Control: Biological, Physical, and Selected Chemical Methods,* pp. 77–88. See also, Beatrice Trum Hunter, *Gardening without Poisons* (Boston: Houghton Mifflin Company, 1964), pp. 181–202.

[21] Hunter, *op. cit.,* pp. 191–92.

[22] UPI dispatch, "Approval Asked on Use of Virus as Pesticide," Los Angeles *Times,* September 13, 1969.

[23] Kenneth Mellanby, *Pesticides and Pollution* (London, William Collins Sons and Co., 1967), pp. 100–70.

[24] Tanada, *op. cit.,* pp. 76–77.

[25] Bryan P. Beirne, "Present and Future Role of Parasites and Predators for Insect Control," *Symposium,* p. 67.

[26] Dr. DeBach predicted disasters for many of the developing African nations, which share the notion that "if pest problems arise, call the biggest pest control operator." Others

agree about the "point of no return" having been passed with some domestic crops. Dr. Robert Van den Bosch said recently that cotton in California is unquestionably "on the threshold of economic collapse." The San Joaquin Valley, which has been invaded by the pink bollworm, "is a two-bale cotton area," he noted. Farmers have to produce 1¾ bales to break even—a margin of $50 to $75. "And as they go into $30 and $40 insecticide programs they are just not going to stay in business." *Chemical Fallout: Current Research on Persistent Pesticides,* ed. Morton W. Miller and George G. Berg (Springfield, Ill.: Charles C. Thomas, Publisher, 1969), p. 110.

CHAPTER 13   INTEGRATED CONTROL

[1] The material about the Fillmore Protective Control District was given to me by Howard Lorbeer during a personal interview on August 15, 1969, and in subsequent correspondence.

[2] Ray F. Smith and Robert Van den Bosch, "Integrated Control," *Pest Control: Biological, Physical, and Selected Chemical Methods,* ed. Wendell W. Kilgore and Richard L. Doutt (New York: Academic Press, 1967), p. 328.

[3] Lester A. Swan, *Beneficial Insects* (New York: Harper & Row, Publishers, 1964), pp. 38–82.

[4] Smith and Van den Bosch, *op. cit.,* pp. 329–32.

[5] *Ibid.,* pp. 333–34.

[6] *Ibid.*

CHAPTER 14   SOUND AND LIGHT

[1] Hubert and Mable Frings, "Behavioral Manipulation," *Pest Control: Biological, Physical, and Selected Chemical*

Methods, ed. Wendell W. Kilgore and Richard L. Doutt (New York: Academic Press, 1967), point out that some confusion exists about ultrasound—sound with frequencies higher than 15,000 cycles per second. Because earlier biological studies on ultrasonics dealt mainly with the destructive effects of underwater ultrasound on tissues and small organisms, and because of the "seeming mystery" of sounds that could not be heard by human ears, many have come to regard ultrasound "as a somehow mysterious form of energy." They point out that "all the destructive effects of ultrasound can be duplicated with ordinary sound." (p. 398)

[2] Shooting to kill seems to be of little value so far as many bird pests are concerned. England, where the Ministry of Agriculture had subsidized cartridges used for "pigeon shoots," removed the subsidy recently because the shooting made so little difference to the pigeon population. (Kenneth Mellanby, *Pesticides and Pollution* (London: William Collins Sons and Co., Ltd., 1967), p. 177.

[3] S. O. Nelson and J. L. Seubert, "Electromagnetic Energy and Sound for Use in Control of Certain Pests," *Pest Control by Chemical, Biological, Genetic, and Physical Means: A Symposium* (Washington, D.C.: Agricultural Research Service, USDA, 1964), p. 187.

[4] *Ibid.,* p. 184.

[5] Kenneth D. Roeder and Arthur E. Treat, "The Detection and Evasion of Bats by Moths," *American Science,* June 1961, pp. 127–58.

[6] Nelson and Seubert, *op. cit.,* p. 184.

[7] A. C. Hoffman and L. S. Henderson, "The Fight against Insects," *USDA Yearbook of Agriculture, 1966* (Washington, D.C.: Government Printing Office, 1966), p. 31.

[8] *Ibid.*

[9] Frings and Frings point out (*op. cit.*) that many factors must be considered before sound application can be used successfully; however acoustical communication controls are generally reasonably priced, do allow precise manipulation of pest species, "have no fire or soiling hazards, and leave no troublesome residues." (pp. 447–48)

[10] Beatrice Trum Hunter, *Gardening without Poisons* (Boston: Houghton Mifflin Company, 1964), p. 144.

[11] *Ibid.*, pp. 130–37. Useful discussion of simple effective traps is also found in Lester A. Swan, *Beneficial Insects* (New York: Harper & Row, Publishers, 1964), pp. 330–34.

[12] *Ibid.*, p. 138.

[13] Nelson and Seubert, *op. cit.*, p. 180.

[14] H. O. Deay, J. G. Taylor, and E. A. Johnson, "Results of 1960 Purdue University and USDA Field Tests of Electric Light Traps," reprint from *Proceedings of the American Entomological Society, 1959.*

[15] Eldon E. Fredericks, "Insects See the Light," *Report,* Purdue University Agricultural Extension Service, Agricultural Experiment Station, Summer 1959).

[16] *Ibid.*

[17] *Ribicoff Hearings,* Part 8, p. 1557–65. (See Chapter 2, Note 14.)

[18] The amount varied with tobacco products, with cigars being most heavily contaminated. At a time when permissible DDT residue on foods was 7 p.p.m., cigar residues went as high as 53 p.p.m. Cigars, cigarettes, and pipe tobacco were also loaded with other toxic residues—TDE and endrin—and bore "trace elements" amounting to 37 p.p.m. of other substances. *Ribicoff Hearings,* pp. 1565–69.

[19] *Ibid.*, p. 1602.

[20] The USDA did ban endrin in February 1964—or as *Tobacco* put it politely (September 18, 1964), "the Entomology Research Division no longer recommends endrin for the control of tobacco insects." (p. 112)

[21] "Use of Light Traps Supplemented with Late Season Stalk Cutting for Control of Hornworms in Tobacco," USDA Agricultural Research Service, February 3, 1965.

[22] USDA, Agricultural Research Bulletin #33-119, June 1967.

[23] Grant Hegranes, Insect Management Corporation, personal interview, October 16, 1969.

[24] "Scarcity of Tobacco Insects Limits Evaluation of Blacklight Traps in Oxford, N.C., Area," press release, USDA Agricultural Research Service, Oxford, N.C., May 5, 1969.

[25] *Ibid.*, p. 2.

[26] *Ibid.*

[27] Of obvious importance is having an area large enough so that light-trapped fields will not be continually invaded by pests from untrapped areas.

[28] Press release cited, p. 3.

[29] Material given to me by Kenneth Suggs in a personal interview 1969.

[30] "How Light Kayos the Patio Bugs," *Popular Science,* July 1968.

[31] Copy of letter to Mr. Hegranes, April 17, 1969.

[32] Copy of letter to Mr. Hegranes, July 6, 1967.

[33] *Cotton Farming,* July 1968, p. 2.

[34] A comparable experience occurred in California in 1965. A study on the use of light traps to control cotton pests was made by the Stanford Research Institute over an extended period of time in 1964. Dr. John N. Simons, senior entomologist, made a short report on it at the October meeting of the San Joaquin Entomology Association in Bakersfield, during which he cited the favorable results obtained. In February 1965 an article appeared in the Fresno *Bee.* Signed by J. Hodge Black, Kern County farm adviser; the article's chief theme was that "no definite conclusions could be drawn from the 1964 trials." (Mr. Black, incidentally, was one of the agriculture department employees who appeared as witness for the Kern County Agricultural Commissioner and the Kern County Agricultural Chemical Association in order to counteract the testimony of Dr. Robert Van den Bosch at the court hearing on the UFWOC petition to have spray records released.)

What particularly incensed the Stanford expert, according to his letter of protest (February 16, 1965) to the director of the university extension service, was not merely that Mr. Black had taken it upon himself to report the study of the Stanford Research Institute, but that he had "never seen the data."

[35] First announcement of Senator Anderson's interest was made by Seth Kantor, Albuquerque *Tribune* Washington correspondent, August 9, 1969. He said that USDA research chiefs had been vague in answering the senator's questions about why funds or testing grounds had not been made available. One of the government officials, Mr. Kantor said, told Senator Anderson that if they were, "the chemical producers would howl."

CHAPTER 15   STERILE SEX

[1] Assuming a fertile insect population of one million in the parent generation and a release of 9 million sterile insects, only 100,000 insects would reproduce. That would mean

500,000 fertile insects in the first generation. If another 9 million sterile insects were released for mating, the number of insects reproducing would drop to 26,316. A third release would cut the number of insects reproducing in the next generation to 1,907; under similar conditions, successive drops would be ten and then zero. Control by insecticides at a 90 percent level would leave 62,500 descendants of the original one million reproducing at the end of the fourth generation. Models by Dr. Knipling presented by Leo E. LaChance, C. H. Schmidt, and R. C. Bushland, "Radiation-Induced Sterilization, *Pest Control: Biological, Physical, and Selected Chemical Methods*, ed. Wendell W. Kilgore and Richard L. Doutt (New York: Academic Press, 1967), p. 152.

2 In 1946, Knipling directed his colleagues to intensify research on the mating habits of screwworms and to conduct tests with a variety of organic chemicals to find a male sterilant. "Since none of the compounds tested were effective, the results were not published." *Ibid.*, p. 166. Others who played a significant part in the project were R. Melvin and D. E. Hopkins, also with the USDA in Texas.

3 A. W. Lindquist of the Corvallis, Oregon, laboratory called Knipling's attention to a report by Muller in 1950, in which Muller said that ionizing radiation could cause male sterility by inducing dominant lethal mutations in the sperm. Knipling asked Muller about the possibility of producing competitive sterile male screwworms by irradiation; the response was encouraging.

4 Beatrice Trum Hunter, *Gardening without Poisons* (Boston: Houghton Mifflin Company, 1964), p. 213.

5 LaChance, Schmidt, and Bushland, *op. cit.*, p. 167.

6 L. D. Christenson, "Application of Sterilization Techniques for Controlling and Eradicating Insect Pests," *Pest Control by Chemical, Biological, Genetic, and Physical Means: A Symposium* (Washington, D.C.: Agricultural Research Service, USDA, 1964), p. 98.

[7] *Ibid.*

[8] *Ibid.*

[9] *USDA Yearbook of Agriculture, 1966* (Washington, D.C.: Government Printing Office, 1966), p. 35.

[10] Christenson, *op. cit., Symposium,* p. 98.

[11] LaChance, Schmidt, and Bushland, *op. cit., Pest Control,* p. 174. Infestation was reduced to 0.08 larvae per fruit from 4.72 in untreated area.

[12] *Ibid.,* pp. 174–75.

[13] *Ibid.,* p. 175.

[14] Christenson, *op. cit., Symposium,* p. 100.

[15] *Ibid.*

[16] Wendell W. Kilgore, "Chemosterilants," *Pest Control,* p. 200.

[17] *Ibid.,* pp. 202–4.

[18] *Ibid.,* p. 236.

[19] *Pesticides and Pollution* (London: William Collins Sons and Co., Ltd., 1967), p. 198.

[20] John Barbour, "Poisonless Pesticides," *Science Year, The World Science Book Annual, 1967* (Chicago: Field Publishing Co., 1967), pp. 122–23.

[21] Harry Nelson, "Highly Sexual, Sterile Male Rat Strain Bred," *Los Angeles Times,* March 31, 1969. Chemosterilants are also being intensively investigated to control rats. See, Benny D. Pate and Ruth L. Hays, "Histological Studies of Testes in Rats Treated with Certain Insect Chemoster-

ilants," *Journal of Economic Entomology*, February 15, 1968, pp. 32–34.

22 E. F. Knipling, "Introduction," *Symposium*, pp. 1–3.

23 LaChance, Schmidt, and Bushland, *op. cit., Pest Control*, pp. 189–92.

24 William Endicott, "Worm Will Turn Against Worm in Fight to Save Cotton Crop," Los Angeles *Times*, March 16, 1970.

25 Christenson, *op. cit., Symposium*, p. 101. He predicted that some day "pests may be eradicated in this manner from whole continents."

26 Irradiated flies can be produced at less than $80 a million; since they help to breed the species out of existence and there seems to be no way of developing resistance to irradiation, after the treatments the cost drops. Quite the reverse occurs with ordinary chemical pesticides, since protection becomes more costly as pests develop resistance. Also, when eradication is sought, costs mount as numbers diminish with chemicals. Knocking out the last one percent is sometimes far more expensive than getting rid of the first 90 or 95 percent. J. C. Headley and J. N. Lewis, *The Pesticide Problem: An Economic Approach to Public Policy* (Washington, D.C.: Resources for the Future, Inc., 1967), p, 55, note the efficiency of the sterile insect method in contrast to insecticides as pest populations decline. They, too, caution about overoptimism about chemosterilants, since they "cannot be used by individuals as ordinary agricultural chemicals are used." (p. 32)

CHAPTER 16 "SUE THE BASTARDS"

1 Statements by Victor J. Yannacone, Jr., unless otherwise indicated, were taken from a personal interview with him

and his family on June 12, 1969, and from subsequent letters and telephone conversations in 1969 and 1970.

2 Commenting on Carol Yannacone's suit, *Time* noted that judges "have begun to listen to conservationists." "Conservation: A New Say in Court," October 24, 1969, p. 54.

3 Professor Reich, quoted by Ralph Nader, "Law Schools and Law Firms," *The New Republic*, October 11, 1969, p. 23. Nader noted that until recently law schools had encouraged recruits for law firms whose practice "militated against representation of public interest."

4 "Litigation—Civilization's Alternative to Revolution," speech prepared for the National Environmental Teach-In, April 1970. (Typed copy, pp. 19–20)

5 Dr. Woodwell and Dr. Wurster, quoted by Luther J. Carter, "DDT: The Critics Attempt to Ban Its Use in Wisconsin," *Science*, February 7, 1969, p. 549.

6 "EDF—New Threat to Pesticides," *Farm Chemicals*, January 1968, p. 34.

7 Environmental Defense Fund brochure, no date.

8 "DDT and the Constitution," *The Nation*, March 10, 1969, p. 308.

9 "Lawyer Drags Conservation Causes into Court," *The National Observer*, April 22, 1968.

10 *Ibid.*

11 "Beetles and Dieldrin: By What Right?" *Science*, January 17, 1969, p. 229.

12 *Ibid.*

13 Denn Curran, "Local Clean Air Case May Have National Import," *The Missoulian*, November 21, 1968.

14 "Two Groups Combine to Press Anti-Pollution Suit," *The Missoulian*, November 23, 1968.

15 "Mankind Is Standing Trial as a Mass Poisoner," Los Angeles *Times*, December 24, 1968.

16 Petitioners' brief filed by Yannacone and Yannacone on behalf of the Citizens Natural Resources Association, Inc., and Wisconsin Division Izaak Walton League of America, Inc.

17 Carter, *op. cit.*, p. 549.

18 "The 'New Citizenship' for Survival," *Progressive*, April 1970, p. 34.

19 Yannacone, quoted by Gilbert Rogin, "All He Wants to Save Is the World," *Sports Illustrated*, February 3, 1969, p. 26.

20 *The National Observer*, article cited.

21 "DDT—The Ban That Isn't," *Sierra Club Bulletin*, March 1970, p. 11. Secretary Finch had announced on November 12, 1969, that DDT would be banned in two years. At the same time, he denied the petition to set zero tolerances for DDT on the grounds that it would continue to contaminate most foodstuffs long after people stopped using it. Moorman pointed out: "His reasoning, it would seem, was that because the problem was out of hand, Finch felt he couldn't act." The Sierra Club petition had suggested that zero tolerances be set *except* for all DDT released into the environment prior to the order. Moorman said: "The practical effect of such an order would be to make new releases untenable and to put pressure on Agriculture to cancel registrations and suspend uses immediately."

[22] At a seminar on pesticide problems sponsored by the University of Iowa's Institute of Agricultural Medicine, Professor Hines told public health administrators and laboratory directors that government regulations to protect the public against the hazards of pesticide exposure may be less strict than the standards imposed by the civil courts. University of Iowa *Spectator*, June 1969, p. 2.

[23] Although it is difficult for an individual to prove liability when his injury results from indirect or multiple exposure to pesticide chemicals, Professor Hines said, recent cases indicate that is being done. (Letter, July 21, 1969)

[24] Phil Young, "Pollution: The Costly Nuisance," *The Farm Quarterly*, Spring Planning Issue, 1968, p. 82.

[25] "Boy Made Ill by Pesticide Wins Claim," Los Angeles *Times*, February 1, 1969.

[26] David Sanford, "Giving the Consumer Class," *The New Republic*, July 26, 1969.

[27] A letter, dated June 23, 1970.

[28] "UFWOC Demands Ban on Dangerous Pesticides," *El Malcriado*, February 1–28, 1970.

[29] *Ibid.*

[30] "Talks Stalled on Poison Use," *El Malcriado*, July 15–31, 1969.

[31] Philip Hager, "Extradition Sought on Pollution Charges," Los Angeles *Times*, February 22, 1970.

[32] "Crackdown on Water Polluters," *National Wildlife*, February–March 1970, p. 14.

[33] *Ibid.*, p. 16.

³⁴ Robert Buckmaster, chairman of the Iowa Water Pollution Control Commission," quoted by George Nathan, "U.S. Orders Iowa: Clean Up the Rivers," *The National Observer,* November 3, 1969.

³⁵ New York Times News Service, "Ban on Pesticides Issued by Hickel," Los Angeles *Herald-Examiner,* June 18, 1970.

³⁶ Edward P. Morgan, "War on Pollution," Los Angeles *Herald-Examiner,* January 25, 1970.

³⁷ Larry Green, "Water Pollution Suits May Be Only the Beginning," *The National Observer,* February 16, 1970.

³⁸ Among the victories chalked up by Charles A. O'Brien's office have been actions halting pollution of Los Angeles water supplies by faulty underground pipelines. Cities in the area, which franchise the pipelines and which are supposed to make regular checks, had been turning over their authority to gas and oil producers without imposing on them any obligation to notify the water quality board about mishaps. As a consequence, water pollution was widespread. One water well in a Los Angeles cemetery had been found to pump pure gasoline; another broken pipeline had allowed more than 100,000 gallons of gasoline to seep into the ocean off the coast.

³⁹ UPI dispatch, "Polluters May Face Citizen Suit," Los Angeles *Times,* March 19, 1970.

CHAPTER 17   A LASTING TRUCE

¹ Carl Klein, assistant secretary of the Department of Interior, quoted by Harry Kelly, "U.S. Shies from 1899 Refuse Act Prosecutions," Los Angeles *Herald-Examiner,* June 14, 1970. The situation clearly indicates how poor legislation can defeat good. Violators of the act have been in compliance with federal-state water pollution standards set later. Thus, in advising its 93 U.S. attorneys against pressing com-

plaints, the Department of Justice argued that action would be "unfair and cause legal confusion."

2 UPI dispatch, "Pesticides Still Easy to Obtain?" Los Angeles *Herald-Examiner*, June 18, 1970.

3 AP dispatch, "Henry II May Regret He Had a Better Idea," Los Angeles *Times*, February 1, 1970.

4 UPI dispatch, "Dow Chemical Chief Joins Fight Against Pollution," Los Angeles *Herald-Examiner*, April 3, 1970.

5 Sweden has proposed the creation of a world monitoring network and data bank to measure air and ocean pollution; it also has urged that control measures be drafted to prevent further contamination. Delegates will be asked to sign a series of pollution control treaties at the 1972 United Nations conference on world environment. Earl W. Foell, "Worldwide Monitoring of Environment Urged," Los Angeles *Times*, March 11, 1970.

6 Results of the questionnaire were shown to me by John Heritage, Senator Nelson's assistant, during an interview in Washington, June 15, 1969. Arizona, Michigan, New York, Wisconsin, California, and others have acted, mostly to limit or ban DDT and some of the other chlorinated hydrocarbons. In 1970 Maryland went beyond that to impose restrictions on the use of some of the organic phosphates, including parathion, except when recommended by the Secretary of Health and Mental Hygiene as well as the Board of Agriculture.

7 "Earth Day," *Look*, April 21, 1970, p. 33.

8 SSRS Central Office, 221 Rock Hill Road, Bala Cynwyd, Pa., 19004, will provide further information about this organization.

9 The six firms filing appeal, according to the USDA, were Allied Chemical, Black Leaf Products, Carolina Chemicals,

Diamond Shamrock Corporation, Lebanon Chemical Corporation, and Stauffer Chemical Corporation. Los Angeles *Herald-Examiner,* January 7, 1970.

10 Stanley Williford and Howard Hertel, "Singer Johnny Cash Pays $82,000 to U.S. in Fire Case," Los Angeles *Times,* July 3, 1969.

11 Professor Karl Ruppenthal, quoted by George Getze, "Stanford Professor Wants Polluters to Pay for Restoration," Los Angeles *Times,* February 24, 1969.

12 "A Capital Colloquy," *Ecotactics: The Sierra Club Handbook for Environmental Activists,* p. 188. Congressman Ottinger has also advocated tax incentives to encourage industry to clean up. And he has cited telling instances of companies that have found pollution control profitable— e.g., a company polluting its neighborhood with chlorine gas installed devices to recover lost chlorine at a cost of $19 a ton. The value of the chlorine, $60 a ton. Another company, which processes minerals, is now recovering dust so purified that it is worth $5 a ton more than the original product. With an $8,000 machinery investment, it grosses $25,000 a year. "The Economics of Pollution: The $300 Billion Market," (copy of a speech made by Congressman Ottinger).

13 John Foster, "Pollution Control—A Big Business Begins to Get Bigger," *Exchange,* March 1970, pp. 3–4.

14 "Environmental Traps," *Earth Day—The Beginning,* ed. The National Staff of Environmental Action (New York: Bantam Books, 1970), p. 80.

15 UPI dispatch, "Senate to Get Pesticide Crime Bill," Los Angeles *Herald-Examiner,* July 26, 1970.

16 Good account. John Fuller, *The Gentlemen Conspirators* (New York: Grove Press, 1962.)

[17] *U.S. Consumer Newsletter,* March 18, 1970.

[18] Sister Helen Kelley, quoted by John Dart, "Sister Kelley's Rage Is Quiet But Effective," Los Angeles *Times,* August 31, 1969.

[19] "Salvation: It's Possible," *Progressive,* April 1970, p. 18.

[20] "Duty of Science in the Ecological Crisis," address presented before the Scientists' Institute for Public Information (no date), p. 21.

[21] "Survival U: Prospectus for a Really Relevant University," *The Environmental Handbook* (A Ballantine/Friends of the Earth book), pp. 134–46.

[22] "The Beginning," *Earth Day—The Beginning,* introduction.

[23] Dan L. Thrapp, "Religious Issues Posed by Environmental Crisis," Los Angeles *Times,* April 30, 1970.

[24] *Ibid.*

[25] "Antipollution and Warm Puppies," *Earth Day—The Beginning,* p. 71.

[26] "Garden Insecticides," *Consumer Reports,* July 1969, pp. 407–10.

BIBLIOGRAPHY

Pollution literature is so extensive that listed below are only those works cited in this book. Starred items indicate those available in paperback or of special interest to general readers concerned about pesticides.

Allen, Steve, *The Ground Is Our Table*. Garden City, N.Y.: Doubleday & Company, Inc., 1966.

Ambassador College Research Staff, *Our Polluted Planet*. Pasadena, Calif.: Ambassador College Press, 1969.

Baker, Gladys L., Wayne D. Rasmussen, Vivian Wiser, and Jane M. Porter, *Century of Service: The First 100 Years of the U.S.D.A.* Washington, D.C.: U.S. Department of Agriculture, 1963.

Ballantine, Bill, *Nobody Loves a Cockroach*. Boston: Little, Brown and Company, 1967.

Bishop, James, Jr., and Henry W. Hubbard, *Let the Seller Beware!* Washington, D.C.: The National Press, Inc., 1969.

Brown, A. W. A., *Insect Control by Chemicals*. New York: John Wiley & Sons, Inc., 1951.

———, *Insecticide Resistance in Arthropods*. Geneva: World Health Organization, 1958.

Cannon, Grant G., *Great Men of Modern Agriculture*. New York: The Macmillan Company, 1963.

Carr, Donald E., *Death of the Sweet Waters*. New York: W. W. Norton Company, Inc., 1966.

* Carson, Rachel, *Silent Spring*. Boston: Houghton Mifflin Company, 1962.

* Clarke, Robin, *The Silent Weapons*. New York: David Mc-Kay Company, Inc., 1968.

Cocannouer, Joseph A., *Weeds, Guardians of the Soil*. New York: The Devin-Adair Company, 1950.

* Commoner, Barry, *Science and Survival*. New York: The Viking Press, Inc., 1968.

* Cotton, Steve, ed., *Earth Day—The Beginning*. New York: Arno Press, Inc., 1970.

* Cox, Edward F., Robert C. Fellmeth, John E. Schulz,

Nader's Raiders Report on the Federal Trade Commission.
New York: Grove Press, Inc., 1969.

Crafts, Alden S., and Wilfred W. Robbins, *Weed Control.* New
York: McGraw-Hill Book Company, Inc., 1962.

Curran, C. H., *Insects in Your Life.* New York: Sheridan
House, Inc., 1951.

Davidson, Ralph Howard, and Leonard Marion Peairs, *Insect
Pests of Farm, Garden, and Orchard* (6th edition). New
York: John Wiley & Sons, Inc., 1966.

* DeBach, Paul, ed., *Biological Control of Insect Pests and
Weeds.* New York: Reinhold Publishing Corporation, 1964.

* DeBell, Garrett, ed., *The Environmental Handbook.* New
York: Ballantine Books, Inc., 1970.

Dubos, René, *So Human an Animal.* New York: Charles
Scribner's Sons, 1968.

* Ehrlich, Paul R., *The Population Bomb.* New York: Ballantine Books, Inc., 1968.

Frear, Donald E. H., *Chemistry of the Pesticides.* New York:
D. Van Nostrand Company, Inc., 1955.

* Graham, Frank, Jr., *Since Silent Spring.* Boston: Houghton
Mifflin Company, 1970.

Headley, J. C., and J. N. Lewis. *The Pesticide Problem: An
Economic Approach to Public Policy.* Washington, D.C.:
Resources for the Future, Inc. (Distributed by the Johns
Hopkins Press), 1967.

Held, R. Burnell and Marion Clawson. *Soil Conservation in
Perspective.* Baltimore, Md.: Published for Resources for
the Future, Inc., by the Johns Hopkins Press, 1965.

Herber, Lewis, *Our Synthetic Environment.* New York: Alfred
A. Knopf, Inc., 1962.

* Hunter, Beatrice Trum, *Gardening without Poisons.* Boston:
Houghton Mifflin Company, 1964.

Kilgore, Wendell W., and Richard L. Doutt, *Pest Control:
Biological, Physical, and Selected Chemical Methods.*
New York: Academic Press, 1967.

Klaw, Spencer, *The New Brahmins, Scientific Life in America.*
New York: William Morrow & Company, Inc., 1968.

Klingman, Glenn C., *Weed Control: As a Science.* New York:
John Wiley & Sons, Inc., 1961.

Lane, Mark, *Arcadia.* New York: Holt, Rinehart and Winston,
Inc., 1970.

Lewis, Howard R., *With Every Breath You Take*. New York: Crown Publishers, Inc., 1965.

McCarthy, Richard D., *The Ultimate Folly*. New York: Alfred A. Knopf, Inc., 1969.

McMillen, Wheeler, *Bugs or People?* New York: Appleton-Century-Crofts, 1965.

* Marine, Gene, *America the Raped*. New York: Simon & Schuster, Inc., 1969.

* Marx, Wesley, *The Frail Ocean*. New York: Ballantine Books, Inc., 1969.

* Mellanby, Kenneth, *Pesticides and Pollution*. London: William Collins Sons and Co., Ltd., 1967.

Metcalf, C. L., W. P. Flint, and R. L. Metcalf, *Destructive and Useful Insects*. New York: McGraw-Hill Book Company, Inc., 1962.

Metcalf, R. L., ed., *Advances in Pest Control Research*. New York: Interscience Publishers, Inc. Published annually since 1957.

Mickey, Karl B., *Man and Soil*. Chicago: International Harvester Co., 1948.

Miller, Morton W., and George G. Berg, eds., *Chemical Fallout: Current Research on Persistent Pesticides*. Springfield, Ill.: Charles C. Thomas, Publisher, 1969.

* Mitchell, John G., and Constance L. Stallings, *Ecotactics: The Sierra Club Handbook for Environment Activists*. New York: Pocket Books, 1970.

* Mooney, Booth, *The Hidden Assassins*. Chicago: Follett Publishing Company, 1966.

O'Brien, R. D., *Insecticides: Action and Metabolism*. New York: Academic Press, 1967.

Osborn, Fairchild, *Our Plundered Planet*. Boston: Little, Brown and Company, 1948.

Petrow, Richard, *In the Wake of Torrey Canyon*. New York: David McKay Company, Inc., 1968.

Ridgeway, James, *The Closed Corporation*. New York: Random House, Inc., 1968.

Rienow, Robert, and Leona Train Rienow, *Moment in the Sun*. New York: Ballantine Books, Inc., 1969.

Rodale, J., ed., *Encyclopedia of Organic Gardening*. Emmaus, Pa.: Rodale Press (Distributed by World Publishing), 1967.

Roszak, Theodore, ed., *The Dissenting Academy*. New York: Pantheon Books, 1967.

* Rudd, Robert L., *Pesticides and the Living Landscape*. Madison: University of Wisconsin Press, 1964.

Science Year: The World Book Annual, 1967. Chicago: Field Enterprises Educational Corp., 1967.

Scientific Aspects of Pest Control, A Symposium. Washington, D.C.: National Academy of Sciences-National Research Council, 1966.

Scrimshaw, Nevin S., and John E. Gordon. *Malnutrition, Learning, and Behavior*. Cambridge, Mass.: MIT Press, 1968.

Stewart, George R., *Not So Rich as You Think*. Boston: Houghton Mifflin Company, 1968.

Still, Henry, *The Dirty Animal*. New York: Hawthorn Books, Inc., 1967.

* Storer, John, *The Web of Life*. New York: New American Library, 1953.

* ———, *Man in the Web of Life*. New York: Signet Books, 1968.

Swan, Lester A., *Beneficial Insects*. New York: Harper & Row, Publishers, Inc., 1964.

* Tallian, Laura, *The Pesticide Jungle*. Privately printed, 1966. (Available—Box 34, Phillipsville, Calif. 95559)

* Turner, James S., *The Chemical Feast: Ralph Nader's Study Group Report on the Food and Drug Administration*. New York: Grossman Publishers, 1970.

United Nations Report, Chemical and Bacteriological (Biological) Weapons and the Effects of Their Possible Use. New York: Ballantine Books, Inc., 1970.

Westcott, Cynthia, *The Gardener's Bug Book*. Garden City, N.Y.: Doubleday & Company, Inc., 1956.

* Whiteside, Thomas, *Defoliation*. New York: Ballantine Books, Inc., 1970.

Whitten, Jamie L., *That We May Live*. Princeton, N.J.: D. Van Nostrand Company, Inc., 1966.

Wickenden, Leonard, *Gardening with Nature*. New York: The Devin-Adair Company, 1958.

* ———, *Our Daily Poison*. New York: The Devin-Adair Company, 1956.

GOVERNMENT PUBLICATIONS

Chemicals in Food Products. Hearings Before the House Select Committee to Investigate the Use of Chemicals in Foods and Cosmetics. Eighty-First Congress. Washington, D.C.: U.S. Government Printing Office, 1951. (Delaney Hearings A)

Chemicals in Foods and Cosmetics. Hearings Before the House Select Committee to Investigate the Use of Chemicals in Foods and Cosmetics, House of Representatives. Eighty-Second Congress. Washington, D.C.: U.S. Government Printing Office, 1952–53. Parts 1–4. (Delaney Hearings B)

Deficiencies in Administration of Federal Insecticide, Fungicide, and Rodenticide Act. Hearings Before a Subcommittee of the Committee of Government Operations. Ninety-First Congress. Washington, D.C.: U.S. Government Printing Office, 1969. (Fountain Hearings)

Deficiencies in Administration of Federal Insecticide, Fungicide and Rodenticide Act. Eleventh Report by the Committee on Government Operations. Ninety-First Congress. Washington, D.C.: U.S. Government Printing Office, 1969.

Effects of 2,4,5,-T on Man and the Environment. Hearings before the Subcommittee on Energy, National Resources, and the Environment of the Committee on Commerce of the U.S. Senate. Ninety-First Congress. Washington, D.C.: U.S. Government Printing Office, 1970. (Hart Hearings)

Interagency Coordination in Environmental Hazards. Hearings before the Subcommittee on Reorganization of the Committee on Government Operations, U.S. Senate. Eighty-Eighth Congress. Washington, D.C.: U.S. Government Printing Office, 1963. (Ribicoff Hearings)

Interim Report on Studies of Pesticides and Other Agricultural and Industrial Chemicals. National Cancer Institute, 1969.

Pest Control by Chemical, Biological, Genetic, and Physical Means: A Symposium. Agricultural Research Service, U.S. Department of Agriculture, 1964.

The Pesticide Review 1969. Agricultural Stabilization and Conservation Service of the U.S. Department of Agriculture, Washington, D.C., 1969.

The Regulation of Pesticides in the U.S. Prepared by the U.S. Department of Agriculture and the Department of Health, Education, and Welfare. Washington, D.C.: U.S. Government Printing Office, 1968.

Report of the Secretary's Commission on Pesticides and Their Relationship to Environmental Health (Mrak Commission Report) Department of Health, Education, and Welfare. Washington, D.C.: U.S. Government Printing Office, 1969.

Restoring the Quality of Our Environment. Report of the Environmental Pollution Panel of the President's Science Advisory Committee. The White House, November 1965.

Scientific Aspects of Pest Control: A Symposium arranged and Conducted by the National Academy of Sciences-National Research Council. Publication 1402, National Academy of Sciences-National Research Council. Washington, D.C., 1966.

The Yearbook of Agriculture series prepared by the Yearbook Committee, U.S. Department of Agriculture. Washington, D.C.: U.S. Government Printing Office.

Of particular assistance were the following:

Soil, 1957
Land, 1958
After a Hundred Years, 1962
Consumers All, 1965
Protecting Our Food, 1966
Science for Better Living, 1968

Publications of the World Health Organization's Expert Committee on Pesticides have also been cited—*Pesticide Residues* and *Safe Use of Pesticides in Public Health*—from the technical report services. Geneva, 1967 and 1968.

Documents by state agencies have also been referred to, including the comprehensive discussion prepared by the Human Relations Agency of the California Department of Public Health: *A Report to the 1970 Legislature on the Effects of the Use of DDT and Similar Pesticides on Human Health and the Environment,* December 10, 1969.

Because I have given detailed information about articles, their authors, and the issues in which they appear, it would be repetitious to list here the more than fifty periodicals cited—

scientific and technical journals, trade association publications, consumer magazines, and magazines for general readers.

Instead, listed below are a number of organizations that have taken an active role in combatting pesticide pollution, along with other forms of pollution. Most of them publish informative and instructive material that will be helpful to individuals wishing to participate effectively in the fight to stem the poison tide. Many of them have affiliated organizations in states across the nation:

Committee for Environmental Information
438 North Skinker Boulevard
St. Louis, Missouri 63130

Conservation Foundation
1250 Connecticut Avenue, N.W.
Washington, D.C. 20036

Consumers Union of U.S.
256 Washington Street
Mount Vernon, New York 10550

Defenders of Wildlife
1346 Connecticut Avenue, N.W.
Washington, D.C. 20036

Environmental Action
2000 P Street, N.W.
Washington, D.C. 20036

Environmental Defense Fund
1910 N Street, N.W.
Washington, D.C. 20036

Friends of the Earth
30 East 42nd Street
New York, New York 10017

The Fund For Animals, Inc.
140 W. 57th Street
New York, N.Y. 10019

Izaak Walton League of America
1326 Waukegan Road
Glenview, Illinois 60025

National Audubon Society
1130 Fifth Avenue
New York, New York 10028

Scientists' Institute for Public Information
30 East 68th Street
New York, New York 10021

Sierra Club
1050 Mills Tower
San Francisco, California 94104

Society for Social Responsibility in Science
221 Rock Hill Road
Bala-Cynwyd, Pennsylvania 19004

Wilderness Society
729 15th Street, N.W.
Washington, D.C. 20005

Wildlife Society
3900 Wisconsin Avenue, N.W.
Washington, D.C.

Of special interest to
gardeners:

Bio-Dynamic Farming and
Gardening Association

Route 1
Stroudsburg, Pa. 18360

Organic Gardening
  Association
33 East Minor Street
Emmaus, Pennsylvania 18049

• INDEX